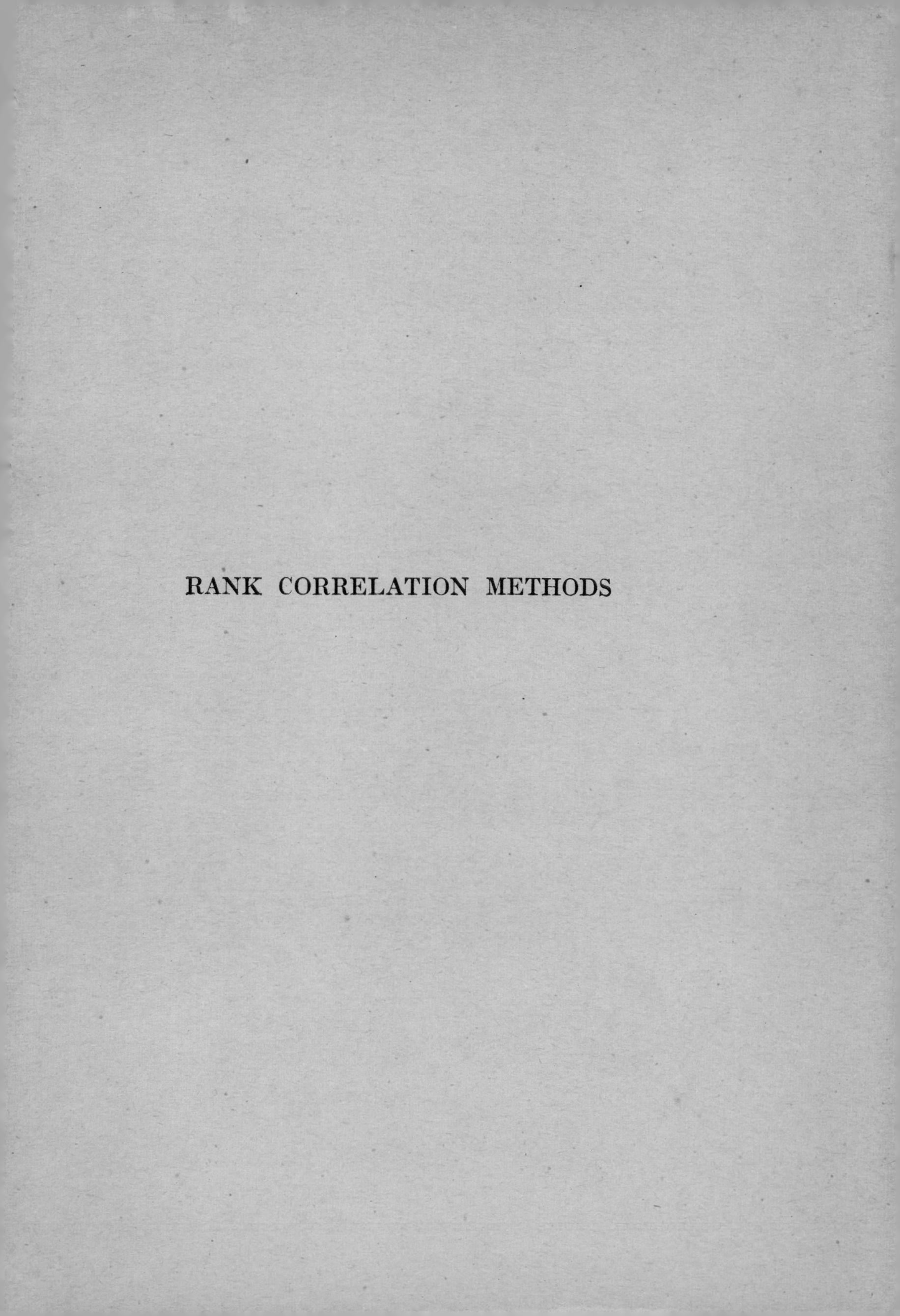

# RANK CORRELATION METHODS

OTHER BOOKS OF INTEREST
TO STATISTICIANS

*The advanced theory of statistics* (two volumes) M. G. Kendall

*Introduction to the theory of statistics*
G. U. Yule & M. G. Kendall

*Exercises in theoretical statistics* .. .. M. G. Kendall

*A statistical primer* .. .. .. .. F. N. David

*The design and analysis of experiment* .. M. H. Quenouille

*Statistical methods in biological assay* .. D. J. Finney

*Sampling methods for censuses and surveys* .. .. F. Yates

*Biomathematics* .. .. .. .. .. C. A. B. Smith

*Probability and the weighing of evidence* .. .. I. J. Good

# RANK CORRELATION METHODS

MAURICE G. KENDALL, Sc.D.
PROFESSOR OF STATISTICS IN THE UNIVERSITY OF LONDON

SECOND EDITION
REVISED AND ENLARGED

CHARLES GRIFFIN & COMPANY LIMITED
42 DRURY LANE — LONDON W.C.2

---

*First published .. 1948*
*Second edition .. 1955*

*Made and Printed in Great Britain*
*by Butler and Tanner Limited, Frome*

# EXTRACT FROM PREFACE TO FIRST EDITION

Until a few years ago rank correlation was a rather neglected branch of the theory of statistical relationship. In the practical field it was generally regarded, except perhaps by psychologists, as a makeshift for the correlation of measurable variables ; and in the theoretical field it seemed to present no interesting or important problems. That situation has changed. Practical applications of ranking methods are not only being extended in psychology and education but are being made in other subjects such as industrial experimentation and economics. The aim of this book is to give an account of the new ranking techniques for the use of those workers who, from choice or necessity, have to employ ranked material.

The theory of this subject is, from the mathematical viewpoint, rather complicated. I had to try to meet the needs both of those readers who are interested solely in applications of the theory and of those who wish to go to the root of the theory. It is doubtful whether the methods themselves, in this or any branch of statistics, can be safely applied without some knowledge of the underlying theory ; on the other hand, few workers in the practical field have the inclination or the time to master the complicated mathematical derivation of the formulae they require. What I have done is to write alternate chapters, one describing the results, their applications and the basic ideas, the other deriving the mathematical results in detail. Thus any reader who is not interested in the mathematics can omit the advanced chapters without seriously interrupting the continuity of his reading and can refer to them later if he wishes.

My thanks are due to Professor Sir Ronald A. Fisher and Messrs. Oliver & Boyd for permission to reproduce Tables 7A, 7B, and 8 from their *Statistical Methods for Research Workers* ; and to Dr. Milton Friedman and Professor S. S. Wilks for permission to reproduce Appendix Table 6 from the *Annals of Mathematical Statistics*. I should be grateful if any readers who detect errors or obscurities would call my attention to them.

M. G. K.

LONDON,
*August*, 1948

## PREFACE TO SECOND EDITION

A great deal of new work has been done on ranking methods since this book was first published. I have therefore revised the work extensively, though adhering to the original plan. Much fresh material has been interspersed in the text and a new chapter 13 added. Table 4, giving some random permutations of the natural numbers, is also new.

It is a pleasure to record my indebtedness to my colleagues Mr. James Durbin and Mr. Alan Stuart, who read the revised material and made many useful suggestions; and to Miss Rita M. Baines, who gave invaluable help, as always, in carrying out the work of revision.

M. G. K.

London,
*March*, 1955

# CONTENTS

## CHAPTER 1

# THE MEASUREMENT OF RANK CORRELATION

### Introductory remarks

**1.1** When a number of individuals are arranged in order according to some quality which they all possess to a varying degree, they are said to be *ranked*. The arrangement as a whole is called a *ranking* in which each member has a *rank*.

**1.2** It is customary, but not essential, to denote the ranks by ordinal numbers 1, 2, . . . $n$ where $n$ is the number of objects. Thus the object or individual which comes fifth in the ranking has the rank 5. In the sequel we shall often operate with these numbers as if they were the cardinals of ordinary arithmetic, adding them, subtracting them and even multiplying them; and it is of some importance to realise exactly what such processes mean.

**1.3** Suppose, for example, that an object has a rank 5 when the set of objects is ranked according to some quality $A$ and a rank 8 according to a second quality $B$. What is implied by saying that the difference of the ranks is 3? We cannot subtract "fifth" from "eighth"; but a meaning can be given to the process nevertheless. To say that the rank according to $A$ is 5 is equivalent to saying that, in arranging according to $A$, four members are given priority over our particular member, or are *preferred* to it. Similarly, seven members are preferred in the ranking according to $B$. Consequently the number of preferences in the $B$-ranking exceeds the number in the $A$-ranking by 3; and this is not an ordinal number but a cardinal number, *i.e.* arises by counting.

This may strike the reader as a precious distinction which is hardly worth making at the present stage. If so, he can put it aside until it arises later. He should realise, however, from the outset that the numerical processes associated with ranking are essentially those of counting, not of measurement.

**1.4** In practice, ranked material can arise in many different ways, some of which may be briefly mentioned:

(*a*) Purely as arrangements of objects which are being considered only by reference to their position in space or time. For instance, if we arrange a pack of cards in some order and then shuffle them, the new order is a ranking which may be compared with the old to see whether the shuffling process is a thorough one. We are interested in the spatial arrangement alone—not, for example, in whether some objects are " greater than " or " less than " others in the intensity of a common quality.

(*b*) According to some quality which we cannot measure on any objective scale. For instance, we might rank a set of mineral specimens according to " hardness " by some such simple criterion as saying that $A$ is harder than $B$ if $A$ scratches $B$ when the two are rubbed together. If $A$ scratches $B$ and $B$ scratches $C$ then $A$ will scratch $C$, so that by making a number of comparisons we can rank the objects without ambiguity (unless two of them are equally hard, a special case we shall consider in Chapter 3). There is, however, no method of *measuring* hardness implicit in this approach. We can always decide whether $A$ is harder than $B$, but we cannot say that it is twice as hard without imposing some scale of measurement on the system.

(*c*) According to some measurable or countable quality. For instance, we may rank individuals according to height, or countries according to size of population. It may not always be necessary to carry out the actual measurement in such cases, as for instance, if we arrange a class of students in order of height " by eye " ; but the quality according to which the ranking is made is capable of practical measurement.

(*d*) According to some quality which we believe to be measurable but cannot measure for practical or theoretical reasons. For instance, we may rank a number of persons according to " intelligence " on the assumption that there is such a quality and that individuals can be ranked according to the degree of intelligence which they possess. In Chapter 11 we shall consider a method which enables us to investigate in some cases whether these assumptions are legitimate. The reason for differentiating this case from that of paragraph (*b*) is that in the latter we know from physical considerations that ranking is possible, whereas in the former the possibility is a hypothesis.

**1.5** In the theory of statistics a quantity which may vary from one member of a population to another is called a *variate*. In particular, a measurable quality provides a variate and, of course, a scale. We can always rank a set of individuals according to their position on a scale and may then be said to replace variate-values by ranks. A ranking may then be regarded as a less accurate way of expressing the ordered relation of the members—less accurate because it does not tell us how close the various members may be on the scale. *Per contra*, what the ranking loses in accuracy it gains in generality, for if we stretch the scale of measurement (and even if we stretch it differently in different regions) the ranking remains unaltered; in mathematical language it is *invariant* under stretching of the scale.

**1.6** Historically the theory of ranks developed as an offshoot of the theory of variates. In the early stages ranks were regarded in the main as makeshifts substituted for variate measurements to save time or trouble or to avoid the difficulties of setting up an objective scale. More recently they have been recognised as having an importance of their own, and in the earlier part of this book we shall consider ranking problems as such without any reliance on an underlying scale. Our methods thus have very considerable generality. The relationship between ranks and variates will be discussed in Chapters 9 and 10.

## Rank correlation

**1.7** Suppose a number of boys are ranked according to their ability in mathematics and in music. Such a pair of rankings for ten boys, denoted by the letters $A$ to $J$, might be as follows:

| Boy: | $A$ | $B$ | $C$ | $D$ | $E$ | $F$ | $G$ | $H$ | $I$ | $J$ |
|---|---|---|---|---|---|---|---|---|---|---|
| Maths.: | 7 | 4 | 3 | 10 | 6 | 2 | 9 | 8 | 1 | 5 |
| Music: | 5 | 7 | 3 | 10 | 1 | 9 | 6 | 2 | 8 | 4 |

. . . (1.1)

We are interested in whether there is any relationship between ability in mathematics and music. A glance at these rankings shows that there is far from being perfect agreement, but that some boys occupy the same or nearly the same position in both subjects. We can see the correspondence more easily if we re-arrange one ranking in the natural order, thus:

| Boy: | $I$ | $F$ | $C$ | $B$ | $J$ | $E$ | $A$ | $H$ | $G$ | $D$ |
|---|---|---|---|---|---|---|---|---|---|---|
| Maths.: | 1 | 2 | 3 | 4 | 5 | 6 | 7 | 8 | 9 | 10 |
| Music: | 8 | 9 | 3 | 7 | 4 | 1 | 5 | 2 | 6 | 10 |

. . . (1.2)

What we wish to do is to measure the degree of correspondence between these two rankings, or to measure the intensity of *rank correlation*. We shall accordingly show how to construct a coefficient for this purpose which will be denoted by the Greek letter $\tau$ (tau).

**1.8** Such a coefficient should have three properties:

(*a*) the agreement between the rankings is perfect, *i.e.* every individual has the same rank in both, $\tau$ should be $+1$, indicating perfect positive correlation;

(*b*) if the disagreement is perfect, *i.e.* one ranking is the inverse of the other, $\tau$ should be $-1$, indicating perfect negative correlation;

(*c*) for other arrangements $\tau$ should lie between these limiting values; and in some acceptable sense increasing values from $-1$ to 1 should correspond to increasing agreement between the ranks.

The first two of these requirements are only conventions, but are by far the most useful conventions to employ.

**1.9** In the first ranking of (1.1) consider any pair of rank members, say *AB*. Their ranks, 7, 4, occur in the inverse order (taking the natural order 1 . . . 10 as the correct order) and hence we will score for this pair the value $-1$. Had the pair been in the right order we should have scored $+1$. In the second ranking the pair *AB* has ranks 5, 7, which is in the right order, and we will, therefore, score $+1$ in this ranking.

We now multiply the scores for this pair in both rankings and hence arrive at the score $-1$. Evidently, for any pair, the resulting score is $+1$ if their ranks are in the same order, $-1$ if they are in different orders. We may say that we score $+1$ or $-1$ according as the pair agree or disagree in the two rankings.

The same procedure is followed for each possible pair from the ranking of 10. There are 45 such pairs and the scores are as follows (we write them down in full so that the reader can follow the method, but in practice, as we show presently, this is unnecessary):

| Pair | Score | Pair | Score | Pair | Score | Pair | Score |
|---|---|---|---|---|---|---|---|
| *AB* | $-1$ | *BF* | $-1$ | *DE* | $+1$ | *FH* | $-1$ |
| *AC* | $+1$ | *BG* | $-1$ | *DF* | $+1$ | *FI* | $+1$ |
| *AD* | $+1$ | *BH* | $-1$ | *DG* | $+1$ | *FJ* | $-1$ |
| *AE* | $+1$ | *BI* | $-1$ | *DH* | $+1$ | *GH* | $+1$ |
| *AF* | $-1$ | *BJ* | $-1$ | *DI* | $+1$ | *GI* | $-1$ |
| *AG* | $+1$ | *CD* | $+1$ | *DJ* | $+1$ | *GJ* | $+1$ |
| *AH* | $-1$ | *CE* | $-1$ | *EF* | $-1$ | *HI* | $-1$ |
| *AI* | $-1$ | *CF* | $-1$ | *EG* | $+1$ | *HJ* | $-1$ |
| *AJ* | $+1$ | *CG* | $+1$ | *EH* | $+1$ | *IJ* | $-1$ |
| *BC* | $+1$ | *CH* | $-1$ | *EI* | $-1$ | | |
| *BD* | $+1$ | *CI* | $-1$ | *EJ* | $-1$ | | |
| *BE* | $-1$ | *CJ* | $+1$ | *FG* | $-1$ | | |

The total of positive scores, say *P*, is 21 and that of negative scores, say $Q$, is $-24$. Adding these two we arrive at a total score, say $S$, of $-3$.

Now if the rankings are identical each of the 45 unit scores will be positive and hence the maximum value of $S$ is 45. Similarly the minimum value of $S$ is $-45$. We therefore calculate $\tau$ as

$$\frac{\text{Actual score} = -3}{\text{Maximum possible score} = 45} = -0{\cdot}07.$$

This is near to zero and indicates very little correlation between the two rankings. A zero value may, in fact, be regarded as indicative of independence—halfway, so to speak, between complete positive dependence and complete negative dependence.

**1.10** Consider now the general case. If we have two rankings of $n$, the number of pairs of comparisons which can be made is equal to the number of ways of choosing two things from $n$, which is $\frac{1}{2}n(n-1)$, sometimes written as $\binom{n}{2}$. This is the maximum value of the score, attained when the rankings are identical. If $S$ is the total score we define the correlation coefficient by

$$\tau = \frac{S}{\frac{1}{2}n(n-1)} \quad . \quad . \quad . \quad . \quad (1.3)$$

If $P$ and $Q$ are the positive and negative scores we have the equivalent form (since $P + Q = \frac{1}{2}n(n-1)$ )

$$\tau = \frac{P - Q}{\frac{1}{2}n(n-1)} \quad . \quad . \quad . \quad . \quad (1.4)$$

$$= 1 - \frac{2Q}{\frac{1}{2}n(n-1)} \quad . \quad . \quad . \quad (1.5)$$

$$= \frac{2P}{\frac{1}{2}n(n-1)} - 1 \quad . \quad . \quad . \quad (1.6)$$

**1.11** The determination of the score $S$ (or equivalently of $P$ or of $Q$) does not require the detailed procedure we have followed above. There are several short-cut methods of which the following are probably the easiest.

(*a*) Consider the rearranged form of (1.2). When one ranking is in the natural order, 1, 2, . . . $n$, all unit scores arising from it are positive. Consequently, the contributions to $P$ will arise only from pairs in the second ranking which are in the right order. These are all we need to count. The second ranking is

$$8 \quad 9 \quad 3 \quad 7 \quad 4 \quad 1 \quad 5 \quad 2 \quad 6 \quad 10$$

Considering first the pairs associated with the first member 8, we see that there are two members greater than 8 on the right of it. The contribution to $P$ is therefore $+ 2$. Taking now pairs associated with 9 (other than 8 9 which has already been taken into account) we find a contribution to $P$ of $+ 1$. Similarly the contribution of pairs associated with 3, arising from members to the right of it, is $+ 5$. Proceeding in this way we find

$$P = 2 + 1 + 5 + 1 + 3 + 4 + 2 + 2 + 1 = 21.$$

Hence, from (1.6),

$$\tau = \frac{42}{45} - 1 = - 0{\cdot}07, \text{ as before.}$$

(*b*) If it is too troublesome to rearrange the rankings so that one of them is in the right order we may proceed thus. In the rankings previously considered write down the natural order above them, thus :

| | 1 | 2 | 3 | 4 | 5 | 6 | 7 | 8 | 9 | 10 |
|---|---|---|---|---|---|---|---|---|---|---|
| *A* | 7 | 4 | 3 | 10 | 6 | 2 | 9 | 8 | 1 | 5 |
| *B* | 5 | 7 | 3 | 10 | 1 | 9 | 6 | 2 | 8 | 4 |

The number 1 in ranking $B$ has a 6 above it in ranking $A$. In the natural ranking 6 has four members to the right. Score 4 and delete the 6 from the natural ranking. Now the number 2 in $B$ has an 8 above it in $A$ and in the natural ranking 8 has two members to the right. Score 2 and strike out the 8 from the natural ranking. Proceeding in this way we find scores of

$$4 + 2 + 5 + 3 + 2 + 1 + 1 + 2 + 1 + 0 = 21,$$

which gives the value of $P$, as found above.

The validity of this rule is evident if we rearrange the rankings so as to put $B$ in the natural order (this being the order in which we have considered the members) :

| | 5 | 8 | 3 | 10 | 1 | 7 | 2 | 9 | 6 | 4 |
|---|---|---|---|---|---|---|---|---|---|---|
| *A* | 6 | 8 | 3 | 5 | 7 | 9 | 4 | 1 | 2 | 10 |
| *B* | 1 | 2 | 3 | 4 | 5 | 6 | 7 | 8 | 9 | 10 |

The contributions to $P$ by method (*b*) are the same as those given by method (*a*) applied to the rankings $B$ and $A$. There are, for instance, 4 members to the right of 6 in $A$ which are greater than 6 ; 2 members to the right of 8 in A which are greater than 8 ; and so on.

**1.12** It may help to give some idea of the values assumed by $\tau$ in particular cases if we set out some rankings of 10 and the corresponding $\tau$ obtained by correlating them with the natural order. The reader should check these values as an exercise.

| Ranking | | | | | | | | | | | Value of $\tau$ |
|---|---|---|---|---|---|---|---|---|---|---|---|
| *a* | 4 | 7 | 2 | 10 | 3 | 6 | 8 | 1 | 5 | 9 | + 0·11 |
| *b* | 1 | 6 | 2 | 7 | 3 | 8 | 4 | 9 | 5 | 10 | + 0·56 |
| *c* | 7 | 10 | 4 | 1 | 6 | 8 | 9 | 5 | 2 | 3 | − 0·24 |
| *d* | 6 | 5 | 4 | 7 | 3 | 8 | 2 | 9 | 10 | 1 | + 0·02 |
| *e* | 10 | 1 | 2 | 3 | 4 | 5 | 6 | 7 | 8 | 9 | + 0·60 |
| *f* | 10 | 9 | 8 | 7 | 6 | 1 | 2 | 3 | 4 | 5 | − 0·56 |

## $\tau$ as a coefficient of disarray

**1.13** The coefficient as we have introduced it provides a kind of average measure of the agreement between pairs of members (" agreement ", that is to say, in respect of order) and thus has evident recommendations as a measure of the concordance between two rankings. There is another instructive way of looking at the coefficient. Consider the two rankings of 7 :

| | | | | | | | |
|---|---|---|---|---|---|---|---|
| *A* | 1 | 2 | 3 | 4 | 5 | 6 | 7 |
| *B* | 6 | 3 | 5 | 7 | 1 | 2 | 4 |

We may transform *B* into *A* by successively interchanging pairs of neighbours. For instance, interchanging 1 with its left-hand neighbours, we have, in four stages—

| | | | | | | |
|---|---|---|---|---|---|---|
| 6 | 3 | 5 | 1 | 7 | 2 | 4 |
| 6 | 3 | 1 | 5 | 7 | 2 | 4 |
| 6 | 1 | 3 | 5 | 7 | 2 | 4 |
| 1 | 6 | 3 | 5 | 7 | 2 | 4 |

Now interchanging 2 we find, after four more stages,

1 2 6 3 5 7 4

Interchanging the 3 and 6 gives us

1 2 3 6 5 7 4

Interchanging with the 4 gives us, in three stages,

1 2 3 4 6 5 7

Finally, interchanging the 6 and 5 gives us the natural order *A*.

This transformation has taken 13 moves, and we could not have made it in fewer. We might have taken more, as for instance if we had interchanged 1 and 2 and back again before making the above sequence of moves. It will be clear that there is a minimum number of moves which transform any ranking into any other ranking of the same number of members. Call this number *s*.

Then we shall show in the next chapter that

$$\left.\begin{aligned} s &= Q, \text{ or equivalently} \\ s &= \tfrac{1}{2}\{\tfrac{1}{2}n(n-1) - S\} \end{aligned}\right\} \quad . \quad . \quad . \quad (1.7)$$

which gives a simple relation between the number of interchanges $s$ and the negative score $Q$ or the total score $S$. In the example we have just considered $S = -5$, $n = 7$, and hence

$$s = \tfrac{1}{2}(21 + 5) = 13, \text{ as found.}$$

From (1.5) and (1.7) it follows that

$$\tau = 1 - \frac{2s}{\frac{1}{2}n(n-1)} \quad . \quad . \quad . \quad (1.8)$$

exhibiting $\tau$ as a simple function of the minimum number of interchanges between neighbours required to transform one ranking into the other—in short, as a kind of coefficient of disarray.

## Spearman's $\rho$

**1.14** We now discuss another coefficient of rank correlation denoted by the Greek letter $\rho$ (rho) and named after C. Spearman, who introduced it into psychological work. Consider again the two rankings of 10 given in (1.1):

| | | | | | | | | | | |
|---|---|---|---|---|---|---|---|---|---|---|
| Mathematics : | 7 | 4 | 3 | 10 | 6 | 2 | 9 | 8 | 1 | 5 |
| Music : | 5 | 7 | 3 | 10 | 1 | 9 | 6 | 2 | 8 | 4 |
| Differences $d$ | 2 | − 3 | 0 | 0 | 5 | − 7 | 3 | 6 | − 7 | 1 |
| ,, $d^2$ | 4 | 9 | 0 | 0 | 25 | 49 | 9 | 36 | 49 | 1 |

We have subtracted the ranks for music from those for mathematics and shown the results in the row called " Differences $d$ ". These differences should sum to zero (which provides an arithmetical check) because the sum is the difference of two quantities each of which is the sum of the numbers 1 to 10. We have also shown the squares of these differences. Denoting now the sum of these squares by $S(d^2)$ we define Spearman's $\rho$ by the equation

$$\rho = 1 - \frac{6S(d^2)}{n^3 - n} \quad . \quad . \quad . \quad (1.9)$$

or, in our present example,

$$\rho = 1 - \frac{6 \times 182}{990}$$
$$= -0{\cdot}103.$$

**1.15** When two rankings are identical all the differences $d$ are zero and from (1.9) it follows that $\rho = 1$. We will now prove that when one ranking is the reverse of the other, $\rho = -1$.

Suppose that $n$ is odd, and is equal to $2m + 1$. We lose no generality by writing one ranking in the natural order, and the rankings and differences may then be expressed as follows:

$$\begin{array}{llllllll} A: & 1, & 2 \ldots & m, & m+1, & m+2, \ldots & 2m, & 2m+1 \\ B: & 2m+1, & 2m \ldots & m+2, & m+1, & m, \ldots & 2, & 1 \\ \hline d: & -2m, & -(2m-2) \ldots & -2, & 0, & 2, \ldots & 2m-2, & 2m \end{array} \qquad (1.10)$$

The sum of squares is thus given by

$$\begin{aligned} S(d^2) &= 8\{m^2 + (m-1)^2 + \ldots + 2^2 + 1^2\} \\ &= 8m(m+1)(2m+1)/6 \\ &= \tfrac{1}{3}(n-1)(n+1)(n) \\ &= \tfrac{1}{3}(n^3 - n). \end{aligned}$$

If we substitute this value in (1.9) we find

$$\rho = 1 - 6/3 = -1.$$

If $n$ is even, say equal to $2m$, we have similarly

$$\begin{array}{llllllll} A: & 1, & 2, \ldots m, & & m+1, \ldots & 2m-1, & m \\ B: & 2m, & 2m-1, \ldots m+1, & & m, \ldots & 2, & 1 \\ \hline d: & -(2m-1), & -(2m-3) \ldots & -1, & 1, \ldots & 2m-3, & 2m-1 \end{array} \qquad (1.11)$$

Thus

$$\begin{aligned} S(d^2) &= 2\{(2m-1)^2 + (2m-3)^2 + \ldots + 3^2 + 1^2\} \\ &= 2\{(2m)^2 + (2m-1)^2 + (2m-2)^2 + \ldots + 3^2 + 2^2 + 1^2\} \\ &\qquad - 2\{(2m)^2 + (2m-2)^2 + \ldots + 2^2\} \\ &= 4m(2m+1)(4m+1)/6 - 8m(m+1)(2m+1)/6 \\ &= \tfrac{1}{3}(n^3 - n) \end{aligned}$$

and, as before, if we substitute in (1.9) we find $\rho = -1$.

The coefficient $\rho$ thus obeys our general requirements that its possible values should range from $-1$ to $+1$, assuming the extreme values only when there is perfect disagreement or agreement between the rankings.

**1.16** The reason for taking the sum of *squares* of the rank-differences will be clear to the reader who is familiar with the calculation of statistical measures of dispersion such as the standard deviation. It is obvious enough that we cannot base a coefficient on the sum of differences $S(d)$, for this is zero. It might be thought, however, that if we disregarded the signs of the differences and summed them a somewhat simpler coefficient could be reached; and indeed this was one of Spearman's original suggestions. The procedure leads to difficulties in the more advanced theory, particularly in connection with sampling questions, and we shall not pursue it.

**1.17** The score $Q$ of equation (1.5) is simply the number of pairs which occur in different orders in the two rankings. We may call any such case an "inversion" and $\tau$ is thus a linear function of the number of inversions. It is interesting to observe that $\rho$ can also be regarded as a coefficient of inversion when each inversion is weighted; in fact, if the pair of ranks $(i, j)$ are inverted and we score $(j - i)$ or $(i - j)$, whichever is positive, for any inversion; and if we sum all such scores to obtain a total $V$, we have

$$V = \tfrac{1}{2}S(d^2) \quad . \quad . \quad . \quad . \quad (1.12)$$

and hence

$$\rho = 1 - \frac{12V}{(n^3 - n)} \quad . \quad . \quad . \quad (1.13)$$

We shall prove this result in the next chapter.

For example, consider the two rankings of 7 of **1.13**, namely

| | | | | | | | |
|---|---|---|---|---|---|---|---|
| *A* | 1 | 2 | 3 | 4 | 5 | 6 | 7 |
| *B* | 6 | 3 | 5 | 7 | 1 | 2 | 4 |

. . . (1.14)

Taking those pairs of ranks which are inverted in the second ranking as compared with the first, we have

| Ranks inverted | Weight |
|---|---|
| 6 3 | 3 |
| 6 5 | 1 |
| 6 1 | 5 |
| 6 2 | 4 |
| 6 4 | 2 |
| 3 1 | 2 |
| 3 2 | 1 |
| 5 1 | 4 |
| 5 2 | 3 |
| 5 4 | 1 |
| 7 1 | 6 |
| 7 2 | 5 |
| 7 4 | 3 |
| | 40 |

The number of inversions is 13, as we found in **1.13**, and

$$\tau = -5/21 = -0{\cdot}24.$$

The sum of weighted inversions is 40 and hence

$$\rho = 1 - \frac{480}{336}$$
$$= -0{\cdot}43.$$

It is easily verified that for the rankings (1.14) we have $S(d^2) = 80$, checking with (1.12).

## Conjugate rankings

**1.18** One property which is common to both $\tau$ and $\rho$ may be noticed. If we correlate a given ranking $A$ with the natural order $B$ $(1, \ldots n)$, and again with the inverse order $B'$ $(n, \ldots 1)$, the values of $\tau$ are the same in magnitude but opposite in sign. This will be seen from the definition of $\tau$, for the effect of reversing the order $B$ is to reverse the sign of each unit score contributing to $S$, and hence the sign of $S$ itself. Thus, corresponding to any two rankings $A$ and $B$ (not necessarily natural orders) with correlation $\tau$ there will be rankings $A$ and $B'$ with correlation $-\tau$. Consider, for instance, the two rankings of 7:

| | | | | | | | |
|---|---|---|---|---|---|---|---|
| $A$ | 4 | 1 | 6 | 7 | 5 | 2 | 3 |
| $B$ | 7 | 6 | 3 | 1 | 4 | 5 | 2 |

. . . (1.15)

Let us rearrange $A$ in the natural order. We then have—

| | | | | | | |
|---|---|---|---|---|---|---|
| 1 | 2 | 3 | 4 | 5 | 6 | 7 |
| 6 | 5 | 2 | 7 | 4 | 3 | 1 |

and the value of $\tau$ is readily found to be $-11/21$ or $-0{\cdot}52$. If we now invert the natural order, giving

| | | | | | | | |
|---|---|---|---|---|---|---|---|
| $C$ | 7 | 6 | 5 | 4 | 3 | 2 | 1 |
| $D$ | 6 | 5 | 2 | 7 | 4 | 3 | 1 |

we find for the correlation of $C$ and $D$ a value of $+0{\cdot}52$. Rearranging so that $D$ becomes $B$ of (1.12), we have

| | | | | | | | |
|---|---|---|---|---|---|---|---|
| $A'$ | 4 | 7 | 2 | 1 | 3 | 6 | 5 |
| $B$ | 7 | 6 | 3 | 1 | 4 | 5 | 2 |

. . . (1.16)

The rankings $A$ and $A'$ may be regarded as conjugate. When correlated with $B$ they give values of $\tau$ which are equal in magnitude but opposite in sign.

**1.19** It is also true, though not so obvious, that the values of $\rho$ between $A$, $B$ and $A'$, $B$ are equal in magnitude but opposite in sign.

We shall prove the general result in the next chapter. The reader may verify as an exercise that for the particular cases (1.15) and (1.16) we have respectively $\rho = -17/28$ and $\rho = +17/28$.

**1.20** In a sense, therefore, the scales of measurement of rank correlation set up by the use of $\tau$ or $\rho$ are symmetrical about the value zero. They range from $-1$ to $+1$, and corresponding to any given positive value of $\tau$ or of $\rho$ there is a negative value of the same magnitude arising from an inversion of one of the rankings. The scales, we may say, are unbiassed.

**1.21** The reader must not expect to find that the numerical values of $\tau$ and $\rho$ are the same for any given pair of rankings, except when there is complete agreement or disagreement. For the rankings of **1.12** correlated with the natural order we have the following values:

| Ranking | $\tau$ | $\rho$ |
|---|---|---|
| *a* | + 0·11 | + 0·14 |
| *b* | + 0·56 | + 0·64 |
| *c* | − 0·24 | − 0·37 |
| *d* | + 0·02 | + 0·03 |
| *e* | + 0·60 | + 0·45 |
| *f* | − 0·56 | − 0·76 |

These will illustrate the sort of differences which arise in practice. The coefficients have different scales, like those of the Centigrade and Fahrenheit thermometers; and they differ in rather more than scale, since $\rho$ gives greater weight to inversions of ranks which are farther apart. In practice we often find that, when neither coefficient is too close to unity, $\rho$ is about 50 per cent greater than $\tau$ in absolute value, but this is not an invariable rule.

## Daniels' inequality

**1.22** It is possible to state certain inequalities connecting the values which $\rho$ and $\tau$ can take for a given ranking. The first such is due to Daniels:

$$-1 \leqslant \frac{3n}{n-2}\tau - \frac{2(n+1)}{n-2}\rho \leqslant 1, \quad . \quad . \quad (1.17)$$

where $n$ is the number in the ranking. For large $n$ this becomes effectively

$$-1 \leqslant 3\tau - 2\rho \leqslant 1 \quad . \quad . \quad . \quad (1.18)$$

If $\tau$ is greater than zero the upper limit may be attained but not the lower limit; when $\tau$ is less than zero the lower limit may be attained but not the upper limit; and when $\tau = 0$ both limits may be attained. Thus, we could have a ranking for which $\tau = 0$ and $\rho = 0{\cdot}5$. It would, however, be a rather peculiar one. Consider, for instance, the rankings

| | | | | | | | | |
|---|---|---|---|---|---|---|---|---|
| *A* | 1 | 2 | 3 | 4 | 5 | 6 | 7 | 8 |
| *B* | 5 | 6 | 7 | 8 | 1 | 2 | 3 | 4 |

$$. \quad . \quad . \quad (1.19)$$

We find

$$\rho = -\,0{\cdot}53, \quad \tau = -\,0{\cdot}14.$$

## The Durbin-Stuart inequality

**1.23** Durbin and Stuart have found other inequalities satisfied by $\rho$ and $\tau$ which enable us to set upper and lower limits to $\rho$ for given $\tau$. They showed that, for any ranking, $V$ of **1.17** is related to $\boldsymbol{Q}$ by

$$V \geqslant \tfrac{2}{3}Q\left(1 + \frac{Q}{n}\right), \quad . \quad . \quad . \quad (1.20)$$

the equality being attainable in certain cases. By using (1.13) and (1.5) we then find

$$\rho \leqslant 1 - \frac{1-\tau}{2(n+1)}\{(n+1)(1-\tau)+4\}, \quad \tau \geqslant 0, \quad . \quad (1.21)$$

which gives an upper limit for $\rho$ given (positive) $\tau$. A lower limit is given by (1.17) as

$$\rho \geqslant \frac{3n\tau - (n-2)}{2(n+1)}, \quad \tau \geqslant 0 \quad . \quad . \quad (1.22)$$

For $n$ large these limits give us

$$\tfrac{3}{2}\tau - \tfrac{1}{2} \leqslant \rho \leqslant \tfrac{1}{2} + \tau - \tfrac{1}{2}\tau^2, \quad \tau > 0 \quad . \quad . \quad (1.23)$$

both limits being attainable. For example when $\tau = 0$, $-\tfrac{1}{2} \leqslant \rho \leqslant \tfrac{1}{2}$. When $\tau = \tfrac{1}{2}$, $\tfrac{1}{4} \leqslant \rho \leqslant \tfrac{7}{8}$; when $\tau = 0{\cdot}9$, $0{\cdot}85 \leqslant \rho \leqslant 0{\cdot}995$.

For $\tau < 0$ we find

$$\tfrac{1}{2}\tau^2 + \tau - \tfrac{1}{2} \leqslant \rho \leqslant \tfrac{3}{2}\tau + \tfrac{1}{2} \quad . \quad . \quad (1.24)$$

We shall prove these results in the next chapter. They illustrate the general remark, made above, that although $\rho$ and $\tau$ are related the relationship is not a simple one.

## Stragglers

**1.24** In general, $\rho$ is an easier coefficient to calculate than $\tau$. We shall see in subsequent chapters that from many other practical and from most theoretical points of view $\tau$ is preferable to $\rho$, and the majority of the work in this book will be based on the former. At this stage we will not argue their relative merits, but there is one interesting practical point which is worth noticing.

It sometimes happens that when a ranking has been made, new individuals are added which necessitate re-ranking. Similarly, in writing down the ranks of a series of individuals which are distinguished by variate-values or marks but are in disorder, we may make mistakes and find at the end of the ranking that a few have been omitted. This will require the calculation of $\rho$ entirely *de novo*, whereas the addition of members to a ranking does not require a complete re-calculation of $\tau$. An example will make the point clear.

*Example 1.1*

A confidential inquiry is sent out to a number of firms asking for the rates of dividend which they propose to declare at their next annual general meetings. We will suppose that they are all able to answer this question, but that there is some possibility that those with the higher dividends in prospect are more reluctant to reply and will delay or will not reply at all. We will also assume that all the rates are different. These are perhaps not very realistic assumptions but they will serve for the purpose of the example.

By a certain date a number of replies have been received and it is then necessary to close the inquiry and to summarise the results. How far can we assume that the replies to hand are representative of the population to which the inquiry was addressed ? Is there any evidence to suggest that those who reply earlier differ from those who reply later ?

Suppose we receive 15 replies in the following order:

| | | | | | | | | | | | | | | | |
|---|---|---|---|---|---|---|---|---|---|---|---|---|---|---|---|
| (A) Order of receipt : | 1 | 2 | 3 | 4 | 5 | 6 | 7 | 8 | 9 | 10 | 11 | 12 | 13 | 14 | 15 |
| (B) Percentage dividend : | 15 | 13 | 12 | 16 | 25 | 8 | 9 | 14 | 17 | 11 | 18 | 20 | 10 | 21 | 19 |
| (C) Rank of percentage : | 8 | 6 | 5 | 9 | 15 | 1 | 2 | 7 | 10 | 4 | 11 | 13 | 3 | 14 | 12 |

If there *is* some relation between the order of receipt and the magnitude of the percentage, it ought to be shown up by the rank correlation between the order of receipt and the order of the percentages according to magnitude. The latter is shown in the last row above. For the correlation of $A$ and $C$ we find $S = 25$,

$$\tau = \frac{25}{105} = +0{\cdot}24.$$

We also find $S(d^2) = 392$,

$$\rho = 1 - \frac{392}{560} = +0{\cdot}30.$$

This suggests some small positive correlation between $A$ and $C$, and in Chapter 3 we shall see how to test its significance. That, however, is not the point of the present example. Suppose that, after these values of $\tau$ and $\rho$ have been worked out, two more replies arrive with percentages 7 and 23. Nearly all the ranks in row $C$ above are affected and have to be re-numbered. The differences $d$ and the sum $S(d^2)$ have to be ascertained anew. If, after this, further replies arrive the work has to be done once more.

On the other hand, the effect of the addition of the two extra values on $S$ can be ascertained very simply. The new member with percentage 7 and rank in the $A$-ranking of 16 merely has to be considered in relation to the other fifteen members, and since it has a lower percentage than any of them it adds $-15$ to the score $S$. Similarly, the new member with percentage 23 adds 14. The new score $S$ is therefore $14 - 15 = -1$ more than the old, *i.e.* is 24, and the new value of $\tau$ is given by

$$\tau = \frac{24}{136} = +0{\cdot}18.$$

In this way a kind of running total of $\tau$ can be ascertained without the necessity of re-ranking at each stage.

It may be remarked that in this example the ranks of ranking $C$ are obtained from a variate, the percentage stated in the reply. Those of the order of receipt are not obtained from a variate, although we could, with sufficient patience, measure the time-intervals elapsing between the receipt of consecutive replies and hence regard the $A$-ranking as arranged according to a time-scale.

**1.25** We conclude with three further examples of the use of rank correlations.

*Example 1.2*

Twelve similar discs are constructed, ranging from light blue to dark blue in colour. Their order is known objectively by a colorimetric test. To test the ability of a dress designer to distinguish shades she is shown these discs and asked to arrange them in order. The results are as follows:

| | | | | | | | | | | | | |
|---|---|---|---|---|---|---|---|---|---|---|---|---|
| Objective order: | 1 | 2 | 3 | 4 | 5 | 6 | 7 | 8 | 9 | 10 | 11 | 12 |
| Order assigned by the subject: | 1 | 4 | 7 | 2 | 3 | 5 | 8 | 12 | 10 | 6 | 11 | 9 |

We require to measure the subject's ability to distinguish the different shades of blue.

For the value of $P$ we have

$$11 + 8 + 5 + 8 + 7 + 6 + 4 + 0 + 1 + 2 + 0 = 52$$

$$\tau = \frac{104}{66} - 1 = +0{\cdot}58.$$

The correlation is positive and substantial, but far from perfect. We shall show how to test its significance in Chapter 3.

In this example we are measuring the agreement between a subjective and an objective order. The subject's failure to achieve complete success may be due to genuine inability to distinguish finer shades, to wandering attention or to other causes; but whatever the cause we can test the subject's ability against a given objective order.

*Example 1.3*

Consider now the case where three judges rank a number of competitors in a beauty contest as follows:

| Judge $A$: | 1 | 2 | 3 | 4 | 5 | 6 | 7 | 8 | 9 |
|---|---|---|---|---|---|---|---|---|---|
| Judge $B$: | 5 | 4 | 1 | 7 | 2 | 8 | 3 | 6 | 9 |
| Judge $C$: | 2 | 5 | 1 | 3 | 4 | 7 | 6 | 9 | 8 |

There is here no objective order such as existed in the previous example. We are interested in how far the judges agree between themselves, not in their agreement with some objective standard.

We find for the correlations between pairs of judges

$$\tau(A \text{ and } B) = 0{\cdot}33$$
$$\tau(B \text{ and } C) = 0{\cdot}44$$
$$\tau(C \text{ and } A) = 0{\cdot}67$$

This indicates that $A$ and $C$ agree more than $A$ and $B$ or $A$ and $C$. The agreement between $A$ and $B$ is poor.

*Example 1.4*

The following Table 1.1 shows, for a number of countries in 1938, the value of external trade (imports plus exports) and the population. In appropriate columns we have ranked the countries according to these two variates.

The value of $P$ will be found to be 83 and hence $\tau = +0{\cdot}22$. This value seems to express fairly well the general relationship between the variables. The countries with the larger populations are, on the whole, those with the greater volume of foreign trade; but Russia and China form notable exceptions, and the relationship is not very strong.

It often happens, with economic data such as these, that the

TABLE 1.1

TRADE AND POPULATION OF CERTAIN COUNTRIES IN 1938

| Country | Trade (Imports plus Exports) £ thousand million | Rank according to Trade | Population (millions) | Rank according to Population |
|---|---|---|---|---|
| United Kingdom . | 1·330 | 1 | 47·6 | 6 |
| U.S.A. . . . . | 1·024 | 2 | 130·0 | 3 |
| Denmark . . . | 0·142 | 11 | 3·8 | 16 |
| France. . . . | 0·450 | 4 | 42·0 | 9 |
| Germany . . . | 0·882 | 3 | 79·2 | 4 |
| Greece . . . . | 0·045 | 17 | 7·1 | 14 |
| Holland . . . | 0·276 | 7 | 8·7 | 12 |
| Italy . . . . | 0·232 | 8 | 43·4 | 8 |
| Japan . . . . | 0·309 | 5 | 72·8 | 5 |
| Norway . . . | 0·098 | 14 | 2·9 | 17 |
| Russia . . . . | 0·105 | 13 | 170·4 | 2 |
| Spain . . . . | 0·052 | 16 | 25·6 | 10 |
| Sweden . . . | 0·201 | 9 | 6·3 | 15 |
| Argentina . . . | 0·180 | 10 | 13·0 | 11 |
| Belgium . . . | 0·307 | 6 | 8·4 | 13 |
| Brazil . . . . | 0·121 | 12 | 44·1 | 7 |
| China (ex. Manchuria) . . . | 0·085 | 15 | 410·0 | 1 |

magnitude differs widely from one individual to another; Norway, for example, having a population of 2·9 million against China's 410 million. In any discussion of relationship based on these variate-values we have to be careful that one or two large items do not swamp the effect of the smaller ones. By ranking the individuals we do something to restore the balance and to give each country a more equal voice, as it were, in the discussion. Whether this is a sound procedure depends on what we are discussing; but it is worth emphasising that there are occasions when the use of variates, though in a sense more accurate, may be more misleading than ranks because they do not correspond exactly to the relationship which we are really trying to measure.

The reader who is familiar with the product-moment correlation coefficient of ordinary statistical theory will see the force of these comments when we say that the coefficient in the above table between trade and population is only $+ 0{\cdot}006$. The effect of including Russia and China in the calculations has been to reduce the average relationship to practically zero, the average being heavily weighted by the size of the populations of these two countries.

## References

The coefficient $\tau$ was considered by Greiner (1909) and Esscher (1924) as a method of estimating correlations in a normal population (see Chapters 9 and 10). The coefficient was rediscovered by Kendall (1938) who considered it purely as a rank coefficient. For $\tau$ as a coefficient of disarray see Haden (1947), Feller (1945) and Moran (1947).

For $\rho$ see papers by Spearman (1904, 1906), K. Pearson (1907), and Kendall and others (1939).

For the inequalities connecting $\rho$ and $\tau$ see Daniels (1950, 1951) and Durbin and Stuart (1951).

## CHAPTER 2

# INTRODUCTION TO THE GENERAL THEORY OF RANK CORRELATION

**2.1** In this chapter we shall begin the development of a general theory of rank correlation and shall demonstrate some results which were stated without proof in the previous chapter. The reader who is interested in practical applications and is prepared to take those results on trust can omit this chapter altogether; but if he has some previous knowledge of the theory of variate-correlation * he may profit from a glance through it to see how the various coefficients in current use may be linked together within the scope of a single theory.

### The general correlation coefficient

**2.2** Suppose we have a set of $n$ objects which are being considered in relation to two properties represented by $x$ and $y$. Numbering the objects from 1 to $n$ for the purposes of identification in any order we please, we may say that they exhibit values $x_1 \dots x_n$ according to $x$ and $y_1 \dots y_n$ according to $y$. These values may be variates or ranks.

To any pair of individuals, say the $i$th and the $j$th, we will allot an $x$-score, denoted by $a_{ij}$, subject only to the condition that $a_{ij} = -a_{ji}$. Similarly we will allot a $y$-score, denoted by $b_{ij}$, where $b_{ij} = -b_{ji}$. Denoting by $\Sigma$ summation over all values of $i$ and $j$ from 1 to $n$, we define a generalised correlation coefficient $\Gamma$ by the equation

$$\Gamma = \frac{\Sigma\, a_{ij}\, b_{ij}}{\sqrt{(\Sigma\, a_{ij}^2\, \Sigma\, b_{ij}^2)}} \quad . \quad . \quad . \quad (2.1)$$

We regard $a_{ij}$ as zero if $i = j$.

### $\tau$ as a particular case

**2.3** This general definition includes $\tau$, $\rho$ and the product-moment correlation $r$ as particular cases which arise when particular methods of scoring are adopted.

Suppose we allot a score $+1$ if $p_j > p_i$ (where $p_i$ is the rank of

* For an account of the statistical theory of correlation see G. Udny Yule and M. G. Kendall, *An Introduction to the Theory of Statistics*, 14th edition. This book will subsequently be referred to as the *Introduction*.

the $i$th member according to the $x$-quality) and $-1$ if $p_j < p_i$. Then

$$a_{ij} = +1 \qquad p_i < p_j \\ \quad = -1 \qquad p_i > p_j \qquad . \quad . \quad . \quad (2.2)$$

and similarly for $b$. Thus the sum $\Sigma\, a_{ij}\, b_{ij}$ is equal to twice the sum $S$ (twice because any given pair occurs once as $(i, j)$ and once as $(j, i)$ in the summation). Furthermore $\Sigma\, a_{ij}^2$ is merely the number of terms $a_{ij}$, that is, $n(n-1)$, and so for $\Sigma\, b_{ij}^2$. It follows from substitution in (2.1) that $\Gamma$ is equal to the coefficient $\tau$ as we defined it in Chapter 1.

## ρ as a particular case

**2.4** Instead of the simple $\pm 1$ let us write

$$a_{ij} = p_j - p_i \quad . \quad . \quad . \quad . \quad (2.3)$$

and similarly

$$b_{ij} = q_j - q_i \quad . \quad . \quad . \quad . \quad (2.4)$$

where $q_i$ is the rank of the $i$th member according to the $y$-quality. Both $p_i$ and $q_i$ range from 1 to $n$, and hence the sum of squares $\Sigma\,(p_j - p_i)^2$ and $\Sigma\,(q_j - q_i)^2$ are equal. From (2.1) we then have

$$\Gamma = \frac{\Sigma\,(p_j - p_i)(q_j - q_i)}{\Sigma\,(p_j - p_i)^2} \quad . \quad . \quad . \quad (2.5)$$

Now

$$\sum_{i,j=1}^{n} (p_j - p_i)(q_j - q_i) = \sum_{i=1}^{n}\sum_{j=1}^{n} p_i q_i + \sum_{i=1}^{n}\sum_{j=1}^{n} p_j q_j - \sum_{i=1}^{n}\sum_{j=1}^{n} (p_i q_j + p_j q_i)$$

$$= 2n \sum_{i=1}^{n} p_i q_i - 2 \sum_{i=1}^{n} p_i \sum_{j=1}^{n} q_j$$

$$= 2n \sum_{i=1}^{n} p_i q_i - \tfrac{1}{2} n^2 (n+1)^2 \quad . \quad . \quad (2.6)$$

since $\Sigma\, p_i$ and $\Sigma\, q_j$ are both equal to the sum of the first $n$ natural numbers, namely $\frac{1}{2}n(n+1)$.

We also have

$$S(d^2) = \sum_{i=1}^{n} (p_i - q_i)^2$$

$$= 2\,\Sigma\, p_i^2 - 2\,\Sigma\, p_i q_i \quad . \quad . \quad . \quad (2.7)$$

and hence, from (2.6),

$$\Sigma (p_j - p_i)(q_j - q_i) = 2n \Sigma p_i^2 - \tfrac{1}{2}n^2(n+1)^2 - nS(d^2) \qquad (2.8)$$

But $\Sigma p_i^2$ is the sum of squares of the first $n$ natural numbers, namely $\frac{1}{6}n(n+1)(2n+1)$, and (2.8) thus reduces on the right to

$$\tfrac{1}{6}n^2(n^2-1) - nS(d^2) \quad . \quad . \quad . \quad (2.9)$$

Further

$$\begin{aligned} \Sigma (p_j - p_i)^2 &= 2n \Sigma p_i^2 - 2 \Sigma p_i p_j \\ &= 2n \Sigma p_i^2 - 2(\Sigma p_i)^2 \\ &= \tfrac{1}{6}n^2(n^2-1) \quad . \quad . \quad . \quad (2.10) \end{aligned}$$

and thus, on substituting from (2.9) and (2.10) in (2.5) we get

$$\Gamma = 1 - \frac{6S(d^2)}{n^3 - n} \quad . \quad . \quad . \quad (2.11)$$

so that in this case $\Gamma$ is reduced to Spearman's $\rho$.

## Product-moment correlation as a particular case

**2.5** Thirdly, suppose we base our scores on the actual variate-values and write

$$\left.\begin{aligned} a_{ij} &= x_j - x_i \\ b_{ij} &= y_j - y_i \end{aligned}\right\} \quad . \quad . \quad . \quad . \quad (2.12)$$

Then

$$\tfrac{1}{2}\sum_{i,j} (x_j - x_i)(y_j - y_i) = n \sum_i x_i y_i - \sum_{i,j} x_i y_j \quad . \quad (2.13)$$

$$\tfrac{1}{2}\sum_{i,j} (x_j - x_i)^2 = n \Sigma x_i^2 - (\Sigma x_i)^2 \quad . \quad . \quad (2.14)$$

Now the expression on the right in (2.13) is $n$ times the covariance of $x$ and $y$, and that on the right of (2.14) is $n$ times the variance of $x$.* From (2.1) we then have

$$\Gamma = \frac{\text{cov}(x, y)}{\sqrt{(\text{var } x \text{ var } y)}} \quad . \quad . \quad . \quad (2.15)$$

so that $\Gamma$ becomes in this case the ordinary product-moment correlation of $x$ and $y$.

**2.6** It follows from the preceding paragraph that $\rho$ itself may be regarded as a product-moment correlation between ranks considered as variates. We will verify this directly.

* For the definition of these terms see 3.10.

For a set of values which are the first $n$ integers we have, as in the previous section,

$$\Sigma p_i = \tfrac{1}{2}n(n+1)$$

and hence the first moment (the mean) is given by

$$\mu_1' = \tfrac{1}{2}(n+1) \quad . \quad . \quad . \quad . \quad (2.16)$$

Similarly

$$\Sigma p_i^2 = \tfrac{1}{6}n(n+1)(2n+1)$$

and hence the variance is given by

$$\mu_2 = \frac{1}{n}\Sigma p_i^2 - \mu_1'^2$$

$$= \tfrac{1}{12}(n^2-1) \quad . \quad . \quad . \quad . \quad (2.17)$$

From (2.7) and (2.10) we find

$$\frac{1}{2}S(d^2) = \frac{1}{12}n(n^2-1) - n\left\{\frac{1}{n}\Sigma p_i q_i - \frac{1}{n}\Sigma p_i \frac{1}{n}\Sigma q_i\right\}$$

so that the first product-moment, which is the expression in curly brackets on the right, is given by

$$\mu_{11} = \frac{1}{12}(n^2-1) - \frac{1}{2n}S(d^2).$$

Thus the product-moment correlation is

$$\frac{\mu_{11}}{\sqrt{\{\mu_2(x)\,\mu_2(y)\}}} = 1 - \frac{6S(d^2)}{n^3-n} = \rho.$$

**2.7** The general coefficient $\Gamma$ of equation (2.1) thus embraces $\tau$, $\rho$ and $r$ as special cases and exhibits how we get different coefficients according to our method of scoring the differences between individuals. The scoring for $\tau$ is the simplest possible and assigns a unit mark, however near or separated the individuals are in the ranking. The scoring for $\rho$ is more elaborate and gives greater weight to differences between individuals if they are further apart (*i.e.* separated by more intervening members of the ranking). The scoring for $r$ attempts to give an objective value to the difference by measuring it on the variate scale, if one exists. The choice between these methods, or a choice of other possible methods, depends on practical considerations.

**2.8** In **1.8** we remarked on three properties which it is desirable for a coefficient of rank correlation to possess. The coefficient $\Gamma$ is easily seen to possess the property of varying from $-1$ to $+1$, in virtue of the Cauchy-Schwartz inequality

$$(\Sigma\, ab)^2 \leqslant \Sigma\, a^2\, \Sigma\, b^2.$$

We shall now prove that under certain conditions it possesses the third property mentioned in **1.8** : namely, if two corresponding pairs of ranks in the two rankings do not agree in order and the members of one pair are interchanged (so that they do agree) the coefficient $\Gamma$ will increase, provided (1) that the scores $a_{ij}$, $b_{ij}$ are not zero and (2) that the scores do not *decrease* with increasing separation of the ranks. These conditions are obeyed by $\tau$, $\rho$ and product-moment $r$.

Following our previous notation, let the rank of the $r$th member, $p_r$, be greater than that of the $s$th member $p_s$; and let the corresponding ranks in the other ranking be $q_r$ and $q_s$. Let $\Sigma''$ denote summation over $i$ and $j$ except $r$ and $s$. Then initially

$$\begin{aligned}\Sigma\, a_{ij}\, b_{ij} &= \Sigma''\, a_{ij}\, b_{ij} + \Sigma''\, a_{rj}\, b_{rj} + \Sigma''\, a_{ir}\, b_{ir} + \Sigma''\, a_{sj}\, b_{sj} \\ &\qquad + \Sigma''\, a_{is}\, b_{is} + a_{rs}\, b_{rs} + a_{sr}\, b_{sr} \\ &= \Sigma''\, a_{ij}\, b_{ij} + 2\,\Sigma''\, a_{rj}\, b_{rj} + 2\,\Sigma''\, a_{sj}\, b_{sj} + 2a_{rs}\, b_{rs} \quad . \quad (2.18)\end{aligned}$$

After interchanging $p_r$ and $p_s$ we have

$$\Sigma\, a_{ij}\, b_{ij} = \Sigma''\, a_{ij}\, b_{ij} + 2\,\Sigma''\, a_{sj}\, b_{rj} + 2\,\Sigma''\, a_{rj}\, b_{sj} - 2a_{rs}\, b_{rs}. \quad (2.19)$$

The difference, namely the increase, is

$$\begin{aligned}-2\,\Sigma''\,(a_{sj} - a_{rj})(b_{sj} - b_{rj}) - 4a_{rs}\, b_{rs} \\ = -2\,\Sigma\,(a_{sj} - a_{rj})(b_{sj} - b_{rj}) \quad . \quad (2.20)\end{aligned}$$

Now if $p_j > p_r$ (and therefore $> p_s$) $a_{sj} > 0$, $a_{rj} \geqslant 0$ and, under our condition on the scores, $a_{sj} \geqslant a_{rj}$. If $p_r > p_j \geqslant p_s$, $a_{sj} \geqslant 0$, $a_{rj} < 0$ and hence $a_{sj} - a_{rj} = a_{sj} + a_{jr} > 0$. If $p_r > p_s > p_j$, $a_{sj} < 0$, $a_{rj} < 0$ and $a_{jr} \leqslant a_{js}$ so that $a_{sj} - a_{rj} \geqslant 0$. Thus in all cases $a_{sj} - a_{rj} \geqslant 0$ and in at least one case we have the strict inequality $a_{sj} - a_{rj} > 0$.

Similarly it will be found that $b_{sj} - b_{rj} \leqslant 0$ and is $< 0$ in at least one case. Hence the summation on the right in (2.20) is negative and the increase must be positive. This completes the proof.

**2.9** We shall make considerable use of the above approach in later chapters, particularly in connection with sampling problems. We now prove two of the assertions in Chapter 1, *viz.*

(*a*)—in section **1.13**—that the minimum number of interchanges between neighbours required to transform one ranking into another is simply related to the score $S$ ; and

(*b*)—in section **1.19**—that the values of $\rho$ obtained by correlating a ranking $A$ with a ranking $B$ and its conjugate $B'$ are equal in magnitude but opposite in sign.

**2.10** We will prove the second one first. It will be sufficient if we consider a ranking $A$ typified by $p_i$ correlated with the natural order $B = 1, \ldots n$ and its inverse $B' = n, \ldots 1$. Denoting the values of $S(d^2)$ for the second by $S'(d^2)$ we have

$$\begin{aligned} S(d^2) &= \Sigma\,(p_i - i)^2 = \Sigma\,p_i^2 + \Sigma\,i^2 - 2\,\Sigma\,ip_i \\ &= \tfrac{1}{3}n(n+1)(2n+1) - 2\,\Sigma\,ip_i \\ S'(d^2) &= \Sigma\,\{p_i - (n+1-i)\}^2 \\ &= \tfrac{1}{3}n(n+1)(2n+1) - 2\,\Sigma\,(n+1-i)p_i \end{aligned}$$

Hence

$$\begin{aligned} S(d^2) + S'(d^2) &= \tfrac{2}{3}n(n+1)(2n+1) - 2\,\Sigma\,(n+1)p_i \\ &= \tfrac{2}{3}n(n+1)(2n+1) - n(n+1)^2 \\ &= \tfrac{1}{3}(n^3 - n) \end{aligned}$$

Thus

$$\begin{aligned} \rho + \rho' &= 2 - \frac{6}{n^3 - n}\{S(d^2) + S'(d^2)\} \\ &= 0 \end{aligned}$$

which establishes the result required.

**2.11** To show that the number of interchanges $s$ is given by

$$s = \tfrac{1}{4}n(n-1) - \tfrac{1}{2}S \quad . \quad . \quad . \quad (2.21)$$

we shall first prove that $s$ is not greater than the value on the right in (2.21) and then that $s$ cannot be less than that value. The equality will follow.

Without loss of generality we can suppose one ranking to be in the natural order $1, 2, \ldots n$; for we are only concerned with interchanges and can re-christen the objects so that one set is in the natural order. Let the object with rank $i$ in the second order have rank $p_i$ in the first, and consider the re-arrangement of the second order.

Define a unit function

$$\left.\begin{aligned} m_{ij} &= 1 \text{ if } p_i > p_j \\ &= 0 \text{ if } p_i < p_j \end{aligned}\right\} \quad . \quad . \quad . \quad (2.22)$$

The object with rank 1 may be transferred to the first place (on the extreme left) by $p_1 - 1$ interchanges. This will move the object with rank 2 to the right by $m_{12}$ places. To transfer this to the second place will then require $p_2 - 2 + m_{12}$ interchanges. Similarly the $i$th object will require

$$p_i - i + m_{1i} + m_{2i} + \ldots + m_{i-1,\,i}$$

interchanges. Adding all these together we find for the total number of interchanges

$$\sum_{i=1}^{n} p_i - \sum_{i=1}^{n} i + \sum_{i<j} m_{ij} = \sum_{i<j} m_{ij} \quad . \quad . \quad (2.23)$$

where $\sum_{i<j}$ denotes summation over values for which $i < j$. Now we may write

$$S = \sum_{i<j} (1 - 2m_{ij}), \quad . \quad . \quad . \quad (2.24)$$

for each unit contribution to $S$ (counting only those pairs for which $i < j$ so as not to count everything twice) is $+ 1$ if $p_i < p_j$ and $- 1$ in the contrary case. Thus the number of interchanges given by (2.23) is equal to

$$\tfrac{1}{2} \sum_{i<j} (1) - \tfrac{1}{2}S = \tfrac{1}{4}n(n - 1) - \tfrac{1}{2}S,$$

since the summation of unity over values for which $i < j$ is half the number of members, which is $\frac{1}{2}n(n - 1)$. Hence, if $s$ is the minimum number of interchanges,

$$s \leqslant \tfrac{1}{4}n(n - 1) - \tfrac{1}{2}S \quad . \quad . \quad . \quad (2.25)$$

Let $T$ be a sequence of interchanges which reduces a given arrangement to the natural order. We classify the interchanges composing $T$ into $n$ groups $T_1, T_2, \ldots T_n$. $T_1$ consists of those which involve the object 1, $T_2$ of those which involve 2 but not 1, and so on, $T_n$ being an empty set.

In any group $T_i$ let $A_i$ be the number of interchanges which move the object to the left and $B_i$ the number which move it to the right. The number of interchanges required in $T_1$ will be at least $p_1 - 1$. These interchanges will move object 2 $m_{12}$ places to the right. The nett result of operations in $T_2$ will be to move the object 2 $A_2 - B_2$ places to the right, and thus the total movement of object 2 is

$$m_{12} + A_2 - B_2,$$

and this must equal $2 - p_2$. Hence

$$B_2 - A_2 = p_2 - 2 + m_{12}$$

and hence

$$B_2 + A_2 \geqslant p_2 - 2 + m_{12}.$$

In a similar way we have

$$B_i + A_i \geqslant p_i - i + m_{1i} + \ldots + m_{i-1,i}$$

Adding such inequalities for $i = 1, \ldots n-1$ and remembering that

$$p_n - n + m_{1n} + \ldots + m_{n-1,n} = 0$$

we have

$$\begin{aligned} s &= \sum_{i=1}^{n-1}(A_i + B_i) \\ &\geqslant \sum p_i - \sum i + \sum_{i<j} m_{ij} \\ &\geqslant \tfrac{1}{4}n(n-1) - \tfrac{1}{2}S \quad . \quad . \quad . \quad . \quad (2.26) \end{aligned}$$

and thus from (2.25) and (2.26) we establish (2.21).

**2.12** We will now prove and develop the result of equations (1.12) and (1.13), exhibiting $\rho$ as a coefficient of weighted inversions. We will suppose, without loss of generality, that one ranking is in the natural order $1, 2, \ldots n$. Defining $m_{ij}$ as in (2.22) we have

$$V = \sum_{i<j} m_{ij}(j-i) \quad . \quad . \quad . \quad (2.27)$$

Adding and subtracting $\sum_{i>j} j\, m_{ij}$ we have

$$\begin{aligned} V &= \sum_{i<j} j\, m_{ij} + \sum_{i>j} j\, m_{ij} - \sum_{i<j} i\, m_{ij} - \sum_{i>j} j\, m_{ij} \\ &= \sum_{i,j} j\, m_{ij} - \sum_{i<j} i(m_{ij} + m_{ji}). \end{aligned}$$

Here $p_j$ is the rank in the first ranking corresponding to $j$ in the second; we sum over $i$ in the first summation and $j$ in the second to find

$$\begin{aligned} V &= \sum_j j(n - p_j) - \sum_i i(n-1) \\ &= \sum_i i^2 - \sum_i i\, p_i \quad . \quad . \quad . \quad . \quad (2.28) \end{aligned}$$

As in (2.7) we have

$$S(d)^2 = 2\sum i^2 - 2\sum i\, p_i,$$

and hence

$$V = \tfrac{1}{2}S(d^2) \quad . \quad . \quad . \quad . \quad . \quad (2.29)$$

It follows at once that

$$\rho = 1 - \frac{12V}{n^3 - n} \quad . \quad . \quad . \quad . \quad (2.30)$$

**2.13** Another form for $\rho$ which is useful in certain contexts, though not as a convenient form for computation, is as follows: let $a_{ij}$, $b_{ij}$ be the unit scores entering into the expression for $\Gamma$. Put

$$a_i = \sum_{j=1}^{n} a_{ij}$$

$$b_i = \sum_{j=1}^{n} b_{ij}$$

Then

$$\rho = \frac{\sum_{i=1}^{n} a_i b_i}{\frac{1}{3}(n^3 - n)} \quad . \quad . \quad . \quad . \quad (2.31)$$

In fact, our scores $a_{ij}$ may be expressed in terms of $m_{ij}$ by the relation

$$a_{ij} = 1 - 2m_{ij},$$

for this is $+1$ if $p_i < p_j$ and $-1$ if $p_i > p_j$. Furthermore the rank of any member may be expressed as

$$p_i = \sum_{j=1}^{n} m_{ij} + 1. \quad . \quad . \quad . \quad (2.32)$$

Hence, we have

$$p_i = -\tfrac{1}{2}\sum_{j} a_{ij} + \tfrac{1}{2}(n+1),$$

and, remembering that the mean of the $p$'s, $\bar{p}$, is $\frac{1}{2}(n+1)$, we find

$$a_i = -2(p_i - \bar{p}). \quad . \quad . \quad . \quad (2.33)$$

Thus, in virtue of the fact that $\rho$ is the product-moment correlation of $p$ and $q$ (2.4) we have

$$\rho = \frac{\frac{1}{4}\sum_i a_i b_i}{\frac{1}{12}(n^3 - n)}$$

$$= \frac{\Sigma\, a_i b_i}{\frac{1}{3}(n^3 - n)},$$

as stated in (2.31).

**2.14** It follows that we can express $\rho$ in the form

$$\rho = \frac{3}{n^3 - n}\Sigma\, a_{ij} b_{ik} \quad . \quad . \quad . \quad (2.34)$$

where the summation extends over all $i, j, k$. Or again, if we consider summation for which $j \neq k$,

$$\rho = \frac{3}{n^3 - n}\left(\sum a_{ij} b_{ij} + \sum_{j \neq k} a_{ij} b_{ik}\right)$$

$$= \frac{3}{(n+1)}\tau + \frac{3}{n^3 - n}\sum_{j \neq k} a_{ij} b_{ik} \quad . \quad . \quad (2.35)$$

It is interesting to consider this form in terms of agreements (with respect to order) of pairs from two rankings. If $a_{ij}$ and $b_{ij}$ are of the same sign we may say that there is a concordance of type 1. (We are dealing only with the case of unitary scores.) If $a_{ij}$ and $b_{ik}$ are of the same sign we may say that there is a concordance of type 2. If the signs are opposite we may speak of *discordances*. Then $\tau$ is simply related to the proportion of concordances of type 1 in the two rankings. The number of possible concordances of type 2 is $n(n-1)(n-2)$, and if we denote this by $k_2$ to distinguish it from the number of concordances of type 1 (equivalent to $2P$ of equation (1.6)), which we will call $k_1$, we have

$$\Sigma\, a_{ij} b_{ij} = k_1 - \{n(n-1) - k_1\}$$

$$= 2k_1 - n(n-1),$$

$$\Sigma\, a_{ij} b_{ik} = 2k_2 - n(n-1)(n-2),$$

and on substitution in (2.35) we find

$$\rho = \frac{6(k_1 + k_2)}{n^3 - n} - \frac{3(n-1)}{n+1} \quad . \quad . \quad . \quad (2.36)$$

### Proof of Daniels' inequality

**2.15** Since relations like $p_i > p_j > p_k > p_i$ are impossible, $a_{ij}$, $a_{jk}$, $a_{ki}$ cannot all have the same sign and hence their sum must be $\pm 1$. Similarly for the $b$-scores. Put

$$(a_{ij} + a_{jk} + a_{ki})(b_{ij} + b_{jk} + b_{ki}) = \varepsilon_{ijk} \quad . \quad . \quad (2.37)$$

Now let the corresponding ranks $p_i$, $p_j$, $p_k$, $q_i$, $q_j$, $q_k$ be renamed according to their order of magnitude, becoming $p_i'$, $p_j'$, etc. For example, a set of $p$-ranks 472 becomes 231. Then $\varepsilon_{ijk}$ is $+1$ or $-1$ according as $p'$ is an even or odd permutation of $q'$, that is to say if it takes an even or odd number of interchanges of consecutive members to go from one to the other. If any pair of $i$, $j$, $k$ are equal $\varepsilon$ is zero.

Summing over all values of the suffixes, we find

$$3n\,\Sigma\, a_{ij} b_{ij} - 6\,\Sigma\, a_{ij} b_{ik} = \Sigma\, \varepsilon_{ijk} \quad . \quad . \quad (2.38)$$

Now there are $n(n-1)(n-2)$ possible triplets of $(i, j, k)$ and $\Sigma\, \varepsilon_{ijk}$ is the number of them which are " even ". Put

$$U = \Sigma\, \varepsilon_{ijk}/n(n-1)(n-2). \quad . \quad . \quad (2.39)$$

We have $\quad -1 \leqslant U \leqslant 1 \quad$ and hence, from (2.38)

$$-1 \leqslant \frac{3n}{n-2}\tau - \frac{2(n+1)}{n-2}\rho \leqslant 1 \quad . \quad . \quad . \quad (2.40)$$

In the limit for $n$ large this becomes

$$-1 \leqslant 3\tau - 2\rho \leqslant 1 \quad . \quad . \quad . \quad (2.41)$$

That the upper limit is attainable is seen from consideration of a ranking in which the $q$'s are the natural order $1, \ldots n$ and the $p$'s are a cyclic permutation of the natural order, say $m+1, m+2, \ldots n, 1, 2, \ldots m$. All the $\varepsilon$'s are then $+1$ and $U$ attains its maximum.

## Proof of the Durbin-Stuart inequality

**2.16** The problem of finding a lower limit of $\rho$ for given $\tau$ is that of finding the smallest value of $V$ for given $Q$. Consider, for example, a population of six with $\tau = 0{\cdot}6$ and hence $Q = 3$. If the first ranking is in the natural order the value of $V$ is least when the second ranking is 214365, for we have constructed three inversions 21, 43, 65 for which the weight has its minimum value unity.

Let us then define a *compact* set of ranks as one whose members form inversions only with each other; no group being subdivisible into subgroups of the same type. All ranks to the left of a compact set are less than every one of its members, those to the right are greater.

Consider any inversion of weight 2, say $r+2, r$. There are three possible orders of the triad $r, r+1, r+2$, namely $r+2, r+1, r$; $r+2, r, r+1$ and $r+1, r+2, r$. In a minimal ranking, *i.e.* a ranking with minimal $V$ for given $Q$, all triads spanned by inversions of weight two must be of type $r+2, r+1, r$, except possibly for the triads of a single compact set. For suppose that in addition to the triad $r+2, r, r+1$ there is a further non-overlapping triad $x+2, x, x+1$. On replacing these by $r+2, r+1, r$ and $x+1, x, x+2$ we reduce $V$ but leave $Q$ unchanged.

There are twelve possible orders of a tetrad spanned by the inversion $r+3, r$ of weight three. Of these the only one which does not contain a triad of types $r+2, r, r+1$ or $r+1, r+2, r$ is $r+3, r+2, r+1, r$. Hence in the minimal ranking all tetrads are of this type, except possibly for one compact set.

By arguing in this way we see that the minimal ranking must consist of sets of the form $q + r, q + r - 1, \ldots r$, except possibly for a single compact set which we shall call the residual set. It is this residual which causes most of the trouble in proving the desired result. In particular it may comprise the whole ranking.

**2.17** Taking first the case when there is no residual set, suppose there are $\alpha_1$ sets of form $r + q_1, \ldots r$; $\alpha_2$ sets of form $r + q_2, \ldots r$; and so on. Then

$$\Sigma \alpha_i q_i = n \quad \ldots \quad (2.42)$$

$$Q = \tfrac{1}{2} \Sigma \alpha_i q_i (q_i - 1)$$
$$= \tfrac{1}{2}(\Sigma \alpha_i q_i^2 - n) \quad \ldots \quad (2.43)$$

$$V = \tfrac{1}{6} \Sigma \alpha_i q_i (q_i^2 - 1)$$
$$= \tfrac{1}{6}(\Sigma \alpha_i q_i^3 - n) \quad \ldots \quad (2.44)$$

Now by the Cauchy–Schwartz inequality

$$(\Sigma \alpha_i q_i)(\Sigma \alpha_i q_i^3) \geqslant (\Sigma \alpha_i q_i^2)^2$$

and on substitution from (2.44) – (2.46) we find

$$V \geqslant \tfrac{2}{3} Q\left(1 + \frac{Q}{n}\right). \quad \ldots \quad (2.45)$$

The equality holds when all $q$'s are equal, as is possible in certain cases.

**2.18** We must now deal with the case when there is a residual set $S$ of $s$ ranks which is not of the form $I = r + s, r + s - 1, \ldots r$. We suppose that $S$ has $q$ inversions of total weight $v$ and that $I$ has $k$ more inversions than has $S$. We may thus proceed from $I$ to $S$ by $k$ interchanges of neighbouring pairs. If we choose such a sequence which gives the greatest reduction in $v$ we arrive at a ranking with $q$ inversions and minimum $v$, which is what we are seeking.

If we start from $I$ the maximum reduction for $k$ interchanges $(k \leqslant s - 1)$ is $\tfrac{1}{2}k(k + 1)$. The sequence of interchanges which gives this reduction is obtained by moving the smallest rank from the extreme right-hand of $I$ towards the left. When the left-hand end is reached, the requirement that $S$ should be a compact set is violated, since the smallest rank then itself forms a single-member compact set.

Further, whenever, starting from $I$, any sequence of $k \geqslant s - 1$ interchanges is carried out, the final result cannot be a residual set forming part of a minimal ranking, for it is always possible, by moving the smallest rank of $I$ through $(s-1)$ interchanges as above, to violate the condition of compactness while producing the same number $q$ of inversions with a smaller $\nu$.

Thus, for a residual set $S$ of $s$ ranks forming part of a minimal ranking, only one rank will be displaced from its position in $I$, and the number of interchanges transforming $I$ to $S$ will be $k \leqslant s-2$.

**2.19** We now show that the inequality (2.45) is satisfied by the residual set alone. In fact the inequality holds strictly, *i.e.*

$$\nu > \frac{2}{3}q\left(1+\frac{q}{s}\right) = \frac{2}{3}\frac{q}{s}(q+s).$$

This is true if

$$\tfrac{1}{6}s(s^2-1) - \tfrac{1}{2}k(k+1) > \tfrac{2}{3}s\{\tfrac{1}{2}s(s-1)-k\}\{\tfrac{1}{2}s(s-1)+s-k\}$$
$$> \tfrac{1}{6}s\{s^2(s^2-1) - 4s^2k + 4k^2\}$$

*i.e.* if

$$k < \frac{s(4s-3)}{3s+4} \quad . \quad . \quad . \quad . \quad (2.46)$$

Now $k \leqslant s-2$, so (2.46) is certainly true if

$$s-2 < \frac{s(4s-3)}{3s+4},$$

*i.e.* if $s^2 - s + 8 > 0$, which is true. Thus the inequality (2.45) holds strictly for the residual set alone.

Let $Q'$ be the number of inversions in the remainder of the ranking apart from the residual set, and let $V'$ be the corresponding weighted sum.

Then
$$Q = Q' + q$$
and
$$V = V' + \nu$$
as a consequence of the definition of compact sets.

Also, from (2.45)

$$V' \geqslant \frac{2}{3}\left(\frac{Q'^2}{n-s} + Q'\right)$$

and

$$\nu > \frac{2}{3}\left(\frac{q^2}{s} + q\right).$$

We require to show that (2.45) is generally true, *i.e.* that

$$V' + \nu \geqslant \frac{2}{3}\left\{\frac{(Q'+q)^2}{n} + Q' + q\right\}.$$

This is satisfied if

$$\frac{Q'^2}{n-s} + \frac{q^2}{s} \geqslant \frac{(Q'+q)^2}{n},$$

*i.e.* if

$$n\{sQ'^2 + (n-s)q^2\} \geqslant s(n-s)(Q'+q)^2$$

which is satisfied if

$$s^2Q'^2 + (n-s)^2q^2 - 2s(n-s)Q'q \geqslant 0,$$

*i.e.* if

$$\{sQ' - (n-s)q\}^2 \geqslant 0,$$

which is true. Thus (2.45) is established. The equality is only attainable when there is no residual set.

Equation (1.21) follows. To find the corresponding expression for negative $\tau$ we replace the ranking concerned by its conjugate. This merely changes the sign of $\rho$ and $\tau$.

## Spearman's footrule

**2.20** To conclude this chapter we will consider briefly a coefficient based, not on $S(d^2)$ like $\rho$, but on $S\,|\,d\,|$ where $|\,d\,|$ stands for the absolute value of $d$, *i.e.* its value without regard to sign. This coefficient, sometimes known as Spearman's " footrule ", is not of the general type of (2.1). Let us put

$$R = 1 - \frac{3S\,|\,d\,|}{n^2 - 1} \quad . \quad . \quad . \quad . \quad (2.47)$$

If two rankings are identical, $S|\,d| = 0$ and $R = 1$ as we should require.

Now if one ranking is the inverse of the other, suppose that $n$ is odd and equals $2m + 1$. Then, as in **1.15**,

$$\begin{aligned} S\,|\,d\,| &= 2\{2m + (2m-2) + (2m-4) + \ldots + 4 + 2\} \\ &= 2m(m+1) \end{aligned}$$

Hence

$$\begin{aligned} R &= 1 - \frac{6m(m+1)}{(2m+1)^2 - 1} \\ &= -0{\cdot}5 \quad . \quad . \quad . \quad . \quad . \quad (2.48) \end{aligned}$$

If $n$ is even, say $2m$, we find similarly

$$S\,|\,d\,| = 2m^2,$$

and hence

$$\begin{aligned} R &= 1 - \frac{6m^2}{4m^2 - 1} \\ &= -0{\cdot}5\left\{1 + \frac{3}{n^2 - 1}\right\} \quad . \quad . \quad . \quad (2.49) \end{aligned}$$

Thus the coefficient $R$ cannot have a minimum value $-1$ unless $n = 2$. For large even $n$ it rapidly approaches $-0{\cdot}5$ and for odd $n$ it must be $-0{\cdot}5$ in all cases. This is a defect which cannot be entirely remedied by taking a different multiplier from $3/(n^2-1)$ for $S|d|$ in (2.47).

If we were to write

$$R' = 1 - \frac{4S|d|}{n^2}$$

$R'$ would become $-1$ for even $n$ and $-1 + 2/n^2$ for odd $n$.

**2.21** Moreover, $R$ is much less sensitive than $\tau$ or $\rho$. If, for example, we write down the 24 permutations of 1 to 4 and correlate them with the natural order we find :

| Values of $\rho$ | Values of $R$ | Frequencies |
|---|---|---|
| 1·0 | 1·0 | 1 |
| 0·8 | 0·6 | 3 |
| 0·6 | 0·2 | 1 |
| 0·4 | 0·2 | 4 |
| 0·2 | 0·2 | 2 |
| 0·0 | − 0·2 | 2 |
| − 0·2 | − 0·2 | 2 |
| − 0·4 | − 0·2 | 4 |
| − 0·6 | − 0·2 | 1 |
| − 0·8 | − 0·6 | 3 |
| − 1·0 | − 0·6 | 1 |
| | | 24 |

For the same value of $R$, *e.g.* 0·2, $\rho$ may vary from 0·2 to 0·6 ; and for $R = -0{\cdot}2$ $\rho$ may vary from 0·0 to $-0{\cdot}6$.

Taking these features into account with the analytical difficulties of dealing with the sampling distribution of $R$, we may safely ignore it in favour of either $\tau$ or $\rho$.

### References

The main paper on generalised coefficients is that of Daniels (1944). See also references to Chapter 1. A powerful but sophisticated paper by Hoeffding in the *Annals of Mathematical Statistics* (1948) considers a very general class of statistic which includes rank coefficients as a special case.

For the property of **2.8** see Daniels (1948). For the inequalities in $\rho$ and $\tau$ see references to Chapter 1.

# CHAPTER 3

## TIED RANKS

**3.1** In practical applications of ranking methods there sometimes arise cases in which two or more individuals are so similar that no preference can be expressed between them. When an observer is ranking members by subjective judgments this effect may be due either to a genuine indistinguishability of the objects or to failure by the observer to distinguish such differences as exist. The members are then said to be *tied*. The arrangement of students in order of merit or by reference to examination marks is a familiar source of ties of this kind.

**3.2** The method which we shall adopt of allocating rank-numbers to tied individuals is to average the ranks which they would possess if they were distinguishable. For instance, if the observer ties the third and fourth members each is allotted the number $3\frac{1}{2}$, and if he ties the second to the seventh inclusive, each is allotted the number $\frac{1}{6}(2 + 3 + 4 + 5 + 6 + 7) = 4\frac{1}{2}$. This is sometimes known as the "mid-rank method". When there is nothing to choose between individuals, we must clearly rank them all alike if we rank them at all; and our method has the advantage that the sum of the ranks for all members remains the same as for an untied ranking.

**3.3** We have now to consider the effect of ties on the calculation of $\tau$ and $\rho$.

In **1.9** we saw that a score of $+1$ or $-1$ was allotted to a pair of members according as their ranks were in the right order or not. If they are tied we shall allot the score zero, midway between the two values which they might assume if they were not tied. The score $S$ is then easily calculated.

**3.4** A new point arises, however, in regard to the calculation of the denominator by which $S$ is to be divided to obtain $\tau$. We have two possibilities:

(*a*) We can use the denominator $\frac{1}{2}n(n-1)$ as for the untied form of $\tau$;

(*b*) We can replace $\frac{1}{2}n(n-1)$ by $\frac{1}{2}\sqrt{\{\Sigma a_{ij}^2 \Sigma b_{ij}^2\}}$, where $a_{ij}$ is the score of the $i$th and $j$th members in one ranking and $b_{ij}$ is the corresponding score in the other.

Where no ties exist, any term $a_{ij}^2$ is unity, so that $\Sigma a_{ij}^2$ reduces to the number of possible terms, namely $n(n-1)$; similarly for $\Sigma b_{ij}^2$ so that the expression $\frac{1}{2}\sqrt{\{\Sigma a_{ij}^2 \Sigma b_{ij}^2\}}$ reduces to $\frac{1}{2}n(n-1)$, as it should. The reason for adopting this expression in the tied case will be clear from **2.2** and **2.3**.

If there is a tie of $t$ consecutive members all the scores arising from any pair chosen from them is zero. There are $t(t-1)$ such pairs. Consequently the sum $\Sigma a_{ij}^2$ is $n(n-1) - \sum_t t(t-1)$, where $\sum_t$ stands for the summation over various sets of ties; for $n(n-1)$ is the sum which would be obtained if no ties were present, and this is to be reduced in virtue of the zero scores arising from the ties. If, therefore, we write

$$T = \tfrac{1}{2}\sum_t t(t-1). \qquad (3.1)$$

for ties in one ranking and

$$U = \tfrac{1}{2}\sum_u u(u-1) \qquad (3.2)$$

for ties in the other, our alternative form of the coefficient $\tau$ for tied ranks may be written

$$\tau = \frac{S}{\sqrt{\{\frac{1}{2}n(n-1) - T\}}\sqrt{\{\frac{1}{2}n(n-1) - U\}}} \qquad (3.3)$$

Before discussing the alternative forms further, let us consider an arithmetical example.

*Example 3.1*

Two rankings are given as follows:

| | | | | | | | | | | |
|---|---|---|---|---|---|---|---|---|---|---|
| *A* | 1 | $2\frac{1}{2}$ | $2\frac{1}{2}$ | $4\frac{1}{2}$ | $4\frac{1}{2}$ | $6\frac{1}{2}$ | $6\frac{1}{2}$ | 8 | $9\frac{1}{2}$ | $9\frac{1}{2}$ |
| *B* | 1 | 2 | $4\frac{1}{2}$ | $4\frac{1}{2}$ | $4\frac{1}{2}$ | $4\frac{1}{2}$ | 8 | 8 | 8 | 10 |

Except for ties, both rankings are in the same order and the correlation is high. Considering the first member in association with the other 9, we see that the contribution to $S$ is 9; the second and third members of $A$ are tied, so that they contribute nothing to $S$, whatever the $B$-score for this pair. The score of members associated with the second member will be found to be 7, and so on. The full score is

$$9 + 7 + 4 + 4 + 4 + 3 + 1 + 1 + 0 = 33.$$

If we adopt alternative ($a$) of **3.4** the value of $\tau$ is then given by

$$\tau_a = \frac{33}{45} = +0{\cdot}733.$$

Under alternative (*b*) we have, for the *A*-ranking,

$$\Sigma a_{ij}^2 = 45 - \tfrac{1}{2}(2 \times 1) - \tfrac{1}{2}(2 \times 1) - \tfrac{1}{2}(2 \times 1) - \tfrac{1}{2}(2 \times 1)$$
$$= 41$$

and for the *B*-ranking

$$\Sigma b_{ij}^2 = 45 - \tfrac{1}{2}(4 \times 3) - \tfrac{1}{2}(3 \times 2)$$
$$= 36.$$

Hence

$$\tau_b = \frac{33}{\sqrt{(41 \times 36)}}$$
$$= +0{\cdot}859.$$

The value given by alternative (*b*) must, of course, be greater than that of (*a*) in all cases. In the present instance it is substantially greater.

**3.5** From the general point of view developed in Chapter 2, the appropriate form of coefficient, as a true measure of correlation between two sets of numbers, is $\tau_b$. For example, if we are measuring the agreement between two judges in arranging a set of candidates in order of merit (no objective order necessarily existing) we should use $\tau_b$. Both judges may be wrong in relation to some objective order, and they may disagree with other judges, but that is not the point. We are measuring their agreement, not their accuracy.

Suppose, for instance, that both rankings are the same, that the last member of each is $n$, and that all the others are tied and hence have rank $\frac{1}{2}n$. Then $\tau_b = 1$, as it should be to express complete agreement between the rankings. But we also have, from (3.1) and (3.2),

$$T = U = \tfrac{1}{2}(n-1)(n-2)$$

and hence

$$\tfrac{1}{2}n(n-1) - T = n - 1.$$

Thus, since the score $S$ is also $n - 1$ (confirming that $\tau_b = 1$), we have

$$\tau_a = \frac{n-1}{\frac{1}{2}n(n-1)} = \frac{2}{n} \quad . \quad . \quad . \quad (3.4)$$

and for large $n$ this is nearly zero. Clearly $\tau_a$ is an inappropriate measure of *agreement.*

**3.6** Nevertheless, there may be cases where $\tau_a$ is a better measure than $\tau_b$. Suppose that there really exists an objective order. The purpose of correlating a ranking assigned by an observer is then to measure his accuracy. The form $\tau_b$ would give weight to the fact that if the observer produces ties the variation of his estimates is reduced. The calculation takes into account, so to speak, the clustering of his values *in spite of the fact that he ought not to produce ties because there really is an objective order.* In such a case it may be argued that the full divisor $\frac{1}{2}n(n-1)$ should be used in calculating $\tau$, *i.e.* that $\tau_a$ is the appropriate form.

Consider the case where our ranking is the natural order $1, \ldots n$ and the other has the first $(n-1)$ members tied (with ranks each $\frac{1}{2}n$) and the last member ranked as $n$. As in (3.4) we have

$$\tau_a = \frac{2}{n},$$

whereas

$$\tau_b = \frac{n-1}{\sqrt{\{\frac{1}{2}n(n-1)^2\}}} = \sqrt{\frac{2}{n}} \quad . \quad . \quad (3.5)$$

For example, with $n = 9$, $\tau_a = 0{\cdot}22$ and $\tau_b = 0{\cdot}47$. The first value seems nearer to what we should expect of a measure of agreement with an objective order. The observer has not got any pair in the wrong order, and has ranked one member correctly ; but he has been unable to distinguish between the first nine, and a value of 0·22 as a measure of his ability seems as much as he deserves. On the other hand, if the first ranking were not known to be objective but was just an expression of opinion from another observer of no greater known reliability, a value of 0·47 seems a fair measure of concordance.

**3.7** There is another interesting way of looking at the problem of tied ranks. Suppose we regard any tied set $t$ as due to inability to distinguish real differences. We may then ask : what is the *average* value of $\tau$ over all the $t!$ possible ways of assigning integral ranks * to the tied members ?

If we replace any tied set $t$ by integral ranks and average for all $t!$ possible orders we get the same result as by replacing the scores $a_{ij}$ for the tied members by zero ; for in the $t!$ arrangements each pair will occur an equal number of times in the order $XY$ and in the order $YX$, so that the allocation of $+1$ in the one case and $-1$ in the other is equivalent to allocating zero on the average. Thus

* The symbol $t!$ (read " factorial $t$ ") stands for the number

$$1 \times 2 \times 3 \times \ldots \times (t-1) \times t.$$

It is the number of different ways of arranging $t$ objects in order. For instance, four objects $A$, $B$, $C$, $D$ can be arranged in 24 different orders.

we may regard $\tau_a$ as an average coefficient, such as would be obtained if the tied ranks were replaced by integral ranks in all possible ways, $\tau$ calculated for each, and an arithmetic mean taken of the resulting values.

**3.8** We turn to consider the analogous problems for the rank correlation coefficient $\rho$. Again we shall have the choice of two denominators and two coefficients, which we may denote by $\rho_a$ and $\rho_b$. If there are sets of ties in the two rankings typified by $t$ and $u$ we define

$$\left.\begin{aligned} T' &= \tfrac{1}{12} \sum_t (t^3 - t) \\ U' &= \tfrac{1}{12} \sum_u (u^3 - u) \end{aligned}\right\} \qquad (3.6)$$

Then we have

$$\rho_a = 1 - \frac{6\{S(d^2) + T' + U'\}}{n^3 - n} \qquad (3.7)$$

$$\rho_b = \frac{\frac{1}{6}(n^3 - n) - S(d^2) - T' - U'}{\sqrt{[\{\frac{1}{6}(n^3 - n) - 2T'\}\{\frac{1}{6}(n^3 - n) - 2U'\}]}} \qquad (3.8)$$

We shall prove these formulae below, but before doing so we will consider an example.

*Example 3.2*

Consider again the two rankings of Example 3.1—

| | | | | | | | | | | |
|---|---|---|---|---|---|---|---|---|---|---|
| *A* | 1 | $2\frac{1}{2}$ | $2\frac{1}{2}$ | $4\frac{1}{2}$ | $4\frac{1}{2}$ | $6\frac{1}{2}$ | $6\frac{1}{2}$ | 8 | $9\frac{1}{2}$ | $9\frac{1}{2}$ |
| *B* | 1 | 2 | $4\frac{1}{2}$ | $4\frac{1}{2}$ | $4\frac{1}{2}$ | $4\frac{1}{2}$ | 8 | 8 | 8 | 10 |

In the first ranking there are four tied pairs ($t = 2$) and hence

$$T' = \tfrac{4}{12}(2^3 - 2) = 2.$$

In the second there is one set for which $t = 4$ and one for which $t = 3$, so that

$$\begin{aligned} U' &= \tfrac{1}{12}(4^3 - 4 + 3^3 - 3) \\ &= 7. \end{aligned}$$

We also find

$$S(d^2) = 13.$$

Hence, from (3.7),

$$\begin{aligned} \rho_a &= 1 - \frac{6(13 + 7 + 2)}{990} \\ &= 0{\cdot}867 \end{aligned}$$

and from (3.8)

$$\rho_b = \frac{165 - 22}{\sqrt{(161 \times 151)}}$$
$$= 0{\cdot}917.$$

**3.9** It is useful to note that (3.8) can be put in the form

$$\rho_b = \frac{\frac{1}{6}(n^3 - n) - S(d^2) - T' - U'}{\{\frac{1}{6}(n^3 - n) - (T' + U')\}\sqrt{\left[1 - \frac{(T' - U')^2}{\{\frac{1}{6}(n^3 - n) - (T' + U')\}^2}\right]}} \quad . \quad . \quad . \quad (3.9)$$

Thus, if $T'$ and $U'$ are small compared with $\frac{1}{6}(n^3 - n)$, we have approximately (and exactly if $T' = U'$)

$$\rho_b = 1 - \frac{S(d^2)}{\frac{1}{6}(n^3 - n) - (T' + U')} \quad . \quad . \quad (3.10)$$

or, slightly more approximately,

$$\rho_b = 1 - \frac{S(d^2)}{\frac{1}{6}(n^3 - n)} \quad . \quad . \quad . \quad (3.11)$$

which is the ordinary formula for $\rho$ in the untied case. We therefore expect that when the ties are not very numerous the use of the formulae (3.9) or (3.10) will make little difference to the numerical values given by the use of (3.11).

For instance, in the data of Example 3.2 we find for the form (3.10)

$$\rho_b = 1 - \frac{13}{165 - 9}$$
$$= 0{\cdot}9167$$

and for the form (3.11)

$$\rho_b = 1 - \frac{13}{165} = 0{\cdot}9212.$$

The value given by (3.8) is 0·9171. All three values agree to the nearest second place of decimals.

**3.10** To establish formulae (3.7) and (3.8) we have to use some of the results of Chapter 2. We saw in **2.6** that $\rho$ may be regarded as the product-moment correlation between the ranks. Suppose we adopt the same viewpoint when some of the ranks are tied.

For a set of untied ranks the sum of squares of ranks is

$$\Sigma p_i^2 = \tfrac{1}{6}n(n + 1)(2n + 1)$$

where $p_i$ is the rank of the $i$th individual; and the sum of ranks is

$$\Sigma\, p_i = \tfrac{1}{2}n(n+1).$$

If a set of $t$ ranks are tied the sum of ranks remains the same but the sum of squares is altered. Suppose the ranks $p_k+1, \ldots p_k+t$ are tied. Then the sum of squares is reduced by

$$\begin{aligned}(p_k+1)^2 + (p_k+2)^2 + \ldots + (p_k+t)^2 - t\{p_k + \tfrac{1}{2}(t+1)\}^2 \\ = tp_k^2 + 2p_k(1+2+\ldots+t) + 1^2 + 2^2 + \ldots + t^2 \\ - t\{p_k^2 + p_k(t+1) + \tfrac{1}{4}(t+1)^2\} \\ = \tfrac{1}{12}(t^3 - t).\end{aligned}$$

It is convenient to introduce at this point (for the reader who has omitted Chapter 2) the idea of variance. This quantity is defined as the mean of the squares of deviations of a set of values from their mean. It is the square of the standard deviation. Thus for an untied ranking the variance is

$$\frac{1}{n}\Sigma\,\{p_i - \tfrac{1}{2}(n+1)\}^2 = \frac{1}{n}\Sigma\, p_i^2 - \tfrac{1}{4}(n+1)^2 = \frac{1}{12}(n^2-1),$$

the summation extending over the $n$ ranks. It follows that for a tied ranking the variance is

$$\begin{aligned}&\frac{1}{12}(n^2-1) - \frac{1}{12n}\Sigma\,(t^3-t) \\ &= \frac{1}{2n}\{\tfrac{1}{6}(n^3-n) - 2T'\} \quad . \quad . \quad . \quad (3.12)\end{aligned}$$

If two quantities $x$ and $y$ are measured from their mean we may similarly define their covariance cov $(x, y)$ as the function $\frac{1}{n}\Sigma\,(xy)$. Since

$$x^2 + y^2 - 2xy = (x-y)^2$$

we have

$$\text{var}\, x + \text{var}\, y - 2\,\text{cov}\,(x, y) = \text{var}\,(x-y)$$

The correlation $\rho_b$ may be defined as

$$\begin{aligned}\rho_b &= \frac{\text{cov}\,(p, q)}{\sqrt{(\text{var}\, p\ \text{var}\, q)}} \\ &= \frac{1}{2}\,\frac{\text{var}\, p + \text{var}\, q - \text{var}\,(p-q)}{\sqrt{(\text{var}\, p\ \text{var}\, q)}} \quad . \quad . \quad (3.13)\end{aligned}$$

It is easily verified that this gives $\rho_b$ for the untied case. Let us apply it to the tied case. Since var $(p - q)$ is still equal to $\frac{1}{n}S(d^2)$ we find from (3.13), on using (3.12),

$$\rho_b = \frac{1}{2}\frac{\frac{1}{6}(n^3 - n) - 2T' + \frac{1}{6}(n^3 - n) - 2U' - 2S(d^2)}{\sqrt{[\{\frac{1}{6}(n^3 - n) - 2T'\}\{\frac{1}{6}(n^3 - n) - 2U'\}]}}$$

which reduces to (3.8). The formula of (3.9) for $\rho_a$ follows in a similar way.

**3.11** What has been said above about the different circumstances in which $\tau_a$ and $\tau_b$ may be preferred applies also to a choice between $\rho_a$ and $\rho_b$. To complete the analogy we need only prove that $\rho_a$ is the average of the values of coefficients which would be obtained if the ties were replaced by integral ranks in all possible ways.

If the $A$-ranking is held fixed, then the average covariance for all $t!$ arrangements of a set of $t$ ranks in the other ranking $B$ is the covariance of the fixed ranks in $A$ and the average of the ranks in $B$; but this latter provides the values of the tied ranks. It follows that the average covariance is the covariance of the tied rankings, for the effects of different sets of ties are additive; and thus the result follows.

*Example 3.3*

If two rankings are identical, the last member in each is ranked $n$, and the other $n - 1$ are tied with rank $\frac{1}{2}n$, we clearly have

$$\rho_b = 1.$$

But for $\rho_a$ we find

$$U' = T' = \tfrac{1}{12}\{(n-1)^3 - (n-1)\}$$
$$= \tfrac{1}{12}n(n-1)(n-2)$$

and $S(d^2) = 0$.
Thus, from (3.7),

$$\rho_a = \frac{\frac{1}{6}(n+1)(n)(n-1) - \frac{1}{6}n(n-1)(n-2)}{\frac{1}{6}(n+1)(n)(n-1)}$$
$$= \frac{3}{n+1}$$

We find the same kind of difference between the two types of $\rho$ as between the two types of $\tau$ in **3.5**.

**3.12** A fairly common problem in psychology is to measure the relationship between two qualities, one of which provides a ranking and the other a *dichotomy* or classification into two classes according as the individual possesses a certain attribute or not. Consider the following ranking of 15 girls and boys according to merit in an examination :

| Rank : | 1 | 2 | 3 | 4 | 5 | 6 | 7 | 8 | 9 | 10 | 11 | 12 | 13 | 14 | 15 |
|---|---|---|---|---|---|---|---|---|---|---|---|---|---|---|---|
| Sex : | *B* | *B* | *G* | *B* | *G* | *G* | *B* | *B* | *B* | *G* | *B* | *G* | *B* | *G* | *G* |

We are interested here in whether there is any connection between sex and success—whether the boys did better than the girls on the average or vice versa.

We will imagine that the division into sex is itself a ranking. There are 8 boys and 7 girls and we will suppose that the first 8 members of the ranking by sex are tied, and so for the next group of 7. The actual values of the tied ranks will be $4\frac{1}{2}$ in the first case and 12 in the second, so that the pair of rankings may be written—

| Ranking *A* : | 1 | 2 | 3 | 4 | 5 | 6 | 7 | 8 | 9 | 10 | 11 | 12 | 13 | 14 | 15 |
|---|---|---|---|---|---|---|---|---|---|---|---|---|---|---|---|
| Ranking *B* : | $4\frac{1}{2}$ | $4\frac{1}{2}$ | 12 | $4\frac{1}{2}$ | 12 | 12 | $4\frac{1}{2}$ | $4\frac{1}{2}$ | $4\frac{1}{2}$ | 12 | $4\frac{1}{2}$ | 12 | $4\frac{1}{2}$ | 12 | 12 |

We may now calculate $\tau_b$ for these rankings. We find

$$S = 7 + 7 - 6 + 6 - 5 - 5 + 4 + 4 + 4 - 2 + 3 - 1 + 2 + 0 = 18$$

$$T = 0$$

$$U = \tfrac{1}{2}(8 \times 7) + \tfrac{1}{2}(7 \times 6) = 49$$

$$\tau = \frac{18}{\sqrt{(105 \times 56)}} = +0{\cdot}24$$

This indicates some positive correlation between order of success and the order of sex, which we have chosen by putting boys first. (Had we put girls first, of course, we should have obtained $\tau = -0{\cdot}24$ leading to the same conclusion.) In short, the boys seem to be better than the girls. Whether the evidence is sufficiently indicative of " real " correlation is a matter of significance which we shall discuss in the next chapter.

*Example 3.4*

A number of workers in a factory were interviewed and an assessment made of their adaptation to living conditions. They were assessed as " efficient " or " overactive ". Statements by the men were also available concerning the frequency of nocturia. For men aged 50–59 years the following was observed :

Ranking according to frequency of nocturia (least nocturia given highest rank)—

| " Efficient " : | $2\frac{1}{2}$ | $2\frac{1}{2}$ | $2\frac{1}{2}$ | $2\frac{1}{2}$ | $6\frac{1}{2}$ | $6\frac{1}{2}$ | 10 | 10 | 10 | 10 | 14 | 14 |
|---|---|---|---|---|---|---|---|---|---|---|---|---|
| " Overactive " : | 5 | 10 | 14 | 16 | 17 | | | | | | | |

A cursory inspection of the figures indicates that the overactive group had the greatest frequency of nocturia. Let us measure the relationship with $\tau_b$. We find, writing $E$ and $O$ for efficient and overactive respectively—

| | | | | | | | | | | | | | | | | |
|---|---|---|---|---|---|---|---|---|---|---|---|---|---|---|---|---|
| Ranking $A$: | $2\frac{1}{2}$ | $2\frac{1}{2}$ | $2\frac{1}{2}$ | $2\frac{1}{2}$ | 5 | $6\frac{1}{2}$ | $6\frac{1}{2}$ | 10 | 10 | 10 | 10 | 10 | 14 | 14 | 14 | 16 | 17 |
| Ranking $B$: | $E$ | $E$ | $E$ | $E$ | $O$ | $E$ | $E$ | $O$ | $E$ | $E$ | $E$ | $E$ | $E$ | $E$ | $O$ | $O$ | $O$ |

If we wish we can replace the $E$'s and $O$'s by rankings, but this is unnecessary for the calculation of $S$. We find

$$\begin{aligned} S &= 5 + 5 + 5 + 5 - 8 + 4 + 4 - 2 + 3 + 3 + 3 + 3 + 2 + 2 \\ &= 34. \\ T &= \tfrac{1}{2}(4 \times 3) + \tfrac{1}{2}(2 \times 1) + \tfrac{1}{2}(5 \times 4) + \tfrac{1}{2}(3 \times 2 \\ &= 20. \\ U &= \tfrac{1}{2}(12 \times 11) + \tfrac{1}{2}(5 \times 4) \\ &= 76 \end{aligned}$$

Thus

$$\tau_b = \frac{34}{\sqrt{(116 \times 60)}} = +\,0{\cdot}41.$$

The reader should check the calculation of $S$. Taking the first member in ranking $A$, for example, we see that no contribution to $S$ can arise from the other members in $A$ with rank $2\frac{1}{2}$, so that it is only subsequent members that need be considered. The first member of ranking $B$, being an $E$, contributes $+1$ only with members which are $O$, of which there are five in the subsequent members.

Similarly for the second, third and fourth members of $A$. When we come to the fifth, with rank 5, all subsequent members of $A$ are liable to contribute. In the $B$-ranking the fifth member is an $O$, and hence contributions of $-1$ arise from subsequent members which are $E$, 8 in number. And so on.

**3.13** If a ranking consists of a dichotomy with $x$ and $n - x = y$ members in the two classes

$$\begin{aligned} \tfrac{1}{2}n(n-1) - T &= \tfrac{1}{2}n(n-1) - \tfrac{1}{2}x(x-1) - \tfrac{1}{2}(n-x)(n-x-1) \\ &= xy. \end{aligned}$$

Thus we have

$$\tau_b = \frac{S}{\sqrt{[xy\{\frac{1}{2}n(n-1) - U\}]}} \quad . \quad . \quad (3.14)$$

**3.14** Consider now the extreme case when both rankings consist of a dichotomy, one, say, into $x$ and $n - x = y$ members, the other into $p$ and $n - p = q$ members. We then have for the denominator in $\tau_b$ the simple expression $\sqrt{(xypq)}$. We may express the data in what is usually known as a $2 \times 2$ table, thus:

First Quality

| | | Possessing | Not-possessing | Totals |
|---|---|---|---|---|
| Second Quality | Possessing | $a$ | $b$ | $p$ |
| | Not-possessing | $c$ | $d$ | $q$ |
| | | $x$ | $y$ | $n$ |

. . . (3.15)

Any member of the class possessing both qualities ($a$ in number) taken with any member of the class not possessing either ($d$ in number) gives a pair with the same order in either ranking and hence contributes $+1$ to $S$. Similarly any member of the $b$-class with any member of the $c$-class contributes $-1$. The others contribute nothing. Hence

$$S = ad - bc$$

and

$$\tau_b = \frac{ad - bc}{\sqrt{(xypq)}} \quad . \quad . \quad . \quad . \quad (3.16)$$

This is one useful form of a coefficient measuring association in a $2 \times 2$ table. There are other coefficients of the same kind, but it is interesting that for the extreme case when both rankings are so tied as to be dichotomous the coefficient $\tau$ becomes one of the measures of association which have been developed in other connections.*

*Example 3.5*

Reverting to the data of Example 3.4, suppose that it was possible

* See, for instance, M. G. Kendall, *The Advanced Theory of Statistics*, Vol. 1, Chapter 13. If $\chi^2$ is the square contingency for the $2 \times 2$ table, calculated in the usual way, $\tau_b^2$ for the table is equal to $\chi^2/n$.

only to grade nocturia into normal and excessive with the following results :

TABLE 3.1

Nocturia

| | | Normal | Excessive | Totals |
|---|---|---|---|---|
| Assessment | Efficient . . . | 10 | 2 | 12 |
| | Overactive . . | 2 | 3 | 5 |
| | TOTAL . . . | 12 | 5 | 17 |

We then have

$$\tau_b = \frac{30 - 4}{\sqrt{(12 \times 5 \times 12 \times 5)}}$$
$$= + 0{\cdot}43$$

which is in good agreement with the value of 0·41 found in Example 3.4.

## Application to ordered contingency tables

**3.15** A similar idea to the one we have used for the 2 × 2 table can be used to provide a measure of association in a contingency

TABLE 3.2

3242 MEN AGED 30–39 ; UNAIDED DISTANCE VISION

(*from A. Stuart* (1953))

Left eye

| | | Highest grade | Second grade | Third grade | Lowest grade | Totals |
|---|---|---|---|---|---|---|
| Right eye | Highest grade . | 821 | 112 | 85 | 35 | 1053 |
| | Second grade . | 116 | 494 | 145 | 27 | 782 |
| | Third grade . | 72 | 151 | 583 | 87 | 893 |
| | Lowest grade . | 43 | 34 | 106 | 331 | 514 |
| | Totals . . . | 1052 | 791 | 919 | 480 | 3242 |

table grouped in rows and columns, provided that there are natural orders in these arrays. Consider, for example, the data in Table 3.2, page 45, showing the grade of vision in the right and left eye of 3242 men aged 30–39. We are interested in the relationship between the grades in right and left eyes and we note that there is an order of rows and columns.

Now goodness of vision (with respect to distance) may be regarded for this purpose as a quality by which the men can be ranked, and any man will have a rank in the two rankings according to right and left eye. We may regard the classification into grades as a rather extensive tying of the 3242 ranks. Thus, for instance, with the right eye, the first 1053 are tied, then the next 782, then the next 893 and finally the last 514. A value of $\tau$ calculated for such a table, with due allowances for ties, will measure the association between the vision of right and left eyes for the group of men as a whole.

**3.16** To calculate such a coefficient we require the sum $S$. There will be a positive contribution from each member of any cell with each member lying below it to the right in the table; *e.g.* from the 821 men in the top left-hand corner there arises a contribution

$$821(494 + 145 + 27 + 151 + 583 + 87 + 34 + 106 + 331).$$

Similarly there will be a negative contribution arising from cells below and to the left; *e.g.* the score associated with the third-grade left eye and second-grade right eye will be

$$145(-72 - 151 - 43 - 34 + 87 + 331).$$

No score will arise from the bottom line of the table. We find

$$\begin{aligned} S &= 821(1958) + 112(1048) + 85(-465) + 35(-1744) \\ &\quad + 116(1292) + 494(992) + 145(118) + 27(-989) \\ &\quad + 72(471) + 151(394) + 583(254) + 87(-183) \\ &= 2,480,223. \end{aligned}$$

For the denominator of $\tau_b$ we have the two contributions

$$\tfrac{1}{2}(3242)(3241) - \tfrac{1}{2}(1053)(1052) - \tfrac{1}{2}(782)(781) - \tfrac{1}{2}(893)(892) - \tfrac{1}{2}(514)(513) = 3,864,293$$

$$\tfrac{1}{2}(3242)(3241) - \tfrac{1}{2}(1052)(1051) - \tfrac{1}{2}(791)(790) - \tfrac{1}{2}(919)(918) - \tfrac{1}{2}(480)(479) = 3,851,609.$$

Hence
$$\tau_b = \frac{2,480,223}{\sqrt{(3,864,293 \times 3,851,609)}} = 0{\cdot}643,$$

which provides a measure of the relationship.

**3.17** Considered as a measure of contingency the alternative form $\tau_a$ has one property (shared by certain other contingency coefficients) of a rather undesirable kind, namely that it cannot attain unity for tables with unequal numbers of rows and columns. This is not a very serious drawback in cases where ties are relatively infrequent, but for heavily tied rankings it may be preferable to use a coefficient for which the limits are attainable.

Consider the maximum score which can be produced by $n$ members arrayed in a table of $u$ rows and $v$ columns. This will be attained when all the observations lie in a longest diagonal of the table and the frequencies in the diagonal cells are as nearly equal as possible. A longest diagonal contains, say, $m$ cells where $m$ is the smaller of $u$ and $v$. If $n$ is a multiple of $m$ the maximum score is

$$2\left(\frac{n}{m}\right)^2\{1+2+\ldots+(m-1)\} = n^2\frac{m-1}{m} \quad . \quad (3.17)$$

When $n$ is not a multiple of $m$ this score is not attainable, but is very nearly so for large $n$ and small $m$. We therefore define

$$\tau_c = \frac{2S}{n^2\frac{m-1}{m}} \quad . \quad . \quad . \quad . \quad (3.18)$$

We have at once

$$\tau_c = \frac{n-1}{n}\frac{m}{m-1}\tau_a \quad . \quad . \quad . \quad (3.19)$$

In the example we considered $n = 3242$ and $m = 4$ so that

$$\tau_c = \frac{2 \times 2,480,223}{\frac{3}{4}(3242)^2} = 0{\cdot}629,$$

as against the value of $\tau_b$ of $0{\cdot}643$.

**3.18** For a table with the same number of rows as columns (as, for example, in the $2 \times 2$ table) $\tau_b$ can attain unity if the frequencies in the table lie only in the main diagonal. In fact, let the frequencies be $f_1, f_2 \ldots f_m$. The score $S$ is

$$f_1(n-f_1) + f_2(n-f_1-f_2) + \ldots f_m(n-f_1-f_2 \ldots -f_m)$$

$$= n\sum f_i - \sum f_i^2 - \sum_{i<j} f_i f_j$$

$$= \tfrac{1}{2}(n^2 - \Sigma f_i^2).$$

The denominator of $\tau_b$ for both row and column totals is

$$\begin{aligned}&\tfrac{1}{2}n(n-1) - \Sigma\,\tfrac{1}{2}f_i(f_i - 1)\\ &= \tfrac{1}{2}(n^2 - \Sigma f_i^2)\end{aligned}$$

and hence $\tau_b$ is unity. The coefficient $\tau_c$ is mainly of use when rows and columns are not the same in number.

## References

See " Student " (1921), Dubois (1939), Woodbury (1940), Kendall (1945, 1947), Sillitto (1947), and Whitfield (1947). For applications to contingency tables, see Kendall (1949) and Stuart (1953).

# CHAPTER 4

## TESTS OF SIGNIFICANCE

**4.1** The rankings with which we deal in practice are usually based on a set of individuals which themselves are only samples from a much larger population. It is of some interest to be able to measure the relationship between mathematical and musical ability in a given class of children; but it is of much greater interest to be able to say, if this class is chosen at random from a certain population of children, how far the results for the sample throw light on the relationship in that population. In this chapter we shall consider the question: given a value of a rank correlation in a sample, how far can we conclude that there exists correlation in the population from which the sample was chosen? In short, we shall try to *test the significance* of observed rank correlations in the special sense of the statistical theory of sampling.

**4.2** Suppose that in the present population there is no relationship between the two qualities under consideration. Then if a sample is chosen at random, any order for the quality $A$ is just as likely to appear with a given order for $B$ as any other $A$-order. If we choose some arbitrary order for $B$ (it does not matter which, so we will take the natural order $1, \ldots n$), then all the $n!$ possible rankings of the numbers 1 to $n$ for $A$ are equally probable. Each accordingly has the probability $1/n!$ (For the present we confine ourselves to the untied case.)

Now to each of the possible arrangements of the $A$-ranking there will correspond a value of $\tau$ or $\rho$. The totality of such values, $n!$ in number, may be classified according to the actual value of $\tau$ or $\rho$, ranging from $-1$ to $+1$, in what is called a *frequency-distribution.* This distribution is fundamental to our present investigation and we proceed to consider it in some detail.

**4.3** For a ranking of four there are 24 possible arrangements. If the reader writes them down and correlates each with the natural order 1, 2, 3, 4 he will find the following values of $S$:

| Value of $S$ | Frequency of Rankings with the Assigned Value of $S$ |
|---|---|
| $-6$ | 1 |
| $-4$ | 3 |
| $-2$ | 5 |
| 0 | 6 |
| 2 | 5 |
| 4 | 3 |
| 6 | 1 |
| TOTAL : | 24 |

Thus the greatest frequency of the values of $S$ is 6, attained when $S = 0$. The distribution is symmetrical about this value, and as $S$ becomes greater in absolute value the frequencies fall away to unity.

**4.4** The corresponding distribution for $n = 8$ is as follows (we show only zero or positive values of $S$, the negative values being given by symmetry):

| Values of $S$ | Frequency of Rankings with the Assigned Value of $S$ |
|---|---|
| 0 | 3,826 |
| 2 | 3,736 |
| 4 | 3,450 |
| 6 | 3,017 |
| 8 | 2,493 |
| 10 | 1,940 |
| 12 | 1,415 |
| 14 | 961 |
| 16 | 602 |
| 18 | 343 |
| 20 | 174 |
| 22 | 76 |
| 24 | 27 |
| 26 | 7 |
| 28 | 1 |
| TOTAL (of whole distribution) : | 40,320 |

In Fig. 4.1 we have drawn a frequency-polygon of this distribution, graphing the frequency ($f$) as ordinate against $S$ as abscissa.

Once again we find a maximum value at $S = 0$ and a steady fall in the frequency as $S$ increases.

**4.5** In the next chapter we shall see how to derive these distributions for various values of $n$. For the present we state without proof—

($a$) that the distributions are always symmetrical. If $\frac{1}{2}n(n - 1)$

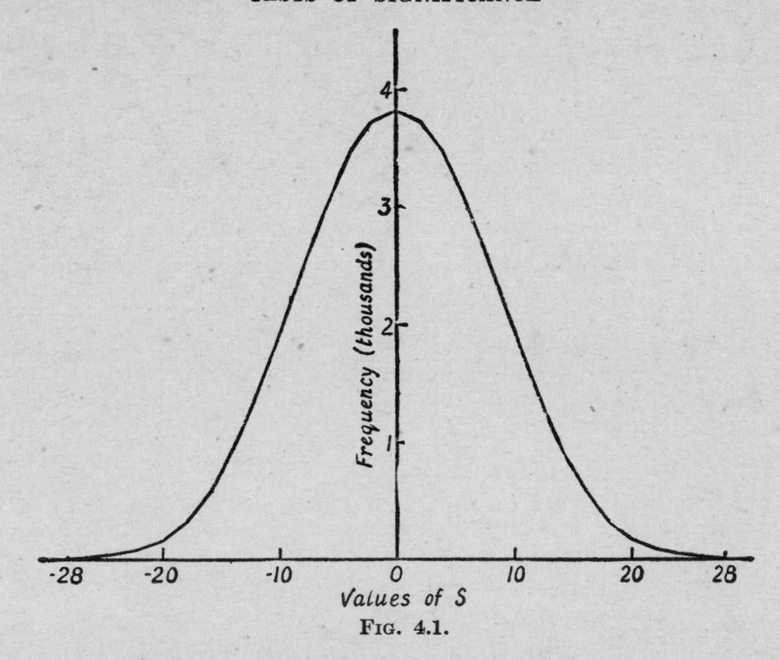


FIG. 4.1.

is even, $S$ can take only even values and there is a maximum frequency for $S = 0$. If $\frac{1}{2}n(n - 1)$ is odd, $S$ can take only odd values and there is a pair of maximum frequencies at $S = \pm 1$;

(b) that the frequencies fall away steadily from the maximum to the value of unity for $S = \pm \frac{1}{2}n(n - 1)$;

(c) that as $n$ increases, the shape of the frequency polygon tends to that of the *normal curve*

$$f(x) = \frac{1}{\sigma\sqrt{(2\pi)}}e^{-\frac{x^2}{2\sigma^2}} \quad . \quad . \quad . \quad (4.1)$$

and that for $n$ greater than 10 this curve provides a satisfactory approximation to the polygon. The parameter $\sigma$ of the curve, which is equal to its standard deviation, is given by

$$\sigma^2 = \tfrac{1}{18}n(n - 1)(2n + 5) \quad . \quad . \quad . \quad (4.2)$$

If the normal curve with this standard deviation were drawn in Fig. 4.1 it would fall so close to the polygon as to be barely distinguishable on this scale.

**4.6** The tendency of the distribution of frequencies to normality is a very useful property which enables us to avoid the calculation of the actual distribution for $n > 10$. For $n \leqslant 10$ the distributions have been worked out and form the basis of Appendix Table 1. This table shows the proportionate frequencies (*i.e.* the actual frequencies divided by $n!$) for which $S$ attains or exceeds a specified value, this being the form in which the information is most often required.

**4.7** Let us now consider the use of these distributions in testing the significance of $\tau$. A test of $\tau$ is equivalent to a test of the corresponding value of $S$, one being a multiple of the other, and we shall find it arithmetically more convenient to deal with $S$.

If there is no connection between the two qualities, a pair of rankings chosen at random will give some value of $S$ lying between the limits $\pm \frac{1}{2}n(n-1)$. The greater part of such values will cluster round the value zero. We shall adopt the following criterion : if the observed value of $S$ is such that it is very improbable that such a value *or greater* in absolute value could have arisen by chance, we shall reject the hypothesis that the two qualities are independent. This amounts to saying that if an observed value of $S$ lies in the " tails " of the distribution of $S$ away from its mean value we shall reject the hypothesis. Just where we draw the line to decide on what are the tails or what is very improbable is a matter of convention. Usually we shall regard a probability of 0·05 or one of 0·01 as small and one of 0·001 as very small. We sometimes speak of a " 5 per cent probability level " of $S$, meaning that value of $S$ which is attained or exceeded with probability 0·05, and similarly for a " 1 per cent probability level " or a " 0·1 per cent probability level ". The corresponding values of $S$ may be termed, for example, the " 5 per cent significance point ". To say that an observed $S$ lies beyond the 5 per cent significance point means that the probability of arriving at such a value or greater (in absolute value) is less than 0·05.

If we suspect beforehand that there is positive correlation we may prefer to consider the probability that $S$ lies in the upper tail only ; and similarly, if negative correlation is expected we may confine attention to the lower tail. This would amount to calculating probabilities that $S$ attained or exceeded some given value or fell short of some value, as the case might be, instead of attaining or exceeding some figure regardless of sign.

*Example 4.1*

In a random sample giving a ranking of 10 we find a value of $\tau$ equal to $-0{\cdot}11$. Is such a value significant ?

The corresponding value of $S$ was $-5$. From Appendix Table 1 we see that the proportion of rankings which give a value of $-5$ or less and $+5$ or more is twice 0·364, namely 0·728. This is quite large and we need not reject the hypothesis of independence of the two qualities. In other words, the observed value is not significant. It could well have arisen by chance from a population in which mathematical and musical ability are unrelated.

Had the observed value of $\tau$ been $+0{\cdot}56$, corresponding to a value of $S = 25$, we find for the probability that $|S| \geqslant 25$ (is greater than or equal to 25 in absolute value) 0·028. This is very small, and we should have concluded that the abilities were not independent in the parent population.

We have based our inference on *absolute* values of $S$, and this appears to be the best course, particularly when the sampling distribution is symmetrical; but if necessary we can draw inferences based on the actual values. If the probability that $S$ is greater than some value $S_0$ in absolute value is $P_0$, say

$$\text{Prob } \{|S| > S_0\} = P_0,$$

then the probability that $S > S_0$, where $S_0$ is positive, is $\frac{1}{2}P_0$, and so is the probability that $S < S_0$ where $S_0$ is negative. For instance, with $S_0 = 25$,

$$\text{Prob } \{S \geqslant S_0\} = 0{\cdot}014,$$

and with $S = -5$

$$\text{Prob } \{S \leqslant -5\} = 0{\cdot}364.$$

In using probability tables the reader should remember which type is being considered. A 5 per cent point where absolute values are employed is only a 2·5 per cent point where actual values are concerned.

## Correction for continuity

**4.8** Where $n$ is greater than 10 we shall use the tables of areas under the normal curve as an approximation to the exact values based on the distribution of $S$. The appropriate areas are given in Appendix Table 3 and show the probability that a given multiple of the standard deviation (*not* in absolute value) will be attained or exceeded. It is a useful rule to remember that for the normal distribution the probability is 0·05 that a value will exceed 1·96 times the standard deviation *in absolute value*, 0·01 that it will exceed

2·58 times the s.d. in absolute value, and 0·001 that it will exceed 3·3 times the s.d. in absolute value.*

In using this table we have to remember that we are replacing the distribution of $S$, which is discontinuous and possesses frequencies separated from one another by two units, by a continuous distribution. To make the approximation better we shall regard the frequency $f$ at $S$, instead of being concentrated at $S$, as spread uniformly over a range from $S - 1$ to $S + 1$. To compare with areas of the normal curve we shall regard the tail as " beginning " at $S - 1$, that is to say, we shall subtract unity from the observed $S$ if it is positive (and add unity if it is negative) before expressing it as a multiple of the standard error. This is known as a " correction for continuity ". The following example will make the procedure clear.

*Example 4.2*

In a pair of rankings of 20 the value of $S$ observed is 58 and accordingly $\tau = 0{\cdot}31$. Is this significant ?

From (4.2) we find

$$\sigma^2 = \text{var } S = \tfrac{1}{18}(20 \times 19 \times 45) = 950$$
$$\sigma = 30{\cdot}82.$$

For $S$ corrected for continuity we have the value 57, and thus

$$S \text{ (corrected)} = \frac{57}{30{\cdot}82}\sigma = 1{\cdot}85\sigma.$$

From Appendix Table 3 we see that the probability of a deviation less than $1{\cdot}85\sigma$ is about 0·9678. The probability that 1·85 is obtained or exceeded in absolute value is thus about $2\ (1 - 0{\cdot}9678) = 0{\cdot}064$. This is small, but not very small. We suspect that the observed value of $\tau$ is significant but cannot reach a very definite decision.

Let us compare a value given by the normal approximation when $n = 9$. Suppose the observed $S$ is 20, corresponding to $\tau = 0{\cdot}56$. From (4.2) we have

$$\sigma = \sqrt{\tfrac{1}{18}(9 \times 8 \times 23)}$$
$$= 9{\cdot}592.$$

* The standard deviation of a distribution of sample values (*i.e.* a sampling distribution) is called the " standard error ". Its square is known as the " sampling variance ", or simply the " variance ", and is written " var ". Thus var $S = \sigma_s^2 = \frac{1}{18}n(n - 1)(2n + 5)$.

With a correction for continuity

$$\frac{S-1}{\sigma} = \frac{19}{9{\cdot}592} = 1{\cdot}981.$$

The probability that this will be attained or exceeded in absolute value is seen, from Appendix Table 3, to be about 0·048. The exact value, from Appendix Table 1, is 0·044. Had we made no correction for continuity we should have found a value of 0·037.

**4.9** When ties are present the above formula (4.2) for the standard error of $S$ requires some modification. If there are ties of extent $t$ in one ranking and $u$ in the other, then the variance of the distribution obtained by correlating one ranking with all $n!$ possible arrangements of the other is given by

$$\text{var } S = \tfrac{1}{18}\{n(n-1)(2n+5) - \sum_t t(t-1)(2t+5) - \sum_u u(u-1)(2u+5)\}$$
$$+ \frac{1}{9n(n-1)(n-2)}\{\sum_t t(t-1)(t-2)\}\{\sum_u u(u-1)(u-2)\}$$
$$+ \frac{1}{2n(n-1)}\{\sum_t t(t-1)\}\{\sum_u u(u-1)\} \quad . \quad . \quad . \quad (4.3)$$

If only one ranking contains ties, so that all $u$'s are zero,

$$\text{var } S = \tfrac{1}{18}\{n(n-1)(2n+5) - \sum_t t(t-1)(2t+5)\} \quad . \quad (4.4)$$

We shall prove these results in the next chapter.

**4.10** As for the untied case, the distribution of $\tau$ for any fixed number of ties tends to normality as $n$ increases, and there is probably little important error involved in using the normal approximation for $n \geqslant 10$, unless the ties are very extensive or very numerous, in which case a special investigation may be necessary. For the case $n < 10$ no complete tables are available owing to the large number of possibilities. The distributions have, however, been tabulated by Sillitto (1947) for any number of tied pairs or tied triplets up to and including $n = 10$.

*Example 4.3*

Consider the two rankings of 12 :

| | | | | | | | | | | | | |
|---|---|---|---|---|---|---|---|---|---|---|---|---|
| *A* | $1\frac{1}{2}$ | $1\frac{1}{2}$ | 3 | 4 | 6 | 6 | 6 | 8 | $9\frac{1}{2}$ | $9\frac{1}{2}$ | 11 | 12 |
| *B* | $2\frac{1}{2}$ | $2\frac{1}{2}$ | 7 | $4\frac{1}{2}$ | 1 | $4\frac{1}{2}$ | 6 | $11\frac{1}{2}$ | $11\frac{1}{2}$ | $8\frac{1}{2}$ | $8\frac{1}{2}$ | 10 |

We find

$$S = 8 + 8 + 1 + 5 + 5 + 5 + 5 - 3 - 2 + 1 + 1 = 34$$

In the first ranking there are ties of extent 2, 2, 3 and in the second of extent 2, 2, 2, 2. From (4.3) we then have—

$$\text{var } S = \tfrac{1}{18}\{(12 \times 11 \times 29) - 6(2 \times 1 \times 9) - (3 \times 2 \times 11)\} + 0$$
$$+ \frac{1}{2 \times 12 \times 11}\{2(2 \times 1) + (3 \times 2)\}\{4(2 \times 1)\}$$
$$= 203{\cdot}30.$$

Thus with a correction for continuity

$$S = \frac{33}{\sqrt{203{\cdot}30}}\sigma = 2{\cdot}31\sigma.$$

The chance of attaining or exceeding such a value in absolute magnitude is about 0·021. This is small, and we incline to attribute significance to the value of $S$.

**4.11** If one ranking degenerates to a dichotomy, as in **3.13,** with $x$ and $n - x = y$ members and ties in the other ranking typified by $t$, we find, on substitution in (4.3), the equation

$$\text{var } S = \frac{xy}{3n(n-1)}\{n^3 - n - \sum_t (t^3 - t)\} \qquad . \qquad (4.5)$$

Finally, if both rankings become dichotomies, as in **3.14,** we find on substitution in (4.5)

$$\text{var } S = \frac{xypq}{n-1} \quad . \quad . \quad . \quad . \qquad (4.6)$$

**4.12** These equations provide us with tests of significance of the appropriate $\tau_a$, $\tau_b$ or $\tau_c$ coefficients, or rather of the values of $S$ from which they are derived. There is, however, one difficulty in regard to corrections for continuity—

(*a*) In the case of a dichotomy and an *untied* ranking the interval between successive values of $S$ is two. The appropriate deduction from $S$ for continuity is one-half of the value, namely unity.

(*b*) For a dichotomy and a ranking composed entirely of ties of the same extent $t$ the interval is $2t$ and the appropriate deduction for continuity is $t$.

(*c*) When both variates are dichotomies the interval is $N$ and the deduction for continuity is $\frac{1}{2}N$.

(*d*) If one variate is dichotomised and the other contains ties of varying extents, there will be varying differences of interval between successive values of $S$ in various parts of the range. In such a case we may use an approximative method, as in Example 4.5 below.

*Example 4.4*

In Example 3.5 we found a value

$$\tau_b = 0{\cdot}43$$

based on $S = 26$. For the variance we have, from (4.6),

$$\sigma_s^2 = \text{var } S = \frac{12 \times 5 \times 12 \times 5}{16}$$

$$\sigma = 15.$$

The correction for continuity is 17/2 and thus we have

$$\frac{S - 8{\cdot}5}{15} = 1{\cdot}167.$$

The probability that this is attained or exceeded in absolute value is 0·24, and the value of $\tau_b$ is not significant.

*Example 4.5*

For the same data but with one variate not dichotomised we have found, in Example 3.4, $\tau_b = 0{\cdot}41$, based on $S = 34$. For the variance we have, from (4.5),

$$\sigma^2 = \text{var } S = \frac{12 \times 5}{3 \times 17 \times 16}\{17^3 - 17 - (4^3 - 4) - (2^3 - 2) - (5^3 - 5) - (3^3 - 3)\}$$

$$= 344{\cdot}6$$

$$\sigma = 18{\cdot}56.$$

Now for the continuity correction we note that the $A$-ranking "jumps" from $2\frac{1}{2}$ to 5 and this involves an interval of 5 in the $S$ score; for if we replace one of the $E$'s corresponding to an $A$-rank by the $O$ corresponding to the $A$-rank of 5, $S$ is reduced by 5, the first five scores being $4 + 4 + 4 - 9 + 4$ instead of $5 + 5 + 5 + 5 - 8$. Similarly the "jump" from 5 to $6\frac{1}{2}$ gives an interval of 3 and so on. We can estimate the mean interval without calculating each individual interval in this way. The total of the $S$-score intervals is twice the number of members in the ranking less the extent of the ties involving the first and last member. In our present case this is

$34 - 4 - 1 = 29$, and the mean interval is thus $29/6 = 4{\cdot}833$. We take half this as the correction for continuity and thus have

$$\frac{S - 2{\cdot}416}{18{\cdot}56} = 1{\cdot}70,$$

giving a probability that $S$ will be equalled or exceeded absolutely as 0·089. The value of $\tau_b$ is still not significant.

It is worth noting that in the previous example we found, for the $2 \times 2$ table, a value of $\tau_b = 0{\cdot}43$, which was not significant. In the present case we find $\tau_b = 0{\cdot}41$, a slightly smaller value which has a probability of 0·089 of being exceeded in absolute value, as against 0·24 for the value based on the $2 \times 2$ table. This is not a discrepancy. In this example we have not dichotomised the second ranking but have taken all the ranks into account. Our method gives more play to values which might be assumed by chance, and hence the probability of exceeding a given value in this more extended field may well differ from the value obtained in the more restricted domain of the double dichotomy.

## The significance of ρ

**4.13** Just as for $\tau$, the set of $n!$ values obtained by correlating all possible (untied) rankings with an arbitrary ranking will provide a set of values of $\rho$ which may be used to test the significance of that coefficient. The distribution of $\rho$ is symmetrical and tends to normality for large $n$; but it is less easy to use than that of $\tau$ for the following reasons:

(*a*) The actual distribution is much more difficult to ascertain and has been worked out fully only up to and including $n = 10$;

(*b*) The distribution tends to normality more slowly than that of $\tau$, and an intermediate form is necessary to bridge the gap between the values for $n = 11$ and the (rather doubtful) point at which the normal approximation is safe;

(*c*) for this intermediate region no simple methods are available for dealing with ties.

**4.14** For the untied case the standard deviation of the distribution of $\rho$ is given by the simple form

$$\text{var } \rho = \sigma_\rho^2 = \frac{1}{n - 1} \qquad . \quad . \quad . \quad (4.7)$$

The corresponding expression for $S(d^2)$ is

$$\text{var } S(d^2) = \left(\frac{n^3 - n}{6}\right)^2 \frac{1}{n-1} \quad . \quad . \quad (4.8)$$

For $n > 20$ it is probably accurate enough to use these expressions on the assumption of normality in the sampling distribution. They apply, of course, only where there is no parent correlation.

*Example 4.6*

In a ranking of 20 the observed value of $S(d^2)$ is 840. We then have

$$\rho = 1 - \frac{6 \times 840}{20 \times 21 \times 19}$$

$$= 0{\cdot}3684.$$

The standard error, from (4.7), is $1/\sqrt{19} = 0{\cdot}2294$. Thus the observed value is $0{\cdot}3684/0{\cdot}2294 = 1{\cdot}61$ times its standard error. This is barely significant.

For such large values of $S(d^2)$ a correction for continuity is of very minor importance, but if we wish to make one we subtract unity from $S(d^2)$. From (4.8) we then have, for the standard error of $S(d^2)$,

$$\sigma = \frac{20^3 - 20}{6}\sqrt{\frac{1}{19}} = 305{\cdot}1.$$

Now $S(d^2)$ varies from 0 to $\frac{1}{3}(n^3 - n)$ with a mean at $\frac{1}{6}(n^3 - n)$, in this case 1330. The deviation of the observed value is then $840 - 1330 = -490$. With a correction for continuity the deviation in absolute value is $\dfrac{489}{305{\cdot}1} = 1{\cdot}60$ times the standard error, leading to the same conclusion as for $\rho$.

Figure 4.2 shows the distribution of $S(d^2)$ as a frequency-polygon for $n = 8$. The sawlike profile of the polygon is unusual, but the correspondence with the normal curve is evidently moderately good, though not good enough for our purposes because in testing significance we are mainly interested in the fit near the tails.

## Continuity correction for ρ

**4.15** Corresponding to the corrections for continuity to $S$ given in **4.12** we have the following corrections to $S(d^2)$ in tied cases:

(*a*) For a dichotomy against an untied ranking the interval between successive values is $n$ and we therefore deduct $\frac{1}{2}n$ from $S(d^2)$.

(*b*) For a dichotomy against a ranking composed entirely of ties of extent $t$ the interval is $nt$ and the appropriate deduction for continuity is $\frac{1}{2}nt$.

(*c*) For a double dichotomy the deduction for continuity is $\frac{1}{4}n^2$.

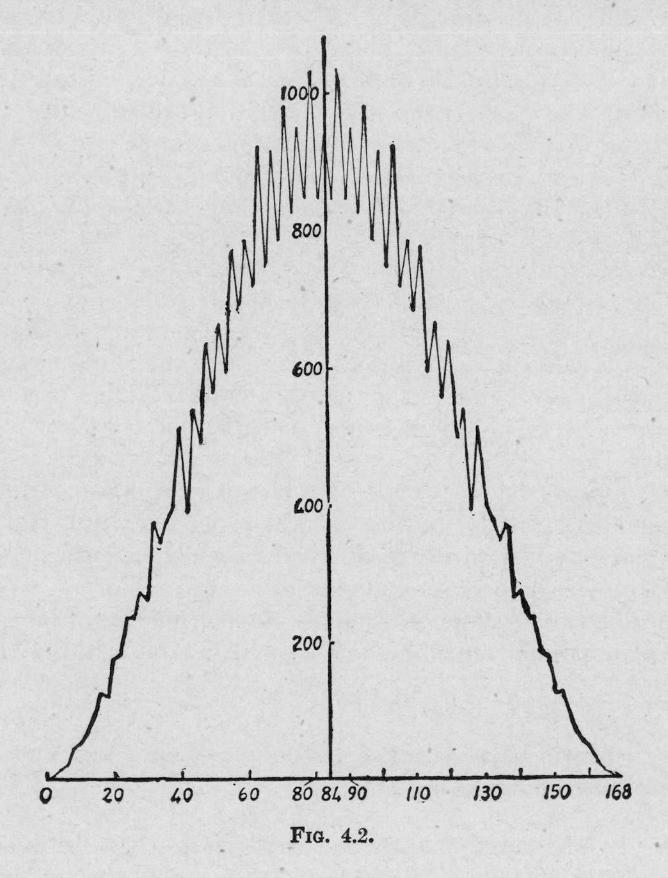


FIG. 4.2.

It is worth noting, however, that for a double dichotomy $\rho_b$ is the same as $\tau_b$ and the formulae for the latter would customarily be used in calculation.

If ties are present no modification is required in the variance of $\rho$, which remains as $1/(n-1)$.

## Tests in the non-null case

**4.16** The tests we have used up to this point are based on the distribution of correlations in a population of values obtained by permuting the ranks in all possible ways. This, effectively, is a test of the hypothesis that the qualities under consideration are independent in the parent population. Our test will then show whether an observed correlation is significant of a departure of the parent correlation *from zero.* But we may also wish to test correlations from a rather different viewpoint, or rather, to assign limits to the parent value in some probabilistic sense. For instance, suppose we arrive at a value of $\tau$ equal to 0·6 and it is found to be significant. Can we say between what values the true correlation probably lies ? Again, if we have a further value from a different sample equal to 0·8, also significant, can we say that the second is significantly greater than the first, or is the difference such as may have arisen by chance ?

**4.17** We shall suppose the whole population $N$ in number to be ranked according to the first variate in the order $1 \ldots N$. This can evidently be done without loss of generality. Suppose the population is laid out in a line in this order, the ranks according to the second variate being $p_i$ for the $i$th member. Then in accordance with our usual technique we may calculate a value of $\tau$ for this population.

Now suppose that a sample of $n$ members is chosen from the $N$. These members will be in the natural order according to the first variate. We may then calculate a value, which we will denote by $t$, for the sample which is the value of $\tau$ for that set of $n$. We merely write $t$ instead of $\tau$ to denote that we are considering a sample value instead of a population value. To each possible sample there will correspond a value of $t$, and since there are $\binom{N}{n} = \frac{N!}{n!\,(N-n)!}$ samples there will be an equivalent number of values of $t$ corresponding to all possible samples.

**4.18** In the next chapter we shall show that for any parent whatsoever the distribution of $t$ tends to normality as $n$, the sample size, increases, provided that the parent $\tau$ is not too near to unity. We shall also show that the mean value of this distribution is $\tau$. So far, so good, but we then encounter difficulties. If the standard deviation of the distribution were dependent only on $\tau$ we could easily test the observed value in the desired manner ; but in fact the standard deviation depends on other unknown quantities.

**4.19** A simple illustration will emphasise the point. Consider the ranking of 9 (according to the second variate)—

5 2 3 1 6 7 8 9 4

There are $\binom{9}{3} = 84$ possible samples of 3 from this " population ". If they are written down and $S$ evaluated for each we find the following distribution :

| Values of $S$ | Frequency |
|---|---|
| 0 | 2 |
| 1 | 15 |
| 2 | 34 |
| 3 | 33 |
| Total : | 84 |

The mean of this distribution will be found to be 13/6 and hence the mean value of the 84 values of $t$ is

$$E(t) = \frac{26/6}{3} - 1 = 0{\cdot}44.$$

It will be found that, for the parent $\tau$, $S = 26$ and hence

$$\tau = \frac{52}{36} - 1 = 0{\cdot}44 = E(t),$$

verifying our statement that the mean value of $t$ is the parent $\tau$. The ranking

1 2 5 9 3 6 7 8 4

also has $\tau = 0{\cdot}44$, but the distribution of $S$ in samples of 3 is now

| Values of $S$ | Frequency |
|---|---|
| 0 | 3 |
| 1 | 16 |
| 2 | 29 |
| 3 | 36 |
| Total : | 84 |

Again the mean value of $t$ is equal to the parent $\tau$, but the distribution of $S$ in the second case is different from that in the first, and its variance is 0·734 against 0·639 in the second case.

**4.20** We are therefore in the difficulty that unless we know something about the arrangement of the ranks in the parent (knowledge which is usually lacking) we cannot express the variance of $t$ in terms of known factors. We shall, however, show in the next chapter that for any parent the variance of $t$ cannot exceed a certain value, namely

$$\text{var } t \leqslant \frac{2}{n}(1 - \tau^2) \quad . \quad . \quad . \quad (4.9)$$

This result will give us a test which is on the safe side. This expression also holds good when ties are present. A corresponding approximate expression for $\rho$ is ($r_s$ denoting the sample value of $\rho$)

$$\text{var } r_s \leqslant \frac{3}{n}(1 - \rho^2) \quad . \quad . \quad . \quad (4.10)$$

for large $n$, but this is not known to be valid for the tied case. The argument will be clear from an example.

*Example 4.7*

In a ranking of 30 a value of $t$ is found to be 0·816. Assuming this ranking to be a random sample, what can be said about the value of $\tau$ in the parent?

For samples of 30 the distribution of $t$ may be taken to be normal, and its mean may be estimated as 0·816. From (4.9) we find that

$$\text{var } t \leqslant \tfrac{2}{30}\{1 - (0{\cdot}816)^2\} = 0{\cdot}022{,}276,$$

giving a standard error of 0·149 *or less*.

Now the probability of a deviation from the mean of 1·96 times the standard deviation or greater (in absolute value) is 0·05. We may therefore say that at the worst, the probability is 0·95 that the true value of $\tau$ lies within $(0{\cdot}149 \times 1{\cdot}96) = 0{\cdot}292$ of 0·816, *i.e.* that the probability is less than or equal to 0·05 that the true value lies outside the range 0·524 to 1·0. Instead of setting limits to the value in the usual statistical manner with an assigned degree of probability, we set limits with a maximum to the degree of probability; or, to put it another way, we set *outside* limits to the range of the parent $\tau$. This may make our inference unnecessarily stringent, but we err on the safe side in the sense that we run no danger of attributing significance to non-significant results, though we may in some cases fail to discern significance where it really exists.

**4.21** We have stated the argument above by relation to standard errors, the form in which it is usually introduced in elementary treatments of statistics.* In order to apply (4.9), however, we need to replace the unknown parent value $\tau$ by the sample value $t$, as has been done in the previous example. Such a procedure may be avoided by recourse to the theory of confidence intervals. If $x$ is the normal deviate corresponding to a probability level of $P$ per cent (*i.e.* if the

* See, for instance, *Introduction*, Chapters 18 and 19. For the theory of confidence intervals see Kendall, *The Advanced Theory of Statistics*, Vol. II, Chapter 19.

probability is $0 \cdot 0P$ that there will occur on random sampling a deviation from the mean of $x$ times the standard deviation or greater in absolute value), then, to this probability at the most, we may assert that

$$\tau_1 \leqslant \tau \leqslant \tau_2 \qquad . \quad . \quad . \quad . \quad (4.11)$$

where $\tau_1$, $\tau_2$ are the roots of

$$t - \tau = x\sqrt{\left\{\frac{2}{n}(1 - \tau^2)\right\}}$$

*i.e.* are given by

$$\tau = \frac{t \pm x\sqrt{\frac{2}{n}}\sqrt{\left\{1 + \frac{2x^2}{n} - t^2\right\}}}{1 + \frac{2x^2}{n}} \qquad . \quad . \quad (4.12)$$

*Example 4.8*

For example, in the data of Example 4.7, $n = 30$, $t = 0 \cdot 816$. The normal deviate corresponding to a probability of 0·05 is 1·96. Substitution in (4.12) then gives

$$\tau = \frac{t \pm 0 \cdot 50607\sqrt{(1 \cdot 2561 - t^2)}}{1 \cdot 2561}$$

$$= 0 \cdot 34 \text{ or } 0 \cdot 96.$$

Thus we may assert that $\tau$ lies between 0·34 and 0·96, being sure of correctness in at least 95 per cent of the cases on the average. This is a more accurate method than that of **4.20.** The limits are, of course, still maxima.

*Example 4.9*

In a sample of 20 a value of $\tau$ equal to 0·8 is observed. A second sample of 20 gives a value of 0·6. Is there any indication that the samples are from different material, or could the different values of $\tau$ arise by chance ?

For a maximum to the variance in the first case we have

$$\text{var } t = \frac{2}{n}(1 - \tau^2)$$

$$= 0 \cdot 036,$$

giving a standard error of 0·19. The second value differs by about this amount, and consequently we cannot attribute significance to the result.

Alternatively, we might argue that the variance of the second value is 0·064. Thus, a maximum to the variance of their difference (being equal to the sum of the variances) is 0·100, the corresponding standard error being 0·32. This is greater than the actual difference of 0·2, and again we conclude that the difference is not significant.

Generally, if we have a number of values of $S$ (even from rankings of different extents) we may add them together and test the significance of the whole set against the sums of the variances of the individual rankings. The validity of this procedure rests on the fact that the variance of the sum of *independent* variables is the sum of their variances. It has been found very useful in field work.

**4.22** The foregoing examples illustrate one rather disappointing feature of rank correlation coefficients, namely the comparatively large standard error which they possess. Whatever $\tau$ may be, the standard error is of the order of $\sqrt{(2/n)}$. This shortcoming, however, is a feature of most correlation coefficients. The standard error of the product-moment coefficient in normal samples, for instance, is $(1 - \rho^2)/\sqrt{n}$ and thus is, in general, of order $1/\sqrt{n}$. It is clearly impossible to locate the parent correlation very closely unless the ranking contains 30 or 40 members. This provides a useful caution against attributing reality to correlation coefficients calculated from rankings of small extent, unless several sample values are available.

For instance, with a ranking of 32 members the maximum standard error is $\frac{1}{4}\sqrt{(1 - \tau^2)}$ and if $t$ is near zero we cannot, on the above basis, locate the parent $\tau$ in a narrower range than twice the standard error, or $\pm$ 0·5. If $t$ is, say, 0·8 the range becomes narrower, but the band of doubt surrounding the true value still extends from 0·5 to 1·0.

**4.23** It is not possible to improve very much on the maximum limits given by (4.9) or (4.11), as we shall show in the next chapter. We shall see, however, that very substantial improvements are possible if the original rankings are available and the investigator has patience to carry out the necessary arithmetic. Apart from this it appears unlikely that any simple improvement is possible without making some assumption about the nature of the variate and its parent distribution, as to which see Chapter 9.

## References

For the distribution of $\tau$ see Kendall (1938), Dantzig (1939), Daniels (1944), Sillitto (1947). For that of $\rho$ see Olds (1938), Kendall and others (1939), Pitman (1937), Hotelling and Pabst (1936) and David and others (1951). For the general joint distribution of correlations see Daniels (1944), Daniels and Kendall (1947), and Hoeffding (1948).

A more extensive table of the distribution of $t$ up to $n = 40$ has been published by Kaarsemaker and Van Wijngaarden (1952).

The result of (4.10) follows from general results given by Hoeffding (1948). If $r_s$ and $t$ are sample values of Spearman's $\rho$ and $\tau$ and

$$k = \frac{1}{n-2}\{(n+1)r_s - 3t\}$$

then
$$\text{var } k \leqslant \frac{3}{n}(1 - \rho_s^2),$$

where $\rho_s$ is Spearman's $\rho$ for a continuous population (cf. 9.5). For large $n$, $k$ tends to equivalence to $r_s$.

# CHAPTER 5

# PROOF OF THE RESULTS OF CHAPTER 4

**5.1** The series of formulae we have used in the last chapter for testing the significance of $\tau$ and $\rho$ requires four types of result, *viz.*

(*a*) the derivation of exact distributions for low value of $n$;
(*b*) the proof that distributions tend to normality for large $n$;
(*c*) the derivation of the means and variances of the limiting distributions;
(*d*) the derivation of the corrections for continuity.

We treat them in that order and conclude the chapter with a more detailed analysis of the non-null case.

## Exact distribution of $\tau$ in the null case

**5.2** If we correlate a fixed ranking of $n$ members with the $n!$ possible rankings (excluding ties) we obtain the same distribution whatever the fixed ranking; for all possibilities occur. We therefore lose no generality in supposing our fixed ranking to be the natural order $1 \ldots n$. Let $u(n, S)$ be the number of values of $S$ in the aggregate of $n!$ possible values obtained by correlating this with all possible rankings.

Consider one such ranking and the effect of inserting a new member $(n + 1)$ at the various places in it, from the first (preceding the first member $p_1$) to the last (following the last member $p_n$). Inserting $(n + 1)$ at the beginning will add $-n$ to $S$; inserting it at the second place adds $-(n - 2)$; at the third place $-(n - 4)$ and so on, the last place adding $n$. It follows that

$$u(n + 1, S) = u(n, S - n) + u(n, S - n + 2) + u(n, S - n + 4) + \ldots \\ + u(n, S + n - 4) + u(n, S + n - 2) + u(n, S + n) \quad . \quad . \quad (5.1)$$

This recurrence formula enables us to ascertain the frequency-distribution of $S$ for $n + 1$ when we know that for $n$; and hence we may build up the series of distributions from the simpler cases for $n = 2$, 3, etc.

**5.3** In practice the procedure may be simplified. For $n = 2$ there are two values of $S$, *viz.* $-1$ and $+1$. If we write the frequencies down three times, one under the other, moving a stage to the right each time, we get

| | | | |
|---|---|---|---|
| 1 | 1 | | |
| | 1 | 1 | |
| | | 1 | 1 |
| **1** | **2** | **2** | **1** |

and the sum gives the frequencies of $S$ for $n = 3$, the actual values ranging from $-\frac{1}{2}n(n-1)$ by units of two to $\frac{1}{2}n(n-1)$, *i.e.* through the values $-3$, $-1$, $+1$, $+3$.

Similarly for $n = 4$ we write down the array for $n = 3$ four times and sum, as follows:

| | | | | | | |
|---|---|---|---|---|---|---|
| 1 | 2 | 2 | 1 | | | |
| | 1 | 2 | 2 | 1 | | |
| | | 1 | 2 | 2 | 1 | |
| | | | 1 | 2 | 2 | 1 |
| **1** | **3** | **5** | **6** | **5** | **3** | **1** |

the frequencies being for values of $S$ from $-6$ by units of 2 to $+6$.

The validity of this rule will be evident from the previous section. To any set of $S$-values for a given $n$, there will correspond in the distribution for $n + 1$ a similar set with values of $S$ increased by $-n$, $-(n-2)$, . . . $(n-2)$, $n$. What we have done is to write these frequencies down, one row for $-n$, one for $-(n-2)$ and so on, and to sum them.

**5.4** Even this procedure may be simplified. We form a numerical triangle as follows:

| $n$ | Frequencies | | | | | | | | | | |
|---|---|---|---|---|---|---|---|---|---|---|---|
| 1 | 1 | | | | | | | | | | |
| 2 | 1 | 1 | | | | | | | | | |
| 3 | 1 | 2 | 2 | 1 | | | | | | | |
| 4 | 1 | 3 | 5 | 6 | 5 | 3 | 1 | | | | |
| 5 | 1 | 4 | 9 | 15 | 20 | 22 | 20 | 15 | 9 | 4 | 1 |
| etc. | | | | | | | | | | | |

In this array a number in the $r$th row is the sum of the number immediately above it and the $(r-1)$ members to the left of that number; *e.g.* in the fifth row $22 = 3 + 5 + 6 + 5 + 3$. The frequencies of values of $S$ for $n = r$ are those so obtained in the $r$th row. This method was used to obtain the frequencies on which Appendix Table 1 is based.

**5.5** The distribution of $S$ is symmetrical; for to any ranking giving a particular value of $S$ there will correspond a conjugate ranking giving $-S$. The mean value of $S$ is therefore zero, as we should expect. That $S$ ranges from $-\frac{1}{2}n(n-1)$ to $\frac{1}{2}n(n-1)$ is evident from the fact that these are the extreme values given when the ranking is the inverse of the natural order or the natural order itself. Further, the interval between successive values of $S$ for given $n$ is 2. This follows from (5.1), or perhaps more simply by the consideration that an interchange of a pair of members in a ranking alters the positive score by $+1$ or $-1$ and hence the difference between positive and negative scores (which is $S$) by $+2$ or $-2$.

## Tendency of $\tau$ to normality in the null case

**5.6** It remains to determine the variance of $S$ and to prove that the distribution tends to normality as $n$ increases.

In the notation of Chapter 2 let us write

$$c_{ij} = a_{ij}\, b_{ij} \quad . \quad . \quad . \quad . \qquad (5.2)$$

where $a$ and $b$ refer to the scores in the different rankings. Put

$$c = \sum_{i,j=1}^{n} c_{ij} \quad . \quad . \quad . \quad . \qquad (5.3)$$

Then

$$c = 2S \quad . \quad . \quad . \quad . \quad . \qquad (5.4)$$

Now

$$\sum_{l=1}^{n} a_{il} = n + 1 - 2i \quad . \quad . \quad . \qquad (5.5)$$

for this is the score associated with the $i$th member and is $(n-i)-(i-1)$. Further,

$$\sum_{i,l=1}^{n} a_{il}^2 = n(n-1) \quad . \quad . \quad . \qquad (5.6)$$

for $a^2$ is $+1$ and this sum is merely the number of possible ways of choosing a pair from $n$ members, each pair being counted twice, once as $XY$ and once as $YX$. It follows from (5.5) that

$$\begin{aligned}\sum_{i,l=1}^{n} a_{il} &= \sum_{i=1}^{n} (n+1-2i)\\ &= n(n+1) - 2\sum_{i=1}^{n} i\\ &= 0,\end{aligned}$$

as is to be expected.

We also find

$$\sum_{i,l,t=1}^{n} a_{il}\, a_{it} = \sum_{i,l} a_{il}\,(n+1-2i)$$
$$= \sum_{i} (n+1-2i)^2$$
$$= \Sigma\,(n+1)^2 - 4(n+1)\,\Sigma\, i + 4\,\Sigma\, i^2$$
$$= n(n+1)^2 - 2n(n+1)^2 + \tfrac{2}{3}n(n+1)(2n+1)$$
$$= \tfrac{1}{3}n(n^2-1) \quad . \quad . \quad . \quad . \quad . \quad . \quad (5.7)$$

Now, writing $E$ to denote mean values on summation over all possible permutations, we have

$$E(c) = E \sum_{i,j=1}^{n} (a_{ij}\, b_{ij})$$
$$= \sum_{i,j} E\,(a_{ij}\, b_{ij})$$

Since $a_{ij}$ and $b_{ij}$ are independent, any fixed value of one being taken with all possible values of the other, and since the mean value $E$ of any term $a_{ij}$ or $b_{ij}$ is zero, we have

$$E(c) = 0, \quad . \quad . \quad . \quad . \quad (5.8)$$

confirming that the mean of $c$ (or of $S$) is zero. For the variance of $c$ we require

$$E(c^2) = E\left\{\sum_{i,j} (a_{ij}\, b_{ij})\right\}^2$$
$$= E\,\{\Sigma\,(a_{ij}^2\, b_{ij}^2) + \Sigma'\,(a_{ij} b_{ij}\, a_{ik} b_{ik}) + \Sigma''\,(a_{ij} b_{ij}\, a_{kl} b_{kl})\} \quad . \quad (5.9)$$

where $i \neq j \neq k = l$. The summations here take place over the terms specified, but any term may arise in more than one way from the expansion of $(\Sigma\, a_{ij}\, b_{ij})^2$.

(i) The term $E\,\Sigma''$ vanishes. To demonstrate this it is enough to show that $E\,\Sigma''\, a_{ij}\, a_{ik}$ vanishes. Now ($\Sigma$ relating to summation over all values of the suffixes)

$$\Sigma\, a_{ij}\, a_{kl} = \Sigma''\, a_{ij}\, a_{kl} + \Sigma'\, a_{ij}\, a_{il} + \Sigma'\, a_{ij}\, a_{ki} + \Sigma'\, a_{ij}\, a_{jl}$$
$$+ \Sigma'\, a_{ij}\, a_{kj} + \Sigma\, a_{ij}\, a_{ij} + \Sigma\, a_{ij}\, a_{ji}.$$

On taking expectations, the terms after the first on the right vanish in pairs in virtue of such relations as $a_{ij} = -a_{ji}$. The term on the left vanishes because (summation extending over all values) $E\,\Sigma\, a_{ij}\, a_{kl} = E\,\Sigma\, a_{ij}\, E\,\Sigma\, a_{kl}$ and $\Sigma\, a_{ij} = 0$. Consequently the first term on the right vanishes.

(ii) Now consider the sum $E \Sigma a_{ij}^2 b_{ij}^2$. An individual term arises from the square of $a_{ij} b_{ij}$ or the product of that term with $a_{ij} b_{ji}$. Thus the sum is twice the sum of $a_{ij}^2 b_{ij}^2$ with $i, j$ from 1 to $n$. There are $n(n-1)$ terms in the sum, and the expectation is thus

$$2n(n-1)E(a_{12}^2 b_{12}^2) = 2n(n-1)E(a_{12}^2)E(b_{12}^2) = 2 \Sigma a_{ij}^2 \Sigma b_{ij}^2/n(n-1).$$

(iii) Similarly the second term on the right in (5.9) is

$$\frac{4}{n(n-1)(n-2)} \Sigma' a_{ij} \Sigma a_{ik} \Sigma' b_{ij} b_{ik}.$$

For the product $a_{ij} a_{ik} b_{ij} b_{ik}$ can arise in four ways, since if we fix $i, j, k$, for the $a$'s the $b$ terms can appear with suffixes $(ij, ik)$, $(ji, ik)$, $(ij, ki)$ and $(ji, ki)$; and there are $n(n-1)(n-2)$ ways of fixing three different suffixes out of $n$. The reader who has trouble with these factors is advised to write out in full the case for $n = 4$.

Furthermore

$$\Sigma' a_{ij} a_{ik} = \Sigma a_{ij} a_{ik} - \Sigma a_{ij}^2$$

Substituting in (5.9) we thus find

$$E(c^2) = \frac{4}{n(n-1)(n-2)} \{\Sigma a_{ij} a_{ik} - \Sigma a_{ij}^2\}\{\Sigma b_{ij} b_{ik} - \Sigma b_{ij}^2\} + \frac{2}{n(n-1)} \Sigma a_{ij}^2 \Sigma b_{ij}^2 \quad . \quad . \quad . \quad (5.10)$$

Now substituting from (5.6) and (5.7) we find

$$E(c^2) = \frac{4}{n(n-1)(n-2)} \{\tfrac{1}{3}n(n^2-1) - n(n-1)\}^2 + \frac{2}{n(n-1)} \{n(n-1)\}^2$$

$$= \frac{2n(n-1)(2n+5)}{9} \quad . \quad . \quad . \quad . \quad . \quad . \quad (5.11)$$

It follows that

$$E(S^2) = \text{var } S = \frac{n(n-1)(2n+5)}{18} \quad . \quad . \quad (5.12)$$

$$\text{var } t = \frac{2(2n+5)}{9n(n-1)} \quad . \quad . \quad . \quad (5.13)$$

(5.12) is the result announced in (4.2).

**5.7** If ties are present, equation (5.10) remains valid but expressions (5.6) and (5.7) require modification. In place of (5.6) we have

$$\Sigma a_{ij}^2 = n(n-1) - \sum_t t(t-1) \quad . \quad . \quad (5.14)$$

where summation $\sum_t$ takes place over the various ties. This follows simply from the consideration that for a pair of tied ranks $a_{ij} = 0$ and consequently the sum of the squares of contributions from a tied set is of the same form as for the ranking as a whole.

In place of (5.7) we have

$$\Sigma a_{ij} a_{ik} = \tfrac{1}{3}n(n^2-1) - \tfrac{1}{3}\sum_t t(t^2-1) \quad . \quad . \quad (5.15)$$

This is not quite so obvious. Consider the effect of tying a set of ranks. The contribution to the sum on the left of (5.15) will be unchanged if the suffix $i$ falls outside this set. If $i$ is inside the set and $j$, $k$ are outside, again the contribution is unchanged. If both $j$, $k$ fall inside no contribution arises, and therefore we have to subtract the term $\frac{1}{3}t(t^2-1)$. If one falls inside and one outside the contribution remains unchanged, for it was zero in the original untied case, each possible pair occurring once to give $+1$ and once to give $-1$.

If we substitute from (5.14) and (5.15) in (5.10) we find, for the variance of $S$ when the rankings contain ties typified by $t$, $u$,

$$\begin{aligned}\text{var}\, S = {} & \tfrac{1}{18}\{n(n-1)(2n+5) - \sum_t t(t-1)(2t+5) - \sum_u u(u-1)(2u+5)\} \\ & + \frac{1}{9n(n-1)(n-2)}\{\Sigma t(t-1)(t-2)\}\{\Sigma u(u-1)(u-2)\} \\ & + \frac{1}{2n(n-1)}\{\Sigma t(t-1)\}\{\Sigma u(u-1)\} \quad . \quad . \quad . \quad (5.16)\end{aligned}$$

This is the result given in (4.3). Equations (4.4), (4.5) and (4.6) follow at once.

**5.8** In proving that the distribution of $S$ tends to normality we shall follow a procedure which, with a few trivial changes, will also prove the normality of $S(d^2)$ and will form an introduction to more general results, due to Daniels (1944), concerning the limiting forms of the general rank correlation coefficients as defined in Chapter 2.

We prove that the moments of the distribution of $S$ tend to those of the normal distribution. It will then follow from what is known as the Second Limit Theorem that the distribution tends to normality.* Since the distribution of $S$ is symmetrical moments

* Kendall, *Advanced Theory*, Vol. I, 4.24.

about the mean of odd order vanish. We have only to show that for the even moments

$$\mu_{2r} = \frac{(2r)!}{2^r\, r!}(\mu_2)^r \quad . \quad . \quad . \quad . \quad (5.17)$$

Consider the mean value of $(\Sigma\, a_{ij}\, b_{ij})^{2r}$. When this expression is expanded it will consist of terms such as

$$\Sigma'\, a_{ij}\, a_{kl}\, a_{mn} \ldots b_{ij}\, b_{kl}\, b_{mn} \ldots$$

When summations extend over values of suffixes which exclude certain values (*e.g.* $i \neq k$) we can replace them by complete summations. Our expanded expression will then, apart from numerical terms, consist of terms such as

$$\Sigma\, a_{ij}\, a_{kl}\, a_{mn} \ldots \Sigma\, b_{ij}\, b_{kl}\, b_{mn} \ldots \quad . \quad . \quad (5.18)$$

where certain suffixes may be the same or " tied " and others will be different and " free ". Consider a term in which the $4r$ suffixes of $a$ are tied in pairs, *e.g.*

$$\Sigma\, a_{ij}\, a_{ik}\, a_{lm}\, a_{ln} \ldots \quad . \quad . \quad . \quad (5.19)$$

There are then $3r$ independent suffixes. Now $\Sigma\, a_{ij}\, a_{ik}$ is of order $\frac{1}{3}n^3$ and consequently (5.19) is of order $(\frac{1}{3}n^3)^r$. In the expansion of $(\Sigma\, a_{ij}\, b_{ij})^{2r}$ terms of this type will arise with a frequency which is the number of ways of tying the $2r$ paired suffixes. This is the product of three factors, *viz.* (i) the number of ways of picking $r$ $a$'s from $2r$, namely $\binom{2r}{r}$; (ii) the number of ways of associating these with the remaining $r$ factors, namely $r!$; (iii) $2^r$ arising from the fact that either suffix of a particular $a$ may be tied. The numerical coefficient is then—

$$\binom{2r}{r} r!\, 2^r = \frac{(2r)!\, 2^r}{r!}$$

Furthermore, if $3r$ suffixes are fixed the remaining members of the ranking can vary in $(n - 3r)!$ ways. Hence $\mu_{2r}$ contains a term

$$\frac{(n-3r)!}{n!}\, \frac{2^r(2r)!}{r!}(\tfrac{1}{3}n^3)^{2r}$$

$$\sim \frac{(2r)!}{2^r\, r!}\left(\frac{4}{9}n^3\right)^r$$

But $\mu_2$ is of order $\frac{4}{9}n^3$ (as we see by putting $r = 1$) and hence $\mu_{2r}$ contains a term

$$\frac{(2r)!}{2^r\, r!}(\mu_2)^r$$

Our demonstration will be complete if we show that all other terms are of lower order in $n$.

If a term in (5.18) contains a pair of suffixes neither of which appears elsewhere, the term vanishes because $\Sigma a_{ij} = 0$. Consider a term where more than two suffixes are tied. The summation of (5.19) is then over not more than $3r - 1$ suffixes and cannot be of greater order than $(n^{3r-1})^2$. If $3r - 1$ or fewer suffixes are fixed the order is then not greater than

$$\frac{(n - 3r + 1)!}{n!} n^{6r-2} \sim n^{3r-1}$$

and is thus lower than that of the term already found. *

## Distribution of ρ in the null case

**5.9** The actual distribution of $\rho$ is much more difficult to determine than that of $\tau$, and no method is known for constructing the distribution for $n + 1$ from that for $n$. Consider the array

$$\begin{matrix} 0 & 1 & 2 & \ldots n-3 & n-2 & n-1 \\ -1 & 0 & 1 & \ldots n-4 & n-3 & n-2 \\ -2 & -1 & 0 & \ldots n-5 & n-4 & n-3 \\ \cdot & \cdot & \cdot & \ldots\ \cdot & \cdot & \cdot \\ -(n-2) & -(n-3) & -(n-4) & \ldots\ -1 & 0 & 1 \\ -(n-1) & -(n-2) & -(n-3) & \ldots\ -2 & -1 & 0 \end{matrix} \quad . \quad . \quad . \quad (5.20)$$

Any permissible set of deviations between the order 1, 2, . . . $n$ and an arbitrary order is given by selecting a member from the array so that no two members appear in more than one row or column. Consider then the array

$$\left\{ \begin{matrix} a^0 & a^1 & a^4 & \ldots a^{(n-3)^2} & a^{(n-2)^2} & a^{(n-1)^2} \\ a^1 & a^0 & a^1 & \ldots a^{(n-4)^2} & a^{(n-3)^2} & a^{(n-2)^2} \\ \cdot & \cdot & \cdot & \ldots\ \cdot & \cdot & \cdot \\ a^{(n-2)^2} & a^{(n-3)^2} & a^{(n-4)^2} & \ldots\ a^1 & a^0 & a^1 \\ a^{(n-1)^2} & a^{(n-2)^2} & a^{(n-3)^2} & \ldots\ a^4 & a^1 & a^0 \end{matrix} \right\} \quad . \quad . \quad . \quad (5.21)$$

The indices in (5.21) are the squares of the entries in (5.20), and if we expand (5.21) we shall get the totality of values of $S(d^2)$. By

* For a simpler proof see Moran (1950*a*) and Silverstone (1950). These proofs depend on more sophisticated ideas and do not generalise to other rank coefficients, but they give the moments of the distribution of any order directly.

" expanding " we mean developing the array by selecting, in the $n!$ possible ways, $n$ factors from (5.21) such that no two have a row or column in common, multiplying them for each set of factors and summing the $n!$ resultants. This method was used to arrive at the distributions which form the basis of Appendix Table 2.

**5.10** Certain simple properties of the distribution of $S(d^2)$ are evident from elementary considerations. First, any value of $S(d^2)$ must be even ; for $\Sigma(d) = 0$ and hence the number of odd values of $d$, and thus $d^2$, must be even. Secondly, the distribution is symmetrical, for to any value of $S(d^2)$ there corresponds a value $\frac{1}{3}(n^3 - n) - S(d^2)$ derived from the conjugate ranking (**2.9**). Thirdly, the mean of the distribution is $\frac{1}{6}(n^3 - n)$. Fourthly, it ranges from 0 to $\frac{1}{3}(n^3 - n)$.

**5.11** We may determine the variance of $S$ in the manner of **5.6**. From the way in which we derived (5.10) in terms of the scores $a$ and $b$ it will be clear that the equation is equally true for $c$ when the scores relate to Spearman's $\rho$, for without loss of generality we may write

$$a'_{ij} = j - i, \quad . \quad . \quad . \quad . \quad . \quad (5.22)$$

where we have added a prime to distinguish it from the score where $\tau$ is concerned. We have at once

$$\sum_{j=1}^{n} a'_{ij} = \tfrac{1}{2}n(n + 1 - 2i) \quad . \quad . \quad . \quad (5.23)$$

and

$$\sum_{i,j=1}^{n} a'^{2}_{ij} = \Sigma(j - i)^2$$

$$= 2n \sum_{j=1}^{n} j^2 - 2\left(\sum_{j=1}^{n} j\right)^2$$

$$= \tfrac{1}{6}n^2(n^2 - 1)$$

and

$$\sum_{i,j,k=1}^{n} a'_{ij}\, a'_{ik} = \tfrac{1}{12}n^3(n^2 - 1) \quad . \quad . \quad . \quad (5.24)$$

Substitution in (5.10) now gives

$$E(c^2) = \frac{n^4(n-1)(n+1)^2}{36} \quad . \quad . \quad . \quad (5.25)$$

Remembering that

$$\rho = 1 - \frac{6S(d^2)}{n^3 - n}$$

and that from (2.9)

$$c = \tfrac{1}{6}n^2(n^2 - 1) - nS(d^2),$$

we find from (5.25)

$$\text{var}\ \rho = E(\rho^2) = \frac{1}{n-1} \quad . \quad . \quad . \quad (5.26)$$

which is the formula (4.7).*

**5.12** By similar methods it may be shown that the fourth moment of $\rho$ is given by

$$\mu_4 = \frac{3(25n^3 - 38n^3 - 35n + 72)}{25n(n+1)(n-1)^3} \quad . \quad . \quad (5.27)$$

The third moment, of course, is zero in virtue of the symmetry of the distribution. Expressions are known for $\mu_6$ and $\mu_8$ (see David and others, 1951), but they are rather cumbrous.

In a normal distribution

$$\mu_4 - 3\mu_2^2 = 0 \quad . \quad . \quad . \quad . \quad (5.28)$$

For the distribution of $\rho$ we find, from (5.27) and (5.26),

$$\mu_4 - 3\mu_2^2 = -\frac{114n^2 + 30n - 216}{25n(n+1)(n-1)^3} \quad . \quad . \quad (5.29)$$

$$= -\frac{4{\cdot}56}{n^3} + 0(n^{-4}) \quad . \quad . \quad . \quad (5.30)$$

This is of lower order than $\mu_2^2$ and equivalently we have

$$\frac{\mu_4}{\mu_2^2} - 3 = -\frac{4{\cdot}56}{n} + 0(n^{-2})\, . \quad . \quad . \quad (5.31)$$

showing that for large $n$ the distribution of $\rho$ has nearly the normal value.

For most ordinary work the tables of exact values together with the normal approximation are sufficient. For more precise work David and others (1951) obtained expansions giving the probability distribution of both $\rho$ and $\tau$ to about four-figure accuracy.

---

* That this formula requires no modification for tied ranks follows from (7.14) with $m = 2$, bearing in mind that (6.6) is to be modified in the tied case. Alternatively, with $c$ as defined in (5.3) and scores $x_j - x_i$, $y_j - y_i$, it may be shown that $E(c^2) = 4n^2\, \Sigma\, (x - \bar{x})^2\, \Sigma\, (y - \bar{y})^2/(n - 1)$, whence (5.26) follows whether ranks are tied or not.

**Joint distribution of $\tau$ and $\rho$**

**5.13** The tendency of $\rho$ to normality may be demonstrated by making a few alterations in the proof of the normality of $\tau$ in **5.8.** Both results are particular cases of a more general theorem due to Daniels (1944) which we now prove.

We shall show, in fact, that the joint distribution of $\tau$ and $\rho$ tends to the bivariate normal form as $n$ tends to infinity. Indeed, under certain non-restrictive conditions, any two coefficients of the general type defined in **2.2** tend to joint bivariate normality.

Suppose that $a$, $a'$ refer to scores in two such coefficients, and similarly for $b$ and $b'$. Then we shall show that the product-moments of the joint distribution of the corresponding $c$ and $c'$ tend to those of the normal bivariate form.

The $p$th order product-moments of this joint distribution are sums of terms containing

$$\Sigma' a_{gh} a_{ij} a_{kl} \ldots \Sigma' b_{rs} b_{tu} b_{vw} \ldots \quad (5.32)$$

where groups of suffixes within the $\Sigma'$'s may be tied or free. Each $\Sigma'$ involves products of $p$ scores which may belong to either system. Every such $\Sigma'$ is in turn a linear combination of the corresponding $\Sigma$ having the same suffixes and other $\Sigma$'s in which additional tied suffixes appear. No $\Sigma$ may contain a pair of free suffixes attached to one score, for it would then vanish by virtue of the fact that $\Sigma a_{ij} = 0$.

We discuss first the moments of even order. Let $p = 2m$. Consider a $\Sigma$ in which the $2m$ scores are divided into $m$ pairs each having one tied suffix, so that there are in all $3m$ independent suffixes, *e.g.*

$$\Sigma a_{ij} a_{ik} a_{lr} a_{ls} a_{tu} a_{tv} \ldots \quad (5.33)$$

It may be written as

$$(\Sigma a_{ij} a_{ik})^{\lambda} (\Sigma a_{ij} a'_{ik})^{\mu} (\Sigma a'_{ij} a'_{ik})^{\nu} \quad (5.34)$$

where $\lambda + \mu + \nu = m$ and $\lambda$, $\mu$, $\nu$ are the number of times the scores are paired in the combinations indicated.

As is always possible, suppose the numerically largest value of $a_{ij}$ to be made equal to unity. We now impose the condition that $\Sigma a_{ij} a_{ik}$ is of order $n^3$, whether $a_{ij}$ and $a_{ik}$ belong to the same or different systems of scores. This, in particular, is satisfied by $\tau$ and $\rho$, when max. $a_{ij} = 1$. With this condition it is seen that $\Sigma$'s of the above type are of order $n^{3m}$.

Other ways of tying suffixes give $\Sigma$'s of lower order of magnitude.

For the order of magnitude of the expression is not reduced on replacing each $a_{ij}$ by $+1$; consequently if further suffixes are tied the order of $\Sigma$ is made less than $n^{3m}$ since there are fewer than $3m$ summations from 1 to $n$. It follows that the dominant term in a $\Sigma'$ is the corresponding $\Sigma$ having the same array of suffixes.

Moreover, every non-vanishing $\Sigma$ involving $3m$ independent suffixes can only be a permutation of type (5.32), while those with more than $3m$ different suffixes must all vanish. This will be clear by considering how the $3m$ suffixes can be arrayed between the $2m$ scores. Begin by assigning $3m$ different suffixes at random among the $4m$ available places. At least $m$ scores will receive their full complement of suffixes, all of which will be different. There cannot be more than $m$ such completed scores, for if $\Sigma$ is not to vanish at least one suffix of each complete pair must be tied, and this can only be done by repeating one suffix from every complete pair in each of the remaining places to be filled, of which there are only $m$. We are thus led to a permutation of the type of $\Sigma$ discussed above. If there had been more than $3m$ different suffixes to begin with, there would not have remained sufficient empty places to prevent the existence of at least one score with a pair of free suffixes. Hence all $\Sigma$'s with more than $3m$ different suffixes must vanish.

Any $2m$th product-moment is the sum of terms like

$$\frac{(n-f)!}{n!} A \, \Sigma' a_{ij} a_{kl} \ldots \Sigma' b_{rs} b_{tu} \ldots$$

where $f$ is the number of independent suffixes in the $\Sigma'$'s and $A$ is a coefficient which is of unit order so far as $n$ is concerned. From the preceding argument the maximum value of $f$ is $3m$, in which case the term is of order $n^{-3m} \times n^{3m} \times n^{3m} = n^{3m}$. When $f \leqslant 3m - 1$ the term is of order not greater than $n^{-3m+1} \times (n^{3m-1})^2 = n^{3m-1}$ and hence such terms may be neglected. Write

$$\left.\begin{aligned} h_{11} &= \Sigma\, a_{ij} a_{ik} \Sigma\, b_{tu} b_{tv} \\ h_{12} &= \Sigma\, a_{ij} a'_{ik} \Sigma\, b_{tu} b'_{tv} \\ h_{22} &= \Sigma\, a'_{ij} a'_{ik} \Sigma\, b'_{tu} b'_{tv} \end{aligned}\right\} \quad . \quad . \quad . \quad (5.35)$$

Then if lower-order terms are neglected, the even product-moment $\mu_{rs}$, $r + s = 2m$ is given by the sum of terms like

$$n^{-3m} A_{\lambda\mu\nu} h_{11}^{\lambda} h_{12}^{\mu} h_{22}^{\nu}, \quad 2\lambda + \mu = r, \quad \mu + 2\nu = s \quad . \quad (5.36)$$

over all possible values of $\lambda$, $\mu$, $\nu$. The coefficient $A_{\lambda\mu\nu}$ is determined by the following argument. Consider a $\Sigma$ whose array of suffixes is such that it can be factorised as $(\Sigma\, a_{ij} a_{ik})^{\lambda} (\Sigma\, a_{ij} a'_{ik})^{\mu} (\Sigma\, a'_{ij} a'_{ik})^{\nu}$. Its suffix pairs can be permuted in $r!\, s!$ ways within the sets of scores of the two types $a$ and $a'$, but of these $\lambda!\,(2!)^{\lambda}\,\mu!\,\nu!\,(2!)^{\nu}$ give essentially the same $\Sigma$. The suffixes within pairs attached to each score may also be rearranged in $2^{2m}$ ways without affecting the result. Hence

$$A_{\lambda\mu\nu} = \frac{r!\,s!\,2^{2m}}{\lambda!\,\mu!\,\nu!\,2^{\lambda+\nu}} = \frac{r!\,s!\,2^{m+\mu}}{\lambda!\,\mu!\,\nu!} \quad . \quad . \quad (5.37)$$

From (5.35), (5.36) and (5.37) it follows that the calculation of $\mu_{rs}$ is tantamount to determining the coefficient of $t_1^r t_2^s$ in

$$\frac{2^m}{n^{3m}\,m!}(h_{11}t_1^2 + 2h_{12}t_1t_2 + h_{22}t_2^2)^m \quad . \quad . \quad (5.38)$$

We now consider the odd moments. For $\rho$ and $\tau$ these vanish by symmetry, but even in the more general case it can be shown that they are negligible to order $n^{-\frac{1}{2}}$. For a $\Sigma$ containing $2m + 1$ scores cannot have more than $3m + 1$ suffixes. This follows by a similar argument to that employed above for the even-order moments. Hence the order of magnitude of any $(2m + 1)$th moment is at most $n^{3m+1}$. The $2m$th moments were shown to be of order $n^{3m}$. A $(2m + 1)$th moment is of order at most $n^{\frac{3}{2}(2m+1)} \times n^{-\frac{1}{2}}$. The odd moments are therefore of lower order $(n^{-\frac{1}{2}})$ compared with the even moments.

Finally, it follows from (5.38) that the moment $\mu_{rs}$ is the coefficient of $t_1^r t_2^s$ in

$$\exp \frac{2}{n^3}(h_{11}t_1^2 + 2h_{12}t_1t_2 + h_{22}t_2^3) \quad . \quad . \quad (5.39)$$

This is the moment-generating function of a bivariate normal distribution (Kendall, *Advanced Theory*, Vol. I, **15.12**). The result is proved.

**5.14** It is of some interest to consider the product-moment correlation between $\rho$ and $\tau$. In exactly the same manner as in the derivation of (5.10) we find, for the mean value $E(cc')$

$$E(cc') = \frac{4}{n(n-1)(n-2)}\{\Sigma\, a_{ij}\, a'_{ik} - \Sigma\, a_{ij}\, a'_{ij}\}\{\Sigma\, b_{ij}\, b'_{ik} - \Sigma\, b_{ij}\, b'_{ij}\}$$

$$+ \frac{2}{n(n-1)}\,\Sigma\, a_{ij}\, a'_{ij}\, \Sigma\, b_{ij}\, b'_{ij}\,. \quad . \quad . \quad (5.40)$$

In the particular case when $c$ relates to $S$ and $c'$ to $S(d^2)$ we find

$$\sum_{i,j,k} a_{ij}\, a'_{ik} = \tfrac{1}{6}n^2(n^2 - 1) \quad . \quad . \quad . \quad (5.41)$$

$$\sum_{i,j} a_{ij}\, a'_{ij} = \tfrac{1}{3}n(n^2 - 1) \quad . \quad . \quad . \quad (5.42)$$

and on substitution in (5.40), we find

$$E(cc') = \tfrac{1}{9}n^2(n-1)(n+1)^2 \quad . \quad . \quad (5.43)$$

Thus the product-moment correlation between $S$ and $S(d^2)$, which is the same as that between $\tau$ and $\rho$, is given by

$$\frac{E(cc')}{\sqrt{\{E(c^2)\,E(c'^2)\}}} = \frac{2(n+1)}{\sqrt{\{2n(2n+5)\}}} \quad . \quad . \quad (5.44)$$

For large $n$ this tends to unity. Even for moderate $n$ it is quite high. For $n = 5$ it is 0·980 and for $n = 20$ it is 0·990.

## Corrections for continuity

**5.15** We turn now to the question of corrections for continuity, the rules for which were given in **4.12** and **4.15**.

(*a*) Consider first the case where one ranking is untied and the other contains ties, and may in the extreme case be a dichotomy. We may imagine the untied ranking in the natural order and the other in any arbitrary order. If we interchange a pair of neighbouring members in the untied ranking the only scores affected are those involving both members. Either the two ranks in the second ranking are untied or they are tied. In the first case the score $S$ alters by two units, in the latter it remains unchanged. However many ties there are in the second ranking (short of the whole set being completely tied) there must be one interchange of neighbouring members in the first ranking which alters $S$ by 2. Thus all intervals between successive values of $S$ in the distribution of $S$ are two units, and the appropriate correction for continuity is one unit.

(*b*) If now the first ranking consists entirely of ties of extent $t$ and the second is dichotomised, a change of two neighbours from different tied groups can at the most—and will at least for some rankings of the second variate—alter $S$ by $2t$, and the continuity correction is $t$.

(*c*) If both variates are dichotomised then, as in **3.14**, $S = ad - bc$. The least change that can result is an increase or decrease of a unit in $a$, and in such a case (say an increase) the increase in $S$ is

$$(a+1)(d+1) - (b-1)(c-1) - (ad - bc) = a + b + c + d = N.$$

The continuity correction is thus $\tfrac{1}{2}N$.

(*d*) When both rankings contain ties it is not possible to lay down any general rule for continuity corrections. If the point is important some special consideration such as that in Example 4.5 is necessary.

**5.16** For the continuity corrections to $\rho$, consider a ranking in the natural order and a dichotomy into $k$ and $n - k$ individuals, the corresponding midranks being $\frac{1}{2}(k+1)$ and $\frac{1}{2}(n+k+1)$. If two members of the first ranking are $x$ and $y$ and their interchange results in the interchange of two members in the second, one from each part of the dichotomy, the change in $S(d^2)$ is

$$\{x-\tfrac{1}{2}(k+1)\}^2+\{y-\tfrac{1}{2}(n+k+1)\}^2-\{x-\tfrac{1}{2}(n+k+1)^2\} \\ -\{y-\tfrac{1}{2}(k+1)\}^2=n(x-y).$$

Thus there will be one interchange of neighbouring members ($y=x+1$) which increases or decreases $S(d^2)$ by $n$. The appropriate deduction is therefore $\frac{1}{2}n$.

If the members of the first ranking are all tied to extent $t$, the minimum (and realisable) change is $nt$, giving a correction of $\frac{1}{2}nt$.

Finally, if the first ranking is dichotomised the minimum change is $\frac{1}{2}n^2$ and the correction $\frac{1}{4}n^2$.

### The non-null case

**5.17** We turn now to the more difficult case where parental correlation exists. We denote the parent value by $\tau$ and the sample value by $t$. We prove in the first place that the mean value of $t$ over all possible samples is $\tau$.

Consider the $\binom{N}{n}$ samples of $n$ from a population of $N$ members. Any particular pair of members will occur in $\binom{N-2}{n-2}$ samples, that is, all pairs occur equally frequently in the totality of all samples. Thus the total score for all samples is $\binom{N-2}{n-2}$ times the score for the population, say $\Sigma$. Thus

$$E(t)=\frac{\binom{N-2}{n-2}\Sigma}{\frac{1}{2}n(n-1)\binom{N}{n}}=\frac{\Sigma}{\frac{1}{2}N(N-1)}=\tau \qquad . \quad (5.45)$$

**5.18** Next we derive an expression for the variance of $t$. Let $c^{(n)}$ be the quantity $c$ for a sample ranking of $n$, and $c$ be the parent value. Then

$$t=\frac{c^{(n)}}{n(n-1)} \qquad . \quad . \quad . \quad . \quad (5.46)$$

and

$$c^{(n)} = \Sigma^{(n)} c_{ij}, \quad . \quad . \quad . \quad . \quad (5.47)$$

where $\Sigma^{(n)}$ denotes summation over those values of $i$ and $j$ occurring in the sample.

We require $E(t^2)$, so consider

$$\sum_n \{c^{(n)}\}^2 = \sum_n \Sigma^{(n)} c_{ij} c_{kl}, \quad . \quad . \quad . \quad (5.48)$$

$\Sigma$ denoting summation over all selections of the sample of $n$ from the population of $N$ members. Let us enumerate the number of ways in which $c_{ij} c_{kl}$ and similar products with tied suffixes occur in the sum.

(i) When $i, j, k, l$ are all different, the term $c_{ij} c_{kl}$ may occur with $\binom{N-4}{n-4}$ selections of the remaining members of the sample, and the contribution of such terms to $\sum_n$ is

$$\binom{N-4}{n-4} \Sigma' c_{ij} c_{kl},$$

$\Sigma'$ as usual denoting summation over unequal values of $i, j, k, l$ from 1 to $N$.

(ii) The term $c_{ij} c_{il}$ similarly occurs in $\binom{N-3}{n-3}$ ways and there are four ways of tying one suffix. The contribution is thus

$$4\binom{N-3}{n-3} \Sigma' c_{ij} c_{il}.$$

(iii) Terms like $c_{ij}^2$ similarly contribute

$$2\binom{N-2}{n-2} \Sigma' c_{ij}^2.$$

Thus

$$\sum_n \{c^{(n)}\}^2 = \binom{N-4}{n-4} \Sigma' c_{ij} c_{kl} + 4\binom{N-3}{n-3} \Sigma' c_{ij} c_{ik} + 2\binom{N-2}{n-2} \Sigma' c_{ij}^2$$

Expressing the $\Sigma'$'s in terms of $\Sigma$'s and dividing by $\binom{N}{n}$ we find

$$E\{c^{(n)}\}^2 = \frac{n^{[4]}}{N^{[4]}}(\Sigma c_{ij} c_{kl} - 4 \Sigma c_{ij} c_{il} + 2 \Sigma c_{ij}^2) + \frac{4n^{[3]}}{N^{[3]}}(\Sigma c_{ij} c_{il} - \Sigma c_{ij}^2) + \frac{2n^{[2]}}{N^{[2]}} \Sigma c_{ij}^2 \quad . \quad . \quad (5.49)$$

where $n^{[r]} = n(n-1)\ldots(n-r+1)$. Since $\Sigma\, c_{ij}^2 = N(N-1)$ and $\Sigma\, c_{ij}\, c_{kl} = c^2$ the variance of $t$ for given $\tau$ and $n$ is seen to depend on $\Sigma\, c_{ij}\, c_{kl} = \Sigma\, c_i^2$, where $\Sigma\, c_i = \sum_{j=1}^{N} c_{ij}$.

Let $N$ become large. The quantities $c$ and $\Sigma\, c_i^2$ are respectively of order $N^2$ and $N^3$, so if we write

$$\tau_i = \frac{c_i}{N}. \qquad (5.50)$$

we find

$$E(t^2) \sim \frac{(n-2)(n-3)}{n(n-1)}\tau^2 + \frac{4(n-2)}{n(n-1)}\frac{\Sigma\tau_i^2}{N} + \frac{2}{n(n-1)} \qquad (5.51)$$

Thus, in the limit,

$$\text{var } t = \frac{4(n-2)}{n(n-1)} \text{ var } \tau_i + \frac{2}{n(n-1)}(1-\tau^2) \qquad (5.52)$$

**5.19** Consider now $c_{ij} = a_{ij}\, b_{ij}$. Keeping $b_{ij}$ equal to $\pm 1$, let the $a$'s assume any values, subject to the conditions

$$\Sigma\, a_{ij}^2 = N(N-1), \qquad \Sigma\, a_{ij}\, b_{ij} = c = N(N-1)\tau.$$

The stationary values of $\Sigma\, c_i^2$ occur when the $a$'s satisfy the relations

$$b_{ij}(c_i + c_j) - \lambda\, a_{ij} - \mu\, b_{ij} = 0 \qquad (5.53)$$

where $\lambda$ and $\mu$ are undetermined multipliers. Multiplying by $b_{ij}$ and summing for all $j$, we find

$$c_i = \frac{\mu(N-1) - c}{N-2-\lambda}.$$

Thus, unless the $c_i$ are all to be equal, in which case $\Sigma\, c_i^2$ is a *minimum*, $\lambda$ and $\mu$ must take the values

$$\lambda = N-2, \qquad \mu = c/(N-1).$$

Multiplying (5.53) by $a_{ij}$ and summing over $j$, we have,

$$2\,\Sigma\, c_i^2 - \lambda N(N-1) - \mu c = 0,$$

whence it follows that $\Sigma\, c_i^2$ cannot exceed

$$\tfrac{1}{2}N(N-1)(N-2) + \tfrac{1}{2}c^2/(N-1).$$

For large $N$ this implies that

$$\Sigma\, \tau_i^2/N \leqslant \tfrac{1}{2}(1 + \tau^2).$$

Hence

$$\text{var } \tau_i \leqslant \tfrac{1}{2}(1 - \tau^2)$$

and thus, from (5.52),

$$\text{var } t \leqslant \left\{\frac{2(n-2)}{n(n-1)} + \frac{2}{n(n-1)}\right\}(1 - \tau^2)$$

$$\leqslant \frac{2}{n}(1 - \tau^2) \quad . \quad . \quad . \quad . \quad . \quad (5.54)$$

which is equation (4.11) of the previous chapter.

**5.20** The form of this result suggests using a transformation

$$w = \sin^{-1} t \quad . \quad . \quad . \quad . \quad (5.55)$$

To the same order of approximation we may take $w$ as being normally distributed about $\omega = \sin^{-1} \tau$, and the variance of $w$ will obey the relation

$$\text{var } w \leqslant \frac{2}{n} \quad . \quad . \quad . \quad . \quad (5.56)$$

which has the advantage of being independent of $\omega$. It is not known whether the distribution in this case is nearer to normality than that of the original $t$.

**5.21** The proof that the distribution of $t$ tends to normality for large $n$ follows, in essentials, the demonstrations given earlier in this chapter. We will merely outline it.

Write

$$g_{ij} = c_{ij} - c/N^2$$

so that

$$g_{ij} = g_{ji}, \qquad \Sigma\, g_{ij} = 0 \qquad \text{and} \qquad g_{ii} = -c/N^2 = -(N-1)\tau/N.$$

The $r$th moment of $c^{(n)}$ about its mean value is $E\{\Sigma^{(n)} g_{ij}\}^r$, so consider

$$\sum_n \{\Sigma^{(n)} g_{ij}\}^r = \sum_n \Sigma^{(n)} g_{ij}\, g_{kl}\, g_{uv} \ldots \quad . \quad (5.57)$$

An essential condition is that

$$\Sigma\, g_{ij}\, g_{ik} = 0(N^3), \quad . \quad . \quad . \quad . \quad (5.58)$$

which is true only if $1 - \tau^2$ is of the order of 1, so that the tendency to normality may break down for high correlations.

In the manner of **5.13**, for the moment of order $2m$ the major term arises from expressions like $(\Sigma\, g_{ij}\, g_{ik})^m$ and other terms are of lower order in $m$. With $3m$ suffixes assigned there are $\binom{N-3m}{n-3m}$ ways of selecting the remaining $n - 3m$ members, and the suffixes can be tied in $\frac{(2m)!\,2^{2m}}{m!\,(2!)^m}$ ways to give the same result. Dividing by $\binom{N}{n}$ and noting that for large $N$ and $n$

$$\binom{N-3m}{n-3m}\Big/\binom{N}{n} \sim \frac{n^{3m}}{N^{3m}}$$

we find for the major term in the moment of order $2m$

$$\frac{n^{3m}}{N^{3m}}\frac{(2m)!}{m!}2^m(\Sigma\, g_{ij}\, g_{ik})^m$$

which is of order $n^{3m}$. By the same argument terms with $f < 3m$ different suffixes are of order $n^f$ and may be neglected. Thus,

$$\mu_{2m} \sim \frac{n^{3m}}{N^{3m}}\frac{(2m)!}{m!}2^m(\Sigma\, g_{ij}g_{ik})^m$$

$$\sim \frac{(2m)!}{2^m m!}(\mu_2)^m \quad . \quad . \quad . \quad . \quad (5.59)$$

Further, $\mu_{2m+1}$ is of order $n^{-\frac{1}{2}}$ in comparison. The tendency to normality follows. The variance of $c^{(n)}$ is

$$\frac{4n^3}{N^3}(\Sigma\, g_{ij}\, g_{ik}) = 4n^3 \operatorname{var} \tau_i \quad . \quad . \quad . \quad (5.60)$$

and the variance of $t$ accordingly is $(4/n)$ var $\tau_i$ which agrees with (5.52) to the order considered.

**5.22** We now give reasons for supposing that the limits to the variance of $t$ given by (5.54) cannot very substantially be narrowed.

Consider a ranking such as

5 2 3 1 6 7 8 9 4

The number of positive pairs is 26, so $t = 0{\cdot}44$. Let us transform this so as to bring the 1 to the beginning of the ranking, but move the 9 so as to preserve the score at 26. The 1 passes over three members to go to the beginning and hence adds 3 to the score.

The 9 must therefore proceed to the left over three members so as to subtract 3, and we reach the ranking

1 5 2 3 9 6 7 8 4

Proceeding similarly with the 2 we reach

1 2 5 9 3 6 7 8 4

Had the 9 been contiguous to the 1 and incapable of proceeding further to the left we should have moved the 8, and so on. Continuing the process we ultimately arrive at

1 2 3 4 9 8 7 6 5

All the lower numbers are in the right order and the others in the inverse order. We may call this the " canonical order " for given $S$. It is not always possible to reduce a given ranking to canonical order, but there cannot be more than one individual out of place.

If the parent ranking is inverted $\tau$ becomes $-\tau$. We may reduce this to the canonical form and re-invert the result, so that the coefficient is again $\tau$. This ranking we may call the " inverse canonical form ".*

**5.23** Now consider the canonical case when there are $N$ members together, $R$ at the beginning in the right order and $N - R$ in the inverse order. If we select $n - j$ members from the $R$ and $j$ from the $N - R$ the value of $S$ for the sample of $n$ is $\frac{1}{2}n(n-1) + \frac{1}{2}j(j-1)$ and the relative frequency of $U = \frac{1}{2}n(n-1) - S$ is

$$\binom{R}{n-j}\binom{N-R}{j}\Big/\binom{N}{n}.$$

Now suppose that $N$ tends to infinity and $R/N$ tends to a limit $p$. The relative frequency of $U$ $(= \frac{1}{2}j(j-1))$ then tends to $\binom{n}{j}p^{n-j}q^j$ where $q = 1 - p$. The mean value of $U$ is then

$$\sum_0^n \tfrac{1}{2}j(j-1)\binom{n}{j}p^{n-j}q^j = \tfrac{1}{2}n(n-1)q^2$$

and since

$$t = 1 - \frac{2U}{\frac{1}{2}n(n-1)}$$

we must have

$$q = \{\tfrac{1}{2}(1-\tau)\}^{\frac{1}{2}}.$$

---

* Sundrum (1953) has recently published a proof of the result that the canonical ranking has minimal variance, but Professor Hoeffding has raised objections which seem to me valid.

The variance of $U$ is found to be

$$\text{var}\, U = n(n-1)pq^2\{nq - \tfrac{1}{2}(1-3q)\}$$

and so

$$\text{var}\, t = \frac{16pq^2\{nq - \tfrac{1}{2}(1-3q)\}}{n(n-1)} \quad . \quad . \quad (5.61)$$

If the inverted parent is reduced to canonical form, giving ratios $p'$ and $q'$, we shall have

$$q' = \{\tfrac{1}{2}(1+\tau)\}^{\frac{1}{2}}$$

and

$$\text{var}\, t' = \frac{16p'q'^2\{nq' - \tfrac{1}{2}(1-3q')\}}{n(n-1)} \quad . \quad . \quad (5.62)$$

Then, since $q^2 + q'^2 = 1$,

$$\text{var}\, t' - \text{var}\, t = \frac{16(n+2)}{n(n-1)}(q'-q)(1-q)(1-q').$$

When $\tau$ is positive $q' > q$ and then var $t' >$ var $t$. Taking the inverse canonical ranking when $\tau > 0$ and the direct canonical ranking when $\tau < 0$, we find for the variance of $t$ when $n$ is large

$$\text{var}\, t \sim \frac{4\sqrt{2}}{n}(1 + |\,\tau\,|)^{\frac{3}{2}}[1 - \sqrt{\{\tfrac{1}{2}(1+|\,\tau\,|)\}}] \quad . \quad (5.63)$$

The ratio of this quantity to the upper limit $\frac{2}{n}(1-\tau^2)$ varies from $2(\sqrt{2}-1) = 0{\cdot}83$ when $\tau = 0$ to 1 when $\tau = 1$. Evidently the upper limit to the variance cannot be much improved, since an actual parent ranking has been found whose variance approximates to it for all values of $\tau$ when $n$ is not too small.

## More exact treatment in the non-null case

**5.24** In proving that $t$ tends to normality in the non-null case we have neglected terms of order $1/\sqrt{n}$ and this suggests that the normal approximation may hold good for large $n$ but may be indifferent for small or moderate $n$. We will examine briefly the possibility of improving the approximation in the case of moderate $n$.

Looking again at (5.52),

$$\text{var}\, t = \frac{4(n-2)}{n(n-1)}\,\text{var}\,\tau_i + \frac{2}{n(n-1)}(1-\tau^2) \quad . \quad (5.64)$$

we see that the actual variance of $t$ for large $N$ depends on the unknown functions $\tau_i$ and $\tau$. In the absence of exact knowledge of these quantities we may estimate them from the sample, using the sample values of $c_i$ and $c$ instead of the unknown parent values. In doing so, however, it is better to modify our formulae slightly so as to remove bias. The reader will recall that in the ordinary theory of statistics it is better to use the estimator $\Sigma(x - x)^2/(n - 1)$ for the variance, rather than the actual sample variance $\Sigma(x - \bar{x})^2/n$ because the average of the former over all samples is the parent variance. For similar reasons it is better not to substitute the sample values of $c_i$ and $c$ in (5.64) but to use a formula which, averaged over all samples, gives the exact form of var $t$. Such an unbiassed formula is

$$\text{var } t = \frac{1}{n(n-1)(n-2)(n-3)}\left\{4\,\Sigma\, c_i^2 - \frac{2(2n-3)}{n(n-1)}c^2 - 2n(n-1)\right\} \quad . \quad . \quad . \quad (5.65)$$

where the $c_i$ and $c$ values are sample values. This will give us a "best" estimate of var $t$.

**5.25** We may take matters a little further by considering the third moment of $t$ so as to allow for departures from normality in the sampling distribution. Reference may be made to Daniels and Kendall (1947) for the details. We merely quote the result that if

$$\gamma_1 = \frac{\mu_3(t)}{\{\mu_2(t)\}^{\frac{3}{2}}} \quad . \quad . \quad . \quad . \quad (5.66)$$

then the frequency-distribution of

$$x = \frac{t - \tau}{\sqrt{\mu_2(t)}}$$

is

$$f(x) = \left(1 - \frac{\gamma_1}{6}\frac{d^3}{dx^3}\right)\frac{e^{-\frac{1}{2}x^2}}{\sqrt{(2\pi)}}\{1 + 0(n^{-1})\} \quad . \quad (5.67)^*$$

If $\xi$ is the normal deviate whose chance of being exceeded is $P(\xi)$, the chance of $x$ exceeding $\xi$ is

$$F(\xi) = P(\xi) + \frac{\gamma_1}{6}(\xi^2 - 1)\frac{e^{-\frac{1}{2}\xi^2}}{\sqrt{(2\pi)}}$$

---

* This is a stronger result than would be obtained by the usual expansion of a frequency function in a Gram-Charlier series based on the first three moments only. For such expansions see Kendall, *Advanced Theory*, Vol. I, 6.23–6.33.

If $X$ is the correct limit such that $F(X) = P(\xi)$ it is readily proved by successive approximation that

$$X = \xi + \frac{\gamma_1}{6}(\xi^2 - 1) \quad . \quad . \quad . \quad (5.68)$$

to order $n^{-1}$. For example the 5 per cent value of $\xi$ is $\pm 1{\cdot}96$. The corresponding value of $X$ is

$$\pm 1{\cdot}96 + \frac{(1{\cdot}96)^2 - 1}{6}\gamma_1$$

$$= \pm 1{\cdot}96 + 0{\cdot}474\gamma_1 \quad . \quad . \quad . \quad . \quad (5.69)$$

The corresponding 1 per cent value of $X$ is

$$\pm 2{\cdot}58 + 0{\cdot}941\gamma_1 \quad . \quad . \quad . \quad (5.70)$$

The following example illustrates the use of these results.

*Example 5.1*

The following shows the ranks according to two qualities $A$ and $B$ in a sample of 30 drawn from a population of unknown character. We require to assess the correlation in the parent population.

TABLE 5.1

| *A* | *B* | *A* | *B* | *A* | *B* |
|---|---|---|---|---|---|
| 1 | 5 | 11 | 17 | 21 | 21 |
| 2 | 4 | 12 | 13 | 22 | 29 |
| 3 | 9 | 13 | 24 | 23 | 28 |
| 4 | 3 | 14 | 14 | 24 | 19 |
| 5 | 6 | 15 | 1 | 25 | 23 |
| 6 | 2 | 16 | 12 | 26 | 20 |
| 7 | 15 | 17 | 10 | 27 | 7 |
| 8 | 18 | 18 | 30 | 28 | 26 |
| 9 | 8 | 19 | 22 | 29 | 27 |
| 10 | 11 | 20 | 16 | 30 | 25 |

The correlation $t$ is found to be $+ 0{\cdot}490$.

(*a*) Consider first of all the maximum confidence limits given by (4.12). The 5 per cent limits are

$$- 0{\cdot}02 \leqslant t \leqslant 0{\cdot}80.$$

(*b*) The $\sin^{-1}$ transformation of **5.20** gives

$$w = \sin^{-1} t = 0{\cdot}512$$
$$0{\cdot}01 \leqslant t \leqslant 0{\cdot}85,$$

with results which are not very different from those of (*a*).

TABLE 5.2

| $c_{ij}$ | | | | | | | | | | | | | | | | | | | | | | | | | | | | | | $c_i$ |
|---|---|---|---|---|---|---|---|---|---|---|---|---|---|---|---|---|---|---|---|---|---|---|---|---|---|---|---|---|---|---|
| 0 | − | + | − | + | − | + | + | + | + | + | + | + | + | − | + | + | + | + | + | + | + | + | + | + | + | + | + | + | + | 21 |
| − | 0 | + | − | + | − | + | + | + | + | + | + | + | + | − | + | + | + | + | + | + | + | + | + | + | + | + | + | + | + | 21 |
| + | + | 0 | − | − | − | + | + | − | + | + | + | + | + | − | + | + | + | + | + | + | + | + | + | + | + | − | + | + | + | 17 |
| − | − | − | 0 | + | − | + | + | + | + | + | + | + | + | − | + | + | + | + | + | + | + | + | + | + | + | + | + | + | + | 19 |
| + | + | − | + | 0 | − | + | + | + | + | + | + | + | + | − | + | + | + | + | + | + | + | + | + | + | + | + | + | + | + | 23 |
| − | − | − | − | − | 0 | + | + | + | + | + | + | + | + | − | + | + | + | + | + | + | + | + | + | + | + | + | + | + | + | 17 |
| + | + | + | + | + | + | 0 | + | − | − | + | − | + | − | − | − | − | + | + | + | + | + | + | + | + | + | − | + | + | + | 13 |
| + | + | + | + | + | + | + | 0 | − | − | − | − | + | − | − | − | − | + | + | − | + | + | + | + | + | + | − | + | + | + | 9 |
| + | + | − | + | + | + | − | − | 0 | + | + | + | + | + | − | + | + | + | + | + | + | + | + | + | + | + | − | + | + | + | 19 |
| + | + | + | + | + | + | − | − | + | 0 | + | + | + | + | − | + | − | + | + | + | + | + | + | + | + | + | − | + | + | + | 19 |
| + | + | + | + | + | + | + | − | + | + | 0 | − | + | − | − | − | − | + | + | − | + | + | + | + | + | + | − | + | + | + | 13 |
| + | + | + | + | + | + | − | − | + | + | − | 0 | + | + | − | − | − | + | + | + | + | + | + | + | + | + | − | + | + | + | 15 |
| + | + | + | + | + | + | + | + | + | + | + | + | 0 | − | − | − | − | + | − | − | − | + | + | − | − | − | − | + | + | + | 7 |
| + | + | + | + | + | + | − | − | + | + | − | + | − | 0 | − | − | − | + | + | + | + | + | + | + | + | + | − | + | + | + | 13 |
| − | − | − | − | − | − | − | − | − | − | − | − | − | − | 0 | + | + | + | + | + | + | + | + | + | + | + | + | + | + | + | 1 |
| + | + | + | + | + | + | − | − | + | + | − | − | − | − | + | 0 | − | + | + | + | + | + | + | + | + | + | − | + | + | + | 13 |
| + | + | + | + | + | + | − | − | + | − | − | − | − | − | + | − | 0 | + | + | + | + | + | + | + | + | + | − | + | + | + | 11 |
| + | + | + | + | + | + | + | + | + | + | + | + | + | + | + | + | + | 0 | − | − | − | − | − | − | − | − | − | − | − | − | 5 |
| + | + | + | + | + | + | + | + | + | + | + | + | − | + | + | + | + | − | 0 | − | − | + | + | − | + | − | − | + | + | + | 15 |
| + | + | + | + | + | + | + | − | + | + | − | + | − | + | + | + | + | − | − | 0 | + | + | + | + | + | + | − | + | + | + | 17 |
| + | + | + | + | + | + | + | + | + | + | + | + | − | + | + | + | + | − | − | + | 0 | + | + | − | + | + | − | + | + | + | 19 |
| + | + | + | + | + | + | + | + | + | + | + | + | + | + | + | + | + | − | + | + | + | 0 | − | − | − | − | − | − | − | − | 11 |
| + | + | + | + | + | + | + | + | + | + | + | + | + | + | + | + | + | − | + | + | + | − | 0 | − | − | − | − | − | − | − | 11 |
| + | + | + | + | + | + | + | + | + | + | + | + | − | + | + | + | + | − | − | + | − | − | − | 0 | + | + | − | + | + | + | 15 |
| + | + | + | + | + | + | + | + | + | + | + | + | − | + | + | + | + | − | + | + | + | − | − | + | 0 | − | − | + | + | + | 17 |
| + | + | + | + | + | + | + | + | + | + | + | + | − | + | + | + | + | − | − | + | + | − | − | + | − | 0 | − | + | + | + | 15 |
| + | + | − | + | + | + | − | − | − | − | − | − | − | − | + | − | − | − | − | − | − | − | − | − | − | − | 0 | + | + | + | −11 |
| + | + | + | + | + | + | + | + | + | + | + | + | + | + | + | + | + | − | + | + | + | − | − | + | + | + | + | 0 | + | − | 21 |
| + | + | + | + | + | + | + | + | + | + | + | + | + | + | + | + | + | − | + | + | + | − | − | + | + | + | + | + | 0 | − | 21 |
| + | + | + | + | + | + | + | + | + | + | + | + | + | + | + | + | + | − | + | + | + | − | − | + | + | + | + | − | − | 0 | 19 |

$c = 426$
$n = 30$
$\Sigma c^2 = 7470$

(*c*) To go further we require the values $c_i$ and $c$. Table 5.2 shows the matrix of values $c_{ij}$ for the data, and we find

$$c = 426$$
$$\Sigma c_i^2 = 7470.$$

From (5.65) we then have

$$\text{var}\, t = \frac{1}{30 \times 29 \times 28 \times 27}\left\{4 \times 7470 - \frac{2 \times 57}{30 \times 29} \times 426^2 - 60 \times 29\right\}$$
$$= 0{\cdot}006{,}630$$

giving an estimated standard error of 0·0814. The 5 per cent confidence limits, assuming normality, are then

$$0{\cdot}33 \leqslant t \leqslant 0{\cdot}65.$$

These are much narrower than the values of (*a*) and (*b*).

(*d*) To allow for departures from normality we require to estimate $\gamma_1$, which in turn depends on $\mu_3(t)$. For moderate samples the following formula gives an approximation

$$\mu_3(t) = \frac{8}{n^6}\left\{\sum_{i>j} c_{ij}(c_i + c_j)^2 - \frac{5c\,\Sigma c_i}{n} + \frac{3c^2}{n^3}\right\} \quad . \quad (5.71)$$

where the first term in curly brackets is a summation of $c_{ij}(c_i + c_j)^2$ over all values $i > j$, *i.e.* the values in Table 5.2 below the diagonal. After some tedious computation we find

$$\gamma_1 = -\,0{\cdot}32.$$

The adjusted 5 per cent limits from (5.69) are then

$$0{\cdot}32 \leqslant t \leqslant 0{\cdot}64.$$

The corrections for non-normality are small, and the limits are very similar to those given by (*c*).

**5.26** The arithmetic required by the foregoing examples is more than we should usually have the patience to perform. Sundrum (1953*a*) has investigated the third and fourth moments of $\tau$ in the non-null case and has shown that the latter depends on 10 parameters which can be estimated from the data. This result is of considerable theoretical interest, but again the labour of applying it in practice would be prohibitive unless it could be programmed on a high-speed computer.

One further resource is left to us. If we can assume that the rankings are based on a normal variate (and, presumably, as an approximation if the underlying variate is nearly normal) the variance is narrowed very considerably. See **9.6** *et seq.*

**ρ in the non-null case**

**5.27** As usual, the sampling theory of $\rho$ is more complicated than that of $\tau$ and not much is known about the distribution in the non-null case; except that we are able to derive the expected value of $r_s$, the sample value of $\rho$.

Let us consider the function $V$ of (2.27),

$$V = \sum_{i<j} m_{ij}(j - i) \quad . \quad . \quad . \quad (5.72)$$

The value of $m_{ij}$ for any particular pair of members is the same for both sample and population—this is the basic reason why $E(t) = \tau$. But the factor $(j - i)$ is not.

Consider a pair of members having ranks $I$, $J$ in the population of $N$. Any member between them in the population has probability $\frac{n-2}{N-2}$ of appearing in the sample ranking. The mean number of such ranks appearing in the sample is therefore

$$\frac{n-2}{N-2}(J - I - 1)$$

and hence the mean $j - i$ in the sample is one more than this, namely

$$\frac{N-n}{N-2} + \frac{n-2}{N-2}(J - I) \quad . \quad . \quad . \quad (5.73)$$

Thus the mean value of $V$ is given by

$$E(V) = \frac{\binom{N-2}{n-2}}{\binom{N}{n}} \sum_{I<J} m_{IJ}\left\{\frac{N-n}{N-2} + \frac{n-2}{N-2}(J - I)\right\},$$

where summation takes place over the population; for any pair of ranks can occur in $\binom{N-2}{n-2}$ ways. Hence, expressing $V$ in terms of $r_s$ we find

$$E(1 - r_s) = \frac{12}{N(N-1)(n+1)} \Sigma\, m_{IJ}\left\{\frac{N-n}{N-2} + \frac{n-2}{N-2}(I - J)\right\}. \quad (5.74)$$

Now for our population

$$\Sigma\, m_{IJ} = \frac{N(N-1)}{4}(1 - \tau)$$

$$\Sigma\, m_{IJ}(J - I) = \frac{N(N^2-1)}{12}(1 - \rho)$$

and substituting in (5.74) we find

$$E(r_s) = \frac{1}{(n+1)(N-2)}\{3(N-n)\tau + (n-2)(N+1)\rho\}. \quad (5.75)$$

a general formula obtained independently by Durbin and Stuart (1951) and Daniels (1951).

**5.28** We note that for $N$ large this tends to

$$E(r_s) = \frac{1}{n+1}\{3\tau + (n-2)\rho\} \quad . \quad . \quad (5.76)$$

a result obtained for continuous populations by Hoeffding in 1948. Thus

$$E(r_s) - \rho = \frac{3}{n+1}(\tau - \rho) \quad . \quad . \quad . \quad (5.77)$$

In statistical terminology $r_s$ is a biassed estimator of $\rho$ and for some populations the bias may be appreciable. It is probably well to correct $r_s$ by deducting the " sample bias " $3(t - r_s)/(n-2)$.

## References

See references to Chapter 4. For the distribution of $\tau$ in the null case see Moran (1950*a*), Silverstone (1950) and David and others (1951). For the mean value of the sample Spearman coefficient see Hoeffding (1948), Daniels (1950, 1951) and Durbin and Stuart (1951). Moran (1948) obtained the result in the case of sampling from a normal population.

The normality of $t$ when ties are present follows as a consequence of general results obtained by Hoeffding (1948). A simple proof is not easy to give, but see Terpstra (1952) for the case when only one ranking is tied, and Kruskal (1952).

CHAPTER 6

# THE PROBLEM OF $m$ RANKINGS

**6.1** Up to this point we have been concerned with the correlation between two rankings. We now consider the case when there are several rankings, say $m$ in number, of $n$ individuals and we desire to investigate the general relationship between them. Suppose, for instance, four observers rank six objects as follows:

| | Object | | | | | |
|---|---|---|---|---|---|---|
| | A | B | C | D | E | F |
| Observer $P$ | 5 | 4 | 1 | 6 | 3 | 2 |
| ,, $Q$ | 2 | 3 | 1 | 5 | 6 | 4 |
| ,, $R$ | 4 | 1 | 6 | 3 | 2 | 5 |
| ,, $S$ | 4 | 3 | 2 | 5 | 1 | 6 |
| Totals of ranks: | 15 | 11 | 10 | 19 | 12 | 17 |

. . . (6.1)

In accordance with our known methods we can work out the rank correlation coefficient between each pair of observers, obtaining $\binom{4}{2} = 6$ coefficients. This, however, is not what we usually require. We need a measure of the concordance of the observers taken as a group.

**6.2** Perhaps the most obvious procedure is to average all the possible values of $\tau$ or of $\rho$ between pairs of observers; but this is evidently very tedious when $m$ is large. In a case such as this the quickest method is to consider the sum of ranks allotted by the observers, as shown in the last row of (6.1). These numbers must sum to 84, and in general to $\frac{1}{2}mn(n+1)$, for they are composed of a sum of $m$ sets each of which is the sum of natural numbers 1 to $n$. The mean value of the sums is then $\frac{1}{2}m(n+1)$, in our present example, 14. Consider the deviations about this mean:

$$1, \quad -3, \quad -4, \quad 5, \quad -2, \quad 3 \qquad . \quad . \quad (6.2)$$

If all the rankings were identical the sums in (6.1) would consist of

$$m, \quad 2m, \quad . \; . \; . \; nm$$

(though not necessarily in that order) and their deviations accordingly

$$-\tfrac{1}{2}m(n-1), \quad -\tfrac{1}{2}m(n-3), \ldots \tfrac{1}{2}m(n-1)$$

The sum of squares of these deviations would be given by

$$\tfrac{1}{12}m^2(n^3-n) \quad . \quad . \quad . \quad . \quad (6.3)$$

This is the maximum value which the sum of squares may have. Its extreme value at the other end of the range is exactly zero if $m$ is even or $n$ is odd, or both, and in the contrary case is relatively small.

Let us then write $S$ for the sum of squares of the actual deviations, in our present instance, from (6.2), 64. We define

$$W = \frac{12S}{m^2(n^3-n)} \quad . \quad . \quad . \quad (6.4)$$

and call $W$ the *coefficient of concordance.* In our example,

$$W = \frac{12 \times 64}{16 \times 210} = 0{\cdot}229.$$

**6.3** $W$ measures, in a sense, the communality of judgments for the $m$ observers. If they all agree $W = 1$. If they differ very much among themselves the sums of ranks will be more or less equal, and consequently the sum of squares $S$ becomes small compared with the maximum possible value, so that $W$ is small. As $W$ increases from 0 to 1 the deviations become " more different " and there is a greater measure of agreement in the rankings.

**6.4** The reader may wonder why we have chosen a coefficient ranging from 0 to 1 and not from $-1$ to 1 as for a rank correlation coefficient. The answer is that when more than two observers are involved, agreement and disagreement are not symmetrical opposites. $m$ observers may all agree but they cannot all disagree completely, in the sense here considered. If, of three observers $P$, $Q$, and $R$, $P$ disagrees with $Q$ on a comparison and also disagrees with $R$, then $Q$ and $R$ must agree.

**6.5** If we write $\rho_{av}$ for the mean value of the Spearman coefficient between the $\binom{m}{2}$ possible pairs of observers, then

$$\rho_{av} = \frac{mW-1}{m-1} \quad . \quad . \quad . \quad . \quad (6.5)$$

For if the rank of the $j$th object by the $i$th observer, measured from the mean $\frac{1}{2}(n + 1)$, is $x_{ij}$ the average $\rho$ is

$$\rho_{av} = \frac{1}{m(m-1)} \frac{\sum_{i,k=1}^{m} \sum_{j=1}^{n} x_{ij} x_{kj}}{\frac{1}{12}(n^3 - n)}$$

$$= \frac{12}{m(m-1)(n^3 - n)} \left\{ \sum_{j=1}^{n} \left( \sum_{i=1}^{m} x_{ij} \right)^2 - \sum_{j=1}^{n} \sum_{i=1}^{m} x_{ij}^2 \right\}$$

$$= \frac{12}{m(m-1)(n^3 - n)} \left\{ S - \frac{1}{12} m(n^3 - n) \right\}$$

$$= \frac{mW - 1}{m - 1} \quad . \quad . \quad . \quad . \quad . \quad . \quad . \quad (6.6)$$

When $\rho_{av} = +1$, $W = 1$. When $W = 0$, $\rho_{av} = -1/(m-1)$, and this is the least value which the average $\rho$ can take, a further illustration of the point made at the end of the last section.

The case we are considering is one wherein $\rho$ is a more convenient coefficient than $\tau$. There appears to be no simple method of expressing the average $\tau$ in terms of the sums of ranks.*

**6.6** If some of the rankings contain ties we may write, as in (3.6),

$$T' = \frac{1}{12} \sum_t (t^3 - t) \quad . \quad . \quad . \quad (6.7)$$

In this case we shall define the coefficient $W$ as

$$W = \frac{S}{\frac{1}{12} m^2 (n^3 - n) - m \sum_{T'} T'} \quad . \quad . \quad (6.8)$$

the summation $\sum_{T'}$ taking place over the various rankings.

In this case (6.6) requires some modification.

**6.7** This definition requires a little comment, for the denominator in (6.8) is not necessarily the maximum value which the sum of squares of totals of ranks (measured from their mean) may have. We may, in fact, define $W$ in the untied case by the alternative formula

$$W = \frac{S}{mS'}, \quad . \quad . \quad . \quad . \quad (6.9)$$

where $S'$ is the sum of squares of deviations of all ranks from their mean. This evidently accords with our previous definition, for the

* For the use of $\tau$ in multiple ranking problems see Ehrenberg (1952) and references to Chapter 13.

sum of squares of deviations in any ranking is $\frac{1}{12}(n^3 - n)$ and there are $m$ rankings. The definition (6.9) also accords with (6.8), for, as we have seen in **3.10**, the effect of ties in a ranking providing a number $T'$ is to reduce the sum of squares of deviations by $T'$.

The reason for adopting (6.9) is that it bears an analogy to the analysis of variance.* Suppose we array the ranks (measured from their mean) as

$$\begin{matrix} x_{11} & x_{12} & \dots & x_{1n} \\ x_{21} & x_{22} & \dots & x_{2n} \\ \cdot & \cdot & \dots & \cdot \\ x_{m1} & x_{m2} & \dots & x_{mn} \end{matrix} \qquad (6.10)$$

The sums of rows are all zero with corresponding zero mean. The sum of columns may be written $S_1 \dots S_n$ with means $S_1/m, \dots S_n/m$.

Then the variance of the whole array is $S'/mn$ by definition. The variance of column totals is $\frac{1}{n}\Sigma(S_i/m)^2 = S/m^2n$. The ratio of the two is thus $S/mS' = W$, which is thus exhibited as the ratio of the variance of column totals to the whole variance. This, and still more the ratio $S/(mS' - S)$, is a familiar ratio in the analysis of variance.

*Example 6.1*

Consider the three rankings

| | | | | | | | | | | |
|---|---|---|---|---|---|---|---|---|---|---|
| $P$ | 1 | $4\frac{1}{2}$ | 2 | $4\frac{1}{2}$ | 3 | $7\frac{1}{2}$ | 6 | 9 | $7\frac{1}{2}$ | 10 |
| $Q$ | $2\frac{1}{2}$ | 1 | $2\frac{1}{2}$ | $4\frac{1}{2}$ | $4\frac{1}{2}$ | 8 | 9 | $6\frac{1}{2}$ | 10 | $6\frac{1}{2}$ |
| $R$ | 2 | 1 | $4\frac{1}{2}$ | $4\frac{1}{2}$ | $4\frac{1}{2}$ | $4\frac{1}{2}$ | 8 | 8 | 8 | 10 |
| TOTAL: | $5\frac{1}{2}$ | $6\frac{1}{2}$ | 9 | $13\frac{1}{2}$ | 12 | 20 | 23 | $23\frac{1}{2}$ | $25\frac{1}{2}$ | $26\frac{1}{2}$ |
| Deviations from mean ($16\frac{1}{2}$) | $-11$ | $-10$ | $-7\frac{1}{2}$ | $-3$ | $-4\frac{1}{2}$ | $3\frac{1}{2}$ | $6\frac{1}{2}$ | 7 | 9 | 10 |

For the sum of squares of deviations $S$ we find 591.
For the $T'$-numbers

$$P: \tfrac{1}{12} \times 2(2^3 - 2) = 1$$

$$Q: \tfrac{1}{12} \times 3(2^3 - 2) = 1\tfrac{1}{2}$$

$$R: \tfrac{1}{12}(4^3 - 4 + 3^3 - 3) = 7$$

* See Kendall, *Advanced Theory*, Vol. II, Chapters 21–3.

Thus, from (6.8),

$$W = \frac{591}{742{\cdot}5 - 28{\cdot}5}$$

$$= 0{\cdot}828.$$

The effect of taking ties into account is evidently small.

**6.8** We now consider the testing of the significance of an observed value of $W$. If all the observers are independent in their judgments, then any set of rankings is just as probable as any other set. We shall therefore consider the distribution of $W$ in the $(n!)^m$ possible sets of ranks and use it in the customary way to reject or accept the hypothesis that the observers have no community of preference.

The actual distribution of $W$ has been worked out for lower values of $m$ and $n$ : $n = 3, m = 2$ to $10$ ; $n = 4, m = 2$ to $6$ ; $n = 5, m = 3$. These form the basis of Appendix Tables 5. For higher values we may use two approximations.

(1) For all values other than those in Appendix Tables 5 an approximation may be based on the distribution known in statistics as Fisher's $z$-distribution. We write

$$z = \tfrac{1}{2}\log_e \frac{(m-1)W}{1-W} \quad . \quad . \quad . \quad (6.11)$$

$$\left.\begin{aligned} \nu_1 &= n - 1 - \frac{2}{m} \\ \nu_2 &= (m-1)\nu_1 \end{aligned}\right\} \quad . \quad . \quad . \quad . \quad (6.12)$$

Then, for "degree of freedom" $\nu_1$ and $\nu_2$, $z$ may be tested in the existing tables of Fisher's distribution. Direct use of the tables may be obviated by using Appendix Table 6 which gives the corresponding values of $S$ to those of $z$ at probability levels of 5 per cent and 1 per cent for various values of $m$ from 3 to 20 and for $n$ from 3 to 7. The use of this table will be illustrated in a moment.

(2) Although the above test is generally valid, a simpler test may be used for $n > 7$. If we write

$$\chi_r^2 = m(n-1)W = \frac{S}{\frac{1}{12}mn(n+1)} \quad . \quad . \quad (6.13)$$

then $\chi_r^2$ is distributed in the form known in statistics as $\chi^2$ with $\nu = n - 1$ degrees of freedom.

*Example 6.2*

For 18 rankings of 7 a value of $S$ is found of 1,620 so that

$$W = \frac{1620}{\frac{1}{12} \times 18^2 \times 336} = 0{\cdot}179.$$

From Appendix Table 6 we see that for the 5 per cent level

$$m = 15 \qquad S = 864{\cdot}9$$
$$m = 20 \qquad S = 1158{\cdot}7$$

and for the 1 per cent level

$$m = 15 \qquad S = 1129{\cdot}5$$
$$m = 20 \qquad S = 1521{\cdot}9.$$

For $m = 18$ the appropriate values of $S$ lie between the values for $m = 15$, $m = 20$, and our observed value is greater than the value for 1 per cent. This means that the probability of obtaining a value as great as or greater than the observed value is less than 0·01—the value lies, we may say, beyond the 1 per cent point. It is thus significant if we agree that such small probabilities are significant.

*Example 6.3*

In 28 rankings of 13 a value of $S$ was found of 11,440 and hence

$$W = \frac{11440}{\frac{1}{12} \times 28^2 \times 2184} = 0{\cdot}080.$$

We may test this by the use of (6.13). We have

$$\chi_r^2 = \frac{11440}{\frac{1}{12} \times 28 \times 13 \times 14} = 27.$$

From Appendix Table 8 we see that for $\nu = n - 1 = 12$ degrees of freedom, at the 1 per cent significance level, $\chi^2 = 26{\cdot}217$. Our observed value is slightly greater than this and is thus "just significant" at the 1 per cent point.

*Example 6.4*

In practical cases the number $m$ is often so large that no correction for continuity need be made, but if one is desirable, it may be introduced by adding 2 to the denominator and subtracting unity from the numerator in

$$W = \frac{S}{\frac{1}{12}m^2(n^3 - n)}$$

For instance, consider the case $n = 3$, $m = 9$, and suppose $S = 78$. From Appendix Table 5A we see that the probability of such a value or greater is 0·010, so that this is approximately the 1 per cent point. Suppose we apply the $z$-test to these data. We find, with continuity corrections,

$$W = \frac{78 - 1}{\frac{1}{12}(81 \times 24) + 2} = 0{\cdot}4695$$

$$z = 0{\cdot}979, \qquad \nu_1 = \frac{16}{9}, \qquad \nu_2 = \frac{128}{9}.$$

By linear interpolation of reciprocals in Appendix Table 7B we find, for these values of $\nu_1$ and $\nu_2$, a value of $z$ equal to 0·954 against the exact value of 0·979. Even for such low values of $n$ as 3 the approximation given by the $z$-test is fair.

**6.9** When ties are present the $z$-test requires no modification unless the number or extent of the ties is large.

In the latter case the test becomes more complicated. Let $\mu_{2i}$ be the variance of the $i$th ranking typified by $\frac{1}{12}(n^2 - 1) - \frac{1}{n}T'$.

Write

$$\mu_2(W) = \frac{4}{m^2(n-1)} \frac{\sum\limits_{i,j} \mu_{2i}\,\mu_{2j}}{(\Sigma\,\mu_{2i})^2} \quad . \quad . \quad (6.14)$$

the summation extending over the $\frac{1}{2}m(m-1)$ values $i \neq j$. Then $W$ may be tested with $z$ given by (6.11) and the modified degrees of freedom

$$\left.\begin{aligned} \nu_1 &= \frac{2(m-1)}{m^3\,\mu_2(W)} - \frac{2}{m} \\ \nu_2 &= (m-1)\nu_1 \end{aligned}\right\} \quad . \quad . \quad . \quad (6.15)$$

The appropriate value of $\chi_r^2$ is

$$\chi_r^2 = \frac{S}{\frac{1}{12}mn(n+1) - \frac{1}{n-1}\Sigma\,T'} \quad . \quad . \quad (6.16)$$

## Estimation

**6.10** Suppose now that a value of $W$ has been found to be significant, so that there is evidence of some agreement among the observers. If we go further and suppose that their judgments are more or less accurate according to some objective scale we may ask : What is the true ranking of the objects, or rather, what is the best estimate we can make of that true ranking ?

**6.11** Suppose we have three rankings of eight as follows—

| | Object | | | | | | | |
|---|---|---|---|---|---|---|---|---|
| | A | B | C | D | E | F | G | H |
| Observer $P$ | 4 | 2 | 1 | 7 | 6 | 3 | 5 | 8 |
| ,, $Q$ | 7 | 2 | 1 | 6 | 4 | 5 | 3 | 8 |
| ,, $R$ | 7 | 4 | 2 | 6 | 5 | 3 | 1 | 8 |
| TOTALS : | 18 | 8 | 4 | 19 | 15 | 11 | 9 | 24 |

. . . (6.17)

One procedure which we must dismiss is that of ranking according to the number of " firsts ", " seconds ", etc., obtained by each individual. For instance we might rank $C$ first because it has two " firsts ". Object $G$ has the remaining " first " and we might rank it second. Looking then to the " seconds " we find that $B$ has two so we rank it third. The other second occurred under $C$, which has already been ranked, so we proceed to the " thirds ", and so on. The ranking obtained in this way is

C G B F E A D H . . (6.18)

When we consider the " fourths ", there are two members, $E$ and $A$, having one each, but we give precedence to the former because it has a fifth whereas the latter has only two " sevenths ".

This procedure is not self-consistent. Suppose we start from the other end of the ranking and rank as 8 the individual with the greatest number of " eighths " and so on. Then in our present example we get

C B G F E D A H . . (6.19)

which is not the same as before. In general there is no particular reason for starting at one end rather than at the other, and it is evidently unsatisfactory that the two procedures should give different results.

**6.12** A better procedure is to rank according to the sums of ranks allotted to the individuals. Thus, in (6.17) $C$ has the least total, so we rank it first, $B$ has next lowest, and so on. The ranking thus obtained is

C B G F E A D H . . (6.20)

which, it may be remarked, is different from either (6.18) or (6.19).

It may be shown (as in the next chapter) that this gives a " best " estimate in a certain sense associated with least squares. In fact, the sum of squares of differences between what the totals are and what they would be if all rankings were alike is a minimum when the ranking is estimated by this method. Furthermore, if the ranking arrived at by this method is correlated by Spearman's $\rho$ with the observed rankings, the mean $\rho$ so obtained is larger than for any other estimated ranking. This is not necessarily true for $\tau$ also but will usually be so for rankings of moderate size.

**6.13** A few points require mention in connection with ties.

(*a*) If no observed ranking contains ties and we do not wish to admit them in the estimated ranking, occasional ambiguities may arise.

Suppose that three particular objects are ranked as follows:

| | $X$ | $Y$ | $Z$ |
|---|---|---|---|
| Observer $P$ | 7 | 8 | 10 |
| ,, $Q$ | 9 | 8 | 6 |
| ,, $R$ | 3 | 7 | 6 |
| ,, $S$ | 5 | 1 | 2 |
| TOTALS: | 24 | 24 | 24 |

. . . (6.21)

The totals being the same, our method gives no criterion of choice. If ties are permitted we should rank them all alike. If not, then it seems best to give precedence to that object for which the ranks cluster most closely. Since the totals are the same, this is equivalent to choosing first the object for which the sum of squares of ranks is least. In (6.21) the sums of squares for $X$, $Y$, $Z$ are 164, 178, 176, so we should rank them $X$, $Z$, $Y$.

(*b*) If a rank $j$ is regarded as expressing the fact that $j - 1$ members are preferred, the sum of ranks gives the sum of preferences, less $m$, and hence our method ranks the objects according to preferences. If some ranks are tied, the replacement of integral ranks by ties does not affect the preferences with other members and merely cancels preferences between the tied set. Thus our method continues to rank according to preferences even when ties exist.

**6.14** Little is known about the distribution of $W$ in the non-null case when some community of preference exists. We cannot therefore test the significance of the difference between sets of rankings. Suppose, for example, 8 male teachers each rank a class of 30 boys and the resulting value of $W$ is 0·5, and suppose 6 female teachers rank the same class giving $W = 0{\cdot}7$. This shows that the women have a greater community of preference than the men; but if we regard the men as a sample from male teachers in general (and so for women) we cannot apply a test of significance to the hypothesis that women teachers are more in agreement among themselves than men. This is a gap in our knowledge which it would be useful to fill.

**6.15** The provision of the above tests of significance should not be allowed to obscure the desirability of examining the primary data to see if there are any obvious effects present. When a number of observers are suspected *a priori* to be heterogeneous in their tastes, it may obscure meaningful effects to assemble their rankings into a single group. To take the extreme case, suppose ten observers are in complete agreement about a ranking of six, so that the sums of ranks are

$$10, \quad 20, \quad 30, \quad 40, \quad 50, \quad 60$$

with $W = 1$. Suppose that 10 further observers, also in complete agreement, rank the objects in the inverse order

$$60, \quad 50, \quad 40, \quad 30, \quad 20, \quad 10$$

also with $W = 1$. The sum of the rankings for the 20 observers is, of course, 70 for each object with $W = 0$. For the whole group we might conclude that there was no community of preference, whereas in reality the community of one set of observers has completely masked that of the other.

## Incomplete rankings

**6.16** Cases sometimes occur in which the rankings are incomplete. One case of particular interest arises in experimental designs where we can deliberately arrange for them to be incomplete in a symmetrical way.

Consider, for example, a manufacturer of ice-cream who wishes to test preferences for seven varieties by getting them ranked by a number of observers. He may not wish to present each of the varieties to each observer, either because of economy in time or because the human palate loses its discriminatory power after a few varieties are tasted. Calling the varieties $A$, $B$, $C$, $D$, $E$, $F$, $G$ we will arrange them in sets of three thus :

$$\begin{array}{ccccccc} A & B & C & D & E & F & G \\ B & C & D & E & F & G & A \\ D & E & F & G & A & B & C \end{array} \qquad . \quad . \quad . \quad (6.22)$$

and present one triplet to each of seven observers. The point of this arrangement is that every variety appears an equal number of times in the experiment (thrice, in fact) and each pair of objects also appears (once) an equal number of times, so that all comparisons appear equally often. We can regard this as seven rankings of seven objects with four missing from each ranking.*

**6.17** Suppose the ranks allotted by observers are

| | | | | | | |
|---|---|---|---|---|---|---|
| 2 | 2 | 1 | 1 | 2 | 2 | 3 |
| 1 | 3 | 2 | 3 | 3 | 3 | 1 |
| 3 | 1 | 3 | 2 | 1 | 1 | 2 |

. . . . (6.23)

The total ranks for the seven objects will be as follows—

| *A* | *B* | *C* | *D* | *E* | *F* | *G* |
|---|---|---|---|---|---|---|
| 4 | 4 | 6 | 6 | 6 | 8 | 8 |

. . . (6.24)

If the ranks had been allotted at random within blocks these totals would tend to be equal ; on the other hand, if the ranks corresponded to a strict ordering of the objects the totals would be 3, 4, . . . 9 and would be as different as possible. As usual, therefore, we will let $S$ represent the sum of squares of the numbers in (6.24), taken from their mean, and construct a coefficient by dividing by the maximum $S$. In our numerical example this gives us

$$W = \frac{16}{28} = 0{\cdot}571$$

**6.18** A design of type (6.22) is called a Youden array.† If $n$ objects are presented $k$ at a time and each ranked $m$ times in the experiment the number of blocks of objects is $mn/k$. Within each block there are $\frac{1}{2}k(k-1)$ comparisons between pairs and hence the number of comparisons is $\frac{1}{2}mn(k-1)$. Let $\lambda$ be the number of blocks in which a given comparison occurs. Then

$$\tfrac{1}{2}n(n-1)\lambda = \tfrac{1}{2}mn(k-1)$$

or

$$\lambda = \frac{m(k-1)}{n-1} \quad . \quad . \quad . \quad (6.25)$$

$\lambda$ must be an integer and hence $n-1$ must be a factor of $m(k-1)$. Moreover $k$ must be a factor of $mn$. These conditions impose considerable limitations on the numbers which are admissible for designs of this kind. In our example $n = 7$, $k = 3$ and hence $m$ is a multiple of three (actually three itself) ; and from (6.25) $\lambda = 1$.

* For this reason the design is also known as an incomplete Latin square.

† For a set of designs of this type see W. G. Cochran and G. M. Cox, *Experimental Design*, 1951, John Wiley and Sons, New York.

If there are no ties, let $x_{ij}$ be the rank assigned to the $j$th object in the $i$th replication (meaning the $i$th block if the design is used only once and the $i$th blocks if it is repeated). $S$ is the sum of squares of deviations of $x_j = \sum_{i=1}^{m} x_{ij}$ from the mean of the totals. It attains its maximum when the total ranks are

$$m,\ m + \lambda,\ m + 2\lambda\ \ldots\ m + (n-1)\lambda$$

and hence

$$\text{maximum value of } S^2 = \frac{\lambda^2 n(n^2-1)}{12}.$$

Thus in general

$$W = \frac{12S}{\lambda^2 n(n^2-1)} \quad \ldots \quad (6.26)$$

$$= \frac{12 \sum_1^n x_j^2 - 3nm^2(k+1)^2}{\lambda^2 n(n^2-1)} \quad \ldots \quad (6.27)$$

When ties are present no simple corrections are available, but we may either ignore their existence if they are not numerous or " toss up for it " in assigning them integral ranks. This will not affect tests of significance.

**6.19** We may test the significance of $W$ by taking (for moderate $n$ and large $m$)

$$\chi^2 = \frac{\lambda(n^2-1)}{k+1} W \quad \ldots \quad (6.28)$$

to be distributed as $\chi^2$ with $n-1$ degrees of freedom. A more exact test is given by taking

$$z = \frac{1}{2} \log \frac{\left(\frac{\lambda(n+1)}{k+1} - 1\right) W}{1 - W}. \quad \ldots \quad (6.29)$$

to be distributed with

$$\left.\begin{aligned} \nu_1 &= \frac{mn\left(1 - \frac{k+1}{\lambda(n+1)}\right)}{\left(\frac{nm}{n-1} - \frac{k}{k-1}\right)} - \frac{2(k+1)}{\lambda(n+1)}, \\ \nu_2 &= \left(\frac{\lambda(n+1)}{k+1} - 1\right)\nu_1 \end{aligned}\right\} \quad . \quad (6.30)$$

degrees of freedom.

If $k = n$ and hence $\lambda = m$, these reduce to equations (6.11) and (6.13) as they should.

*Example 6.5* (Durbin, 1951)

Let us suppose that a design of type (6.22) was used three times and the resulting 21 blocks assigned to 21 tasters. The totals of ranks are

| *A* | *B* | *C* | *D* | *E* | *F* | *G* |
|---|---|---|---|---|---|---|
| 20 | 13 | 18 | 25 | 22 | 12 | 16 |

The mean rank of the total is 18. $S = 134$, $n = 7$, $m = 9$, $k = 3$ and hence $\lambda = 3$. Thus

$$W = \frac{12 \times 134}{9 \times 7 \times 48} = 0{\cdot}532.$$

To test the significance we find, on substitution in (6.29) and (6.30),

$$\nu_1 = 5{\cdot}5, \quad \nu_2 = 27{\cdot}5, \quad z = 0{\cdot}87.$$

From Appendix Table 7B we find the following values for $\nu_1 = 5(6)$ and $\nu_2 = 27(28)$:

| | |
|---|---|
| ·6655 | ·6346 |
| ·6614 | ·6303 |

The value is therefore significant at the 1 per cent level. We conclude that the preferences were not random.

## References

See Friedman (1937, 1940), Kendall and Babington Smith (1939) and Wallis.

For the treatment of Youden arrays see Durbin (1951), who also points out that a true ranking in a balanced design of this kind can be estimated after the manner of 6.10 by ranking the objects according to the sums of ranks allotted to them. Such a procedure minimises the sum of weighted inversions in the observed rankings relative to the estimated ranking.

A treatment of the general case when any number of ranks can be missing from any ranking has been given by Benard and van Elteren (1953).

## CHAPTER 7

# PROOF OF THE RESULTS OF CHAPTER 6

**7.1** We shall first establish the validity of the $z$-distribution as providing a test of the concordance coefficient $W$ in the population of $(n!)^m$ possible rankings. A proof for the case of untied rankings is given in Kendall's *Advanced Theory*, Vol. I, **16.33**, and will not be repeated here. As we shall require general results for tied rankings, we give a somewhat more general investigation, due to Pitman (1938).

**7.2** Suppose we have $m$ sets of numbers

$$\begin{array}{cccc} a_1 & a_2 & \ldots & a_n \\ b_1 & b_2 & \ldots & b_n \\ \cdot & \cdot & \ldots & \cdot \\ k_1 & k_2 & \ldots & k_n \end{array} \qquad (7.1)$$

We will suppose that each is measured about the mean of the row in which it occurs, so that the means of rows and the mean of the whole are zero. We then have

$$W = \frac{\frac{1}{m}\sum_{1}^{n}(a_j + b_j + \ldots + k_j)^2}{\sum_{1}^{n} a_j^2 + \sum_{1}^{n} b_j^2 + \ldots + \sum_{1}^{n} k_j^2} \qquad (7.2)$$

The denominator in the expression is a constant and the variability arises solely from the numerator. If $\alpha_2$ represents the second moment of the $a$-row and so on for $b$, $c$, etc., the denominator is $n\Sigma\alpha_2$. Writing

$$R_{ab} = \sum_{1}^{n} a_i b_i \qquad (7.3)$$

$$U = \sum_{1}^{\binom{m}{2}} R_i \qquad (7.4)$$

where $R_i$ stands generally for any $R_{ab}$, we have

$$W = \frac{1}{m} + \frac{2U}{mn\,\Sigma\,\alpha_2} \qquad (7.5)$$

We find first the moments of $R_{ab}$, then those of $U$ and finally those of $W$.

**7.3** We have, writing $E$ for expected values,

$$\begin{aligned}
E(R_{ab}) &= 0 \\
E(R_{ab}^2) &= E(\Sigma\, a_i b_i)^2 \\
&= E(\Sigma\, a_i^2 b_i^2 + \Sigma'\, a_i b_i\, a_j b_j) \\
&= nE(a_i^2 b_i^2) + n(n-1)E(a_i a_j\, b_i b_j) \\
&= nE(a_i^2)E(b_i^2) + \frac{n(n-1)}{n^2(n-1)^2}\{E(\Sigma\, a_i)^2 - E\,\Sigma\, a_i^2\} \\
&\qquad\qquad \times \{E(\Sigma\, b_i)^2 - E\,\Sigma\, b_i^2\} \\
&= n\alpha_2\beta_2 + \frac{n}{n-1}\alpha_2\beta_2 = \frac{n^2\alpha_2\beta_2}{n-1} \qquad (7.6)
\end{aligned}$$

In a similar way—we omit the algebraical details—we find

$$E(R_{ab}^3) = \frac{n^3\alpha_3\beta_3}{(n-1)(n-2)} = \frac{(n-1)(n-2)}{n}\alpha_3'\beta_3' . \qquad (7.7)$$

$$E(R_{ab}^4) = \frac{3n^4\,\alpha_2^2\,\beta_2^2}{(n-1)(n+1)} + \frac{(n-1)(n-2)(n-3)}{n(n+1)}\alpha_4'\beta_4' \qquad (7.8)$$

where we write $\alpha_3$ for the third moment of the $a$-array and $\alpha_3'$, $\alpha_4'$ for its third and fourth $k$-statistics which are defined in terms of the moments by

$$\alpha_3' = \frac{n^2}{(n-1)(n-2)}\alpha_3$$

$$\alpha_4' = \frac{n}{(n-1)(n-2)(n-3)}\{(n+1)\alpha_4 - 3(n-1)\alpha_2^2\}$$

The point of using $k$-statistics is that for normal populations they vanish for degree higher than 2 and may therefore be presumed small for populations reasonably near to normality.

**7.4** To find the moments of $U$ we note that

$E(R_{ij}\, R_{kl}) = 0$ for all suffixes except $i = k$, $j = l$

$E(R_{ij}\, R_{kl}\, R_{mn}) = 0$ unless the suffixes form a " circular " set such as $ij$, $jk$, $ki$.

Similarly with four terms the only type not vanishing is one in which the suffixes are $ij$, $jk$, $kl$, $li$. Hence

$$E(U) = E(\Sigma\, R) = 0 . \qquad (7.9)$$

$$\begin{aligned}
E(U^2) &= E(\Sigma\, R_i^2 + \Sigma'\, R_i R_j) \\
&= \frac{n^2}{n-1}\Sigma\,\alpha_2\beta_2 \qquad (7.10)
\end{aligned}$$

Further

$$E(R_{ij}\,R_{jk}\,R_{ki}) = E(\Sigma\, a_i b_i\, \Sigma\, b_i c_i\, \Sigma\, c_i a_i)$$
$$= E[\{\Sigma\, b_i^2 a_i c_i + \Sigma'\, b_i b_j (a_i c_j + a_j c_i)\}\, \Sigma\, c_i a_i]$$
$$= E[E\, b_i^2\, \Sigma\, a_i c_i + E b_i b_j\, \Sigma\, (a_i c_j + a_j c_i)]\, \Sigma\, c_i a_i$$
$$= (E b_i^2 - E b_i b_j) E(\Sigma\, a_i c_i)^2$$
$$= \left(\beta_2 + \frac{\beta_2}{n-1}\right)\frac{n^2 \alpha_2 \gamma_2}{n-1}$$
$$= \frac{n^3 \alpha_2 \beta_2 \gamma_2}{(n-1)^2}$$

$$\Sigma\, E(R_i^3) = \frac{(n-1)(n-2)}{n}\, \Sigma\, \alpha_3' \beta_3'$$

Hence

$$E(U^3) = \frac{6n^3}{(n-1)^2}\, \Sigma\, \alpha_2 \beta_2 \gamma_2 + \frac{(n-1)(n-2)}{n}\, \Sigma\, \alpha_3' \beta_3' \quad (7.11)$$

Finally—again we omit the algebra—

$$E(U^4) = \frac{3n^4}{(n-1)(n+1)}\, \Sigma\, \alpha_2^2 \beta_2^2 + \frac{(n-1)(n-2)(n-3)}{n(n+1)}\, \Sigma\, \alpha_4' \beta_4'$$
$$+ \frac{3n^4}{(n-1)^2}\{(\Sigma\, \alpha_2 \beta_2)^2 - \Sigma\, \alpha_2^2 \beta_2^2\}$$
$$+ 12(n-2)\, \Sigma\, \alpha_3' \beta_3' \gamma_2 + \frac{72n^4}{(n-1)^3}\, \Sigma\, \alpha_2 \beta_2 \gamma_2 \delta_2 \quad . \quad (7.12)$$

Finally, for the moments of $W$,

$$E(W) = \frac{1}{m} = \overline{W}, \text{ say} \quad . \quad . \quad . \quad (7.13)$$

$$E(W - \overline{W})^2 = \frac{4}{m^2(n-1)} \frac{\Sigma\, \alpha_2 \beta_2}{(\Sigma\, \alpha_2)^2} \quad . \quad . \quad (7.14)$$

and, neglecting terms involving $\alpha_3'$ and $\alpha_4'$ which are of lower order in $n$,

$$E(W - \overline{W})^3 = \frac{48}{m^3(n-1)^2} \frac{\Sigma\, \alpha_2 \beta_2 \gamma_2}{(\Sigma\, \alpha_2)^3} \quad . \quad . \quad . \quad . \quad . \quad (7.15)$$

$$E(W - \overline{W})^4 = \frac{48}{m^4(n-1)^2} \frac{(\Sigma\, \alpha_2 \beta_2)^2}{(\Sigma\, \alpha_2)^4} - \frac{96}{m^4(n-1)^2(n+1)} \frac{\Sigma\, \alpha_2^2 \beta_2^2}{(\Sigma\, \alpha_2)^4}$$
$$+ \frac{1152}{m^4(n-1)^3} \frac{\Sigma\, \alpha_2 \beta_2 \gamma_2 \delta_2}{(\Sigma\, \alpha_2)^4} \quad . \quad (7.16)$$

**7.5** Consider now the case when the ranks are untied. In this case all the variances of rankings are equal and we find

$$E(W) = \frac{1}{m} \qquad . \quad . \quad . \quad . \quad . \quad . \quad (7.17)$$

$$\mu_2(W) = E(W - \bar{W})^2 = \frac{2(m-1)}{m^3(n-1)} \qquad . \quad . \quad . \quad . \quad . \quad (7.18)$$

$$\mu_3(W) = E(W - \bar{W})^3 = \frac{8(m-1)(m-2)}{m^5(n-1)^2} \qquad . \quad . \quad . \quad . \quad (7.19)$$

$$\mu_4(W) = E(W - \bar{W})^4 = \frac{12(m-1)^2}{m^6(n-1)^2} + \frac{48(m-1)(m-2)(m-3)}{m^7(n-1)^3} - \frac{48(m-1)}{m^7(n-1)^2(n+1)} \qquad . \quad (7.20)$$

Now consider the distribution

$$dF = \frac{1}{B(p, q)} W^{p-1}(1 - W)^{q-1}\, dW \qquad . \quad . \quad (7.21)$$

The first two moments are

$$E(W) = \frac{p}{p+q} \qquad . \quad . \quad . \quad . \quad . \quad (7.22)$$

$$\mu_2(W) = \frac{pq}{(p+q)^2(p+q+1)} \qquad . \quad . \quad (7.23)$$

If we equate (7.17) to (7.22) and (7.18) to (7.23) we find

$$\left.\begin{aligned} p &= \tfrac{1}{2}(n-1) - \frac{1}{m} \\ q &= (m-1)p \end{aligned}\right\} \qquad . \quad . \quad . \quad (7.24)$$

The distribution of $W$ is thus an approximation to (7.21) when $p$ and $q$ have these values. The third moment of (7.21) is

$$\frac{8(m-1)(m-2)}{m^4(n-1)(mn-m+2)} = \frac{8(m-1)(m-2)}{m^5(n-1)^2}\left\{1 - \frac{2}{m(n-1)+2}\right\}$$

Comparing this with (7.19) we see that the third moment of (7.21) is approximately equal to the third moment of $W$ unless $m(n-1)$ is small. Again the fourth moment of (7.21) is

$$\frac{12(m-1)}{m^6(n-1)^2}\left[\frac{(m-1)y^2 + 4m^2y - 14(m-1)y}{(y+2)(y+4)}\right]$$

where $y = m(n-1)$, and this is approximately equal to the fourth moment of $W$ if $m(n-1)$ is not too small.

**7.6** This distribution (7.21) has its first two moments exactly, and its third and fourth moments approximately equal to the actual distribution of $W$; and thus we expect it to provide an approximation. The accuracy of the approximation is, in fact, greater than perhaps our rather long proof of the result might foreshadow.

The distribution (7.21) is known in statistical theory as the B- (Beta) or Type I distribution. A simple transformation reduces it to the form of Fisher's $z$-distribution. In fact, putting

$$z = \tfrac{1}{2} \log \frac{(m-1)W}{1-W}$$

we find that (7.21) reduces to

$$dF \propto \frac{e^{2pz}\, dz}{\{(m-1) + e^{2z}\}^{p+q}}$$

which is Fisher's form with

$$\nu_1 = 2p$$
$$\nu_2 = 2q$$

so that, from (7.24),

$$\nu_1 = (n-1) - \frac{2}{m}$$

$$\nu_2 = (m-1)\nu_1$$

as given in (6.12).

**7.7** If ties are present the test needs further consideration.

($a$) In the above derivation we have only used the absence of ties to evaluate the terms $\alpha_2$, and if all rankings are equally tied these variances are still equal and the results hold.

($b$) If the $T'$-numbers appropriate to ties are small compared with $\frac{1}{12}(n^3 - n) = \mathrm{N}$, say, again, the test requires no modification. For then, to the first order in $\Sigma T'/mN$,

$$\frac{\Sigma \alpha_2\beta_2}{(\Sigma \alpha_2)^2} = \frac{\Sigma (N - T'_\alpha)(N - T'_\beta)}{\Sigma (N - T'_\alpha)^2}$$

$$= \frac{(m-1)m}{m^2}\left\{1 - \frac{2}{mN}\, \Sigma T'\right\}\left\{1 - \frac{2}{mN}\, \Sigma T'\right\}^{-1}$$

$$= \frac{m-1}{m}$$

so that, to this order, the second moment of $W$ remains unchanged. The effect on the third and fourth moments is also negligible to this order. Hence our result.

(*c*) If the $T'$-numbers are large then we must calculate $\mu_2(W)$. We shall then find

$$\left.\begin{aligned}\tfrac{1}{2}\nu_1 &= p = \frac{m-1}{m^3\mu_2(W)} - \frac{1}{m}\\ \tfrac{1}{2}\nu_2 &= q = (m-1)p\end{aligned}\right\} \quad . \quad . \quad . \quad (7.25)$$

and the test may be applied with these values of $\nu_1$ and $\nu_2$.

**7.8** We now prove that the statistic

$$\begin{aligned}\chi_r^2 &= m(n-1)W\\ &= \frac{S}{\frac{1}{12}mn(n+1)}\end{aligned} \quad . \quad . \quad . \quad (7.26)$$

tends as $m$ increases to that of the $\chi^2$-distribution

$$dF \propto e^{-\frac{1}{2}\chi^2}\chi^{\nu-1}\,d\chi \quad . \quad . \quad . \quad (7.27)$$

with $\nu = n - 1$.

In the array (7.1) consider the sum of any column, say the first, which we will call $p$. We have

$$\begin{aligned}E(p) &= E(a_1 + b_1 + \ldots + k_1) = 0\\ E(p^2) &= E(\Sigma a)^2 \qquad\qquad = \Sigma \alpha_2\end{aligned}$$

$E(p^{2r+1})$ is of order $\Sigma \alpha_{2r+1} + \Sigma \alpha_{2r-1}\beta_2 +$, etc. $E(p^{2r})$ is of order $\Sigma \alpha_{2r} + \ldots + \Sigma \alpha_2\beta_2 \ldots \varkappa_2$. The same argument as we employed in **5.21** leads to the conclusion that $E(p^{2r+1})$ is of lower order in $m$ and that the dominant term in $E(p^{2r})$ is $\Sigma \alpha_2\beta_2 \ldots \varkappa_2$. Thus in the limit odd moments vanish and

$$\frac{\mu_{2r}}{(\mu_2)^r} \sim \frac{(2r)!}{2^r}\frac{\Sigma \alpha_2\beta_2 \ldots \varkappa_2}{(\Sigma \alpha_2)^r} \quad . \quad . \quad . \quad (7.28)$$

When all $\alpha$'s are equal, or nearly so,

$$\frac{\mu_{2r}}{(\mu_2)^r} \sim \frac{(2r)!}{r!\,2^r}$$

and hence the distribution of $p$ tends to normality with zero mean.

Now $S$ is the sum of squares of $n$ such variates, subject only to the constraint that $\Sigma(p) = 0$. Thus $kS$ is distributed as $\chi^2$ with $\nu = n - 1$, where $k$ is a factor to be determined such that the mean of $kS$ is $n - 1$, the mean of $\chi^2$. But

$$E(kS) = kn\,\Sigma \alpha_2$$

and thus

$$k = \frac{n-1}{n\,\Sigma \alpha_2}$$

and hence

$$\chi_r^2 = \frac{(n-1)S}{n\,\Sigma\,\alpha_2}$$

is distributed as $\chi^2$.

When the rankings contain no ties each has the variance $\frac{1}{12}(n^2-1)$ and thus

$$\chi_r^2 = \frac{S}{\frac{1}{12}nm(n+1)}$$

as given in (7.26).

If ties are present, represented by $T'$-numbers, the appropriate value is

$$\chi_r^2 = \frac{(n-1)S}{n\left\{\frac{1}{12}m(n^2-1) - \frac{1}{n}\,\Sigma\,T'\right\}}$$

$$= \frac{S}{\frac{1}{12}mn(n+1) - \frac{1}{n-1}\,\Sigma\,T'} \quad . \quad . \quad (7.29)$$

Unless the ties are substantial in extent the effect of the second term in the denominator is small.

**7.9** We now indicate the basis of calculating the actual distributions of $W$ (or equivalently of $S$) for the lower values of $m$ and $n$.

For $m = 2$ the values are derivable from the distribution of Spearman's $\rho$. We proceed from the case for given $m$, $n$ to that for $m + 1$, $n$. For example, with $m = 2$, $n = 3$, we have the following values for the sums of ranks measured about their mean:

| Type | | | Frequency |
|---|---|---|---|
| − 2 | 0 | 2 | 1 |
| − 2 | 1 | 1 | 2 |
| − 1 | 0 | 1 | 2 |
| 0 | 0 | 0 | 1 |

Here − 2, 1, 1 and 2, − 1, − 1 are taken to be identical types, for they give the same value of $S$ and will also give similar types when we proceed to the case $m = 3$ as follows.

For $m = 3$ each of the above types will appear added to six permutations of − 1, 0, 1; *e.g.* the type − 2, 0, 2 will give one each of − 3, 0, 3; − 3, 1, 2; − 2, − 1, 3; − 2, 1, 1; − 1, − 1, 2 and $-1, 0, 1$. These types are counted for each of the basic types of $m = 2$, and we get—

| Type | | | Frequency |
|---|---|---|---|
| $-3$ | 0 | 3 | 1 |
| $-3$ | 1 | 2 | 6 |
| $-2$ | 0 | 2 | 6 |
| $-2$ | 1 | 1 | 6 |
| $-1$ | 0 | 1 | 15 |
| 0 | 0 | 0 | 2 |
| | | | 36 |

For $n = 5$ and greater the labour becomes very considerable owing to the large number of different types to be taken into account at each stage. It seems, however, that for all ordinary purposes in testing significance the $z$-distribution provides an adequate approximation for greater values of $n$.

**7.10** We have now to show (as indicated in **6.12**) that the method of estimation there proposed is such as to maximise the average $\rho$-correlation between the estimated and the observed rankings.

Suppose the estimated ranking is $X_1, \ldots X_n$ and let the sums of ranks be $S_1 \ldots S_n$. Then the average $\rho$ is given by

$$\frac{1}{m}\sum_{k=1}^{m}\rho_k = \frac{12}{m(n^3-n)}\sum_{k=1}^{m}\sum_{j=1}^{n}\{X_j - \tfrac{1}{2}(n+1)\}\{x_{jk} - \tfrac{1}{2}(n+1)\}$$

where $x_{jk}$ is the rank of the $j$th object in the $k$th ranking. This is equal to

$$\frac{12}{m(n^3-n)}\sum_{j=1}^{n}\{X_j - \tfrac{1}{2}(n+1)\}\{S_j - \tfrac{1}{2}m(n+1)\}$$

$$= \frac{12}{m(n^3-n)}\left\{\sum_{j=1}^{n}(X_jS_j) - \tfrac{1}{4}mn(n+1)^2\right\} \quad . \quad . \quad (7.30)$$

This is clearly a maximum when $\Sigma(XS)$ is a maximum, *i.e.* when the greatest $S$ is multiplied by the greatest $X$ and so on, the least $S$ being multiplied by the least $X$. Our suggested rule of estimation does in fact ensure that the multiplications take place in this way, and hence the result follows.

If we consider the sum

$$U = \sum_{j=1}^{n}(S_j - mX_j)^2$$

$$= \Sigma S_j^2 + m^2\,\Sigma X^2 - 2m\,\Sigma(XS)$$

we see that, since the first two terms on the right are constants, $U$ is minimised if $\Sigma\,(XS)$ is maximised. Our method of estimation therefore minimises $U$, that is to say, minimises the sum of squares of differences between the actual sums $S$ and what they would be, $mX$, if all rankings were identical.

**7.11** We now establish the test for the case of incomplete rankings considered in **6.16.** With the notation there used let us put

$$U = \sum_j \sum_{i<p} x_{ij}\,x_{pj} \quad . \quad . \quad . \quad (7.31)$$

Then, since

$$\sum x_{ij}^2 = \frac{mn(k^2-1)}{12},$$

we find

$$W = \frac{12}{\lambda^2 n(n^2-1)}\left\{\sum x_{ij}^2 + 2\sum_j \sum_{i<p} x_{ij}\,x_{pj}\right\}$$

$$= \frac{k+1}{\lambda(n+1)} + \frac{24U}{\lambda^2 n(n^2-1)} \quad . \quad . \quad . \quad . \quad (7.32)$$

Now the $j$th object occurs in different blocks in the $i$th and $p$th replication, and an $x$ in any one block is independent of an $x$ in any other block. Hence

$$E(U) = 0 \quad . \quad . \quad . \quad . \quad (7.33)$$

and

$$U^2 = \Sigma\, x_{ij}^2\, x_{pj}^2 + 2\,\Sigma\, x_{ij}\, x_{pj}\, x_{ql}\, x_{rl} \quad . \quad . \quad (7.34)$$

There are $\frac{1}{2}nm(m-1)$ terms in the first of these sums and the expectation of each is $\{E(x_{ij}^2)\}^2 = \frac{1}{144}(k^2-1)^2$. The only terms contributing to the second sum are those for which the $j$th and $l$th objects occur together in different blocks. Now

$$E(x_{ij}\,x_{ql}) = E(x_{pj}\,x_{rl})$$
$$= -\tfrac{1}{12}(k+1),$$

when the $j$th and $l$th object occur in the same block, and is zero in the contrary case. The number of such cases of occurrence together is $\frac{1}{4}n(n-1)\lambda(\lambda-1)$. Hence, substituting in (7.34) we get

$$E(U^2) = \frac{mn(k+1)(k^2-1)}{288}\{(m-1)(k-1)+\lambda-1)\}\,. \quad (7.35)$$

Thus

$$E(W) = \frac{k+1}{\lambda(n+1)}, \quad . \quad . \quad . \quad . \quad . \quad . \quad (7.36)$$

$$\text{var } W = \frac{2(k+1)^2}{mn\lambda^2(n+1)^2}\left(m-1+\frac{\lambda-1}{k-1}\right) \quad . \quad (7.37)$$

**7.12** It is to be noted that we cannot proceed to calculate third and fourth moments in the way employed for the ordinary coefficient because the symmetries holding in virtue of the equal occurrence of objects and pairs of objects do not hold for triads or more complex sets. Arguing (a little heuristically) by analogy from $W$ in the ordinary case we may, however, identify our distribution with that of (7.21) by equating its first and second moments to (7.36) and (7.37) respectively. This gives us

$$\left.\begin{aligned} p &= \frac{mn\left(1 - \dfrac{k+1}{\lambda(n+1)}\right)}{2\left(\dfrac{mn}{n-1} - \dfrac{k}{k-1}\right)} - \frac{k+1}{\lambda(n+1)} \\ q &= \left(\frac{\lambda(n+1)}{k+1} - 1\right)p \end{aligned}\right\} \quad . \quad . \quad (7.38)$$

whence the test of **6.19** follows.

**7.13** To fit a $\chi^2$ distribution, which has $n-1$ degrees of freedom, we put $W = a\chi^2$ and find

$$E(W) = \frac{k+1}{\lambda(n+1)} = a(n-1)$$

and hence, evaluating $a$, we see that

$$\chi^2 = \frac{\lambda(n^2-1)}{k+1}W. \quad . \quad . \quad . \quad (7.39)$$

tends to be distributed as $\chi^2$ with $n-1$ degrees of freedom. The variance of this $\chi^2$ is

$$\begin{aligned} &2(n-1)\left\{1 - \frac{k(n-1)}{mn(k-1)}\right\} \\ &= 2(n-1)\left(1 - \frac{1}{m}\right) \text{ approximately}, \quad . \quad . \quad (7.40) \end{aligned}$$

and this agrees with (7.37) for large $m$.

**References**

See references to the previous chapter together with Pitman (1938), Welch (1937) and Kendall (1942*b*, 1945).

# CHAPTER 8

# PARTIAL RANK CORRELATION

**8.1** In interpreting an observed dependence between two qualities we are constantly faced with the question whether an association or correlation of $A$ with $B$ is really due to the associations or correlations of each with a third quality $C$. In the theory of statistics this kind of problem leads to the theories of *partial* association or correlation which attempt to decide the matter by the consideration of sub-populations in which the variation of $C$ is eliminated. The same problem arises in rank correlation. For instance, if there appears a significant correlation between mathematical and musical abilities in a number of subjects, the question arises whether this may be attributable to the correlation of each with some more fundamental quality such as intelligence. We proceed to consider a method which may be applied in rank correlation theory to an investigation of this kind of problem.

**8.2** Suppose we have three rankings of 6 as follows

$$\left.\begin{array}{llllll} P=1 & 2 & 3 & 4 & 5 & 6 \\ Q=3 & 1 & 4 & 2 & 6 & 5 \\ R=4 & 2 & 1 & 6 & 3 & 5 \end{array}\right\} \quad . \quad . \quad . \quad (8.1)$$

There are $\binom{6}{2}$ possible pairs. Taking some ranking as standard (it does not matter which one, so we will take the one in which the ranking is in the natural order), let us write down all possible pairs and enter + underneath if the pair observed has that order and − in the opposite case. We find :

| | (12) | (13) | (14) | (15) | (16) | (23) | (24) | (25) | (26) | (34) | (35) | (36) | (45) | (46) | (56) |
|---|---|---|---|---|---|---|---|---|---|---|---|---|---|---|---|
| *P* | + | + | + | + | + | + | + | + | + | + | + | + | + | + | + |
| *Q* | − | + | − | + | + | + | + | + | + | − | + | + | + | + | − |
| *R* | − | − | + | − | + | − | + | + | + | + | + | + | − | − | + |

For the coefficients we find :

$$\tau_{PQ} = \tfrac{7}{15}, \qquad \tau_{PR} = \tfrac{3}{15}, \qquad \tau_{QR} = -\tfrac{1}{15}$$

Consider now the following four-fold table, setting out the agreements of rankings $Q$ and $R$ with $P$:

| Ranking Q \ Ranking R | Pairs + (agreeing with $P$) | Pairs − (disagreeing with $P$) | TOTALS |
|---|---|---|---|
| Pairs + (agreeing with $P$) | 6 | 5 | 11 |
| Pairs − (disagreeing with $P$) | 3 | 1 | 4 |
| TOTALS . . | 9 | 6 | 15 |

. . . (8.2)

Here, for example, there are 11 cases in which $Q$ agrees with $P$; in 6 of these $R$ also agrees with $P$, and in the remaining 5 it disagrees.

Generally in three rankings of $n$ we shall have a table of the form

| | | |
|---|---|---|
| $a$ | $b$ | $a + b$ |
| $c$ | $d$ | $c + d$ |
| $a + c$ | $b + d$ | $N = \binom{n}{2} = a + b + c + d$ |

. . . (8.3)

We now define a partial rank correlation coefficient of $Q$ and $R$ with $P$ as

$$\tau_{QR.P} = \frac{ad - bc}{|\sqrt{\{(a + b)(c + d)(a + c)(b + d)\}}|} \quad . \quad (8.4)$$

In our present example this becomes

$$\frac{6 - 15}{\sqrt{(11 \times 4 \times 9 \times 6)}} = -0{\cdot}185$$

as compared with $\tau_{QR} = -0{\cdot}067$.

**8.3** The coefficient of (8.4) is a coefficient of association in a $2 \times 2$ table and we have already met it in another connection in **3.14.** It can vary from $-1$ to $+1$ but not outside those limits, and measures the intensity of association between the agreements of $Q$ with $P$ and those of $R$ with $P$.

If the coefficient is unity we have

$$(ad - bc)^2 = (a + b)(a + c)(b + d)(c + d)$$

giving

$$4abcd + a^2(bc + bd + cd) + b^2(ac + ad + cd) + c^2(ab + ad + bd) + d^2(ac + ab + bc) = 0.$$

Since no $a$, $b$, $c$, $d$ can be negative this can only be true if at least two of them are zero. If two in the same row and column are zero we get the purely nugatory case in which either $Q$ or $R$ is in perfect agreement or disagreement with $P$. We have then to consider only $a = 0$ and $d = 0$ or $b = 0$ and $c = 0$. In the latter case $Q$ and $R$ agree completely upon their concordances with $P$ and $\tau_{QR.P} = 1$. In the former case they disagree completely and the coefficient is $-1$.

**8.4** The reader who is acquainted with the quantity known as $\chi^2$ can easily satisfy himself that

$$\tau_{QR.P} = \sqrt{\frac{\chi^2}{N}} \quad . \quad . \quad . \quad . \qquad (8.5)$$

$\chi^2$, and hence $\tau$, measures the degree of departure from the case when the dichotomy of preferences according to $Q$ is independent of those according to $R$. Suppose, in fact, that they are independent. Then the frequencies in the table will be

$$\begin{array}{cc} \dfrac{(a+b)(a+c)}{N} & \dfrac{(a+b)(b+d)}{N} \\ \\ \dfrac{(a+c)(c+d)}{N} & \dfrac{(c+d)(b+d)}{N} \end{array}$$

The differences between the observed values and these "independence" values will then be typified by

$$\frac{(a+b)(a+c)}{N} - a = \frac{(a+b)(a+c) - a(a+b+c+d)}{N}$$

$$= \frac{bc - ad}{N}.$$

Thus $\chi^2$ is the sum of four terms like

$$\frac{(bc - ad)^2}{N^2} \bigg/ \frac{(a + b)(a + c)}{N}$$

and the sum reduces to

$$\frac{(bc - ad)^2(a + b + c + d)}{(a + b)(a + c)(c + d)(b + d)}$$

from which (8.5) follows.

**8.5** We have therefore constructed a coefficient, capable of varying from $-1$ to $+1$, which measures the extent to which $Q$ and $R$ agree *so far as concerns their agreement with* $P$. If the coefficient is $+1$ they are in complete agreement; if it is zero $ad - bc = 0$ and $a/b = c/d$, so that the preferences are independent; if the coefficient is $-1$ they are in complete disagreement.

We may then say that partial $\tau$ as so defined measures the agreement between $Q$ and $R$ independently of the influence of $P$. Partial $\tau$ is increased by an agreement between $Q$ and $R$ whether they agree with $P$ or not. The point may be clearer from a further examination of the table (8.3). For the ordinary rank correlation between $Q$ and $R$ we shall have

$$\tau_{QR} = \frac{(a + d) - (b + c)}{N} \quad . \quad . \quad . \quad (8.6)$$

In the table, however, we itemise the agreements between $Q$ and $R$ according to whether they do or do not agree with $P$. The row containing $a, b$ shows us how far $Q$ has $+$ or $-$ scores in those items for which $R$ has only $+$ scores. If this row is similar (in the sense of proportionality) to the row containing $c, d$, then $Q$ has $+$ or $-$ scores in much the same proportion whether $R$ has $+$ scores or not. In such circumstances we can hardly regard $Q$ and $R$ as much in agreement, except in so far as they both agree with $P$. Our coefficient of partial $\tau$ measures the departure from this situation towards greater differences of the $Q$ scores whether $R$ is $+$ or $-$, *i.e.* gives a better indication that $Q$ and $R$ are more or less in agreement between themselves, whatever the position in regard to $P$.

**8.6** In addition to (8.6) we have

$$\tau_{PQ} = \frac{(a + b) - (c + d)}{N} \quad . \quad . \quad . \quad (8.7)$$

$$\tau_{PR} = \frac{(a + c) - (b + d)}{N} \quad . \quad . \quad . \quad (8.8)$$

Remembering that $N = a + b + c + d$, we have

$$1 - \tau_{PQ}^2 = \frac{4}{N^2}(a + b)(c + d)$$

$$1 - \tau_{PR}^2 = \frac{4}{N^2}(a + c)(b + d)$$

$$\tau_{QR} - \tau_{PQ}\,\tau_{PR} = \frac{1}{N^2}[(a + b + c + d)\{\overline{a + d} - \overline{b + c}\}$$

$$- \{\overline{a + b} - \overline{c + d}\}\{\overline{a + c} - \overline{b + d}\}]$$

$$= \frac{4}{N^2}(ad - bc)$$

Thus from (8.4),

$$\tau_{QR.P} = \frac{\tau_{QR} - \tau_{PR}\,\tau_{QP}}{\sqrt{\{(1 - \tau_{PR}^2)(1 - \tau_{QP}^2)\}}} \quad . \quad . \quad (8.9)$$

This expresses partial $\tau$ in terms of the coefficients $\tau$ between the original rankings. It is remarkable (but apparently is only a coincidence) that this relationship is formally the same as that expressing a partial product-moment correlation in terms of the constituent correlations.*

*Example 8.1*

Three rankings are given according to (1) intelligence, (2) mathematical ability, (3) musical ability. They are as follows :

| | | | | | | | | | | |
|---|---|---|---|---|---|---|---|---|---|---|
| (1) | 1 | 2 | 3 | 4 | 5 | 6 | 7 | 8 | 9 | 10 |
| (2) | 1 | 4 | 5 | 6 | 2 | 7 | 3 | 9 | 8 | 10 |
| (3) | 4 | 1 | 3 | 5 | 2 | 6 | 7 | 10 | 9 | 8 |

We find

$$\tau_{12} = 0{\cdot}644, \qquad \tau_{13} = 0{\cdot}644, \qquad \tau_{23} = 0{\cdot}556.$$

Thus, from (8.9),

$$\tau_{23.1} = \frac{0{\cdot}556 - (0{\cdot}644)^2}{1 - (0{\cdot}644)^2}$$

$$= 0{\cdot}24.$$

This correlation is weaker than between (2) and (3) above, and we suspect that correlations between (1) and (2), (1) and (3) may be masking the real relationship between (2) and (3). This kind of inference, however, must be made with considerable reserve. It is a suggestion for further inquiry, nothing more unless there are prior grounds for expecting the effect.

* See, for instance, Yule and Kendall, *Introduction*, **12.15.**

**8.7** No tests of significance are yet known for partial $\tau$. The so-called $\chi^2$-test cannot be used because there are dependencies between certain scores entering into the quantities $a, b, c, d$; for instance, if $A$ is ranked before $B$ and $B$ before $C$ then $A$ must be ranked before $C$. Here again we have a branch of the subject which might repay further investigation.

## References

See Kendall (1942*a*). In his 1948 paper Hoeffding gives a rather complicated expression for the variance of partial $\tau$ in the limiting case when $n$ is large. If $\tau_{13} = \tau_{23} = 0$ the distribution of $\sqrt{n}(t_{12.3} - \tau_{12.3})$ is the same, in the limit, as that of $\sqrt{n}(t_{12} - \tau_{12})$.

Moran (1951) has considered partial $\tau$ without reaching any clear conclusions other than that the distributional problem is a very complex one.

Moran also considers a coefficient of multiple correlation defined, for example, in the case of three variates by a formula analogous to the ordinary theory:

$$1 - R^2_{1(23)} = (1 - \tau^2_{13})(1 - \tau^2_{12.3})$$

For small $n$ the distributional theory is again difficult. Moran suggests a test based on the variance-ratio.

## CHAPTER 9

# RANKS AND VARIATE VALUES

**9.1** Up to this point we have considered ranks as the fundamental data of a given statistical situation, irrespective of the manner in which they were reached. In many such situations, however, the ranking takes place (or is supposed to take place) according to the values of a statistical variable or *variate*. It is of considerable interest to consider the relationships between the ranks and the corresponding variate values, or between measures of correlation based on ranks and those based on the variate values.

### Concordances

**9.2** In general we shall require to consider a continuous population, that is to say a population for which the variate values may be any of a continuous range. One point to notice initially is that such a population cannot possess a rank correlation, strictly speaking; for the essence of ranking is that the objects shall be orderable and the totality of values of a continuous variate cannot be ordered in this sense.

**9.3** We can nevertheless connect the ideas of correlation of ranks and correlation of variates by considering *order properties*. Suppose we draw two members $x_i$ and $x_j$ at random from a continuous population. The probability that they coincide is zero and thus the possibility that $x_i = x_j$ can be ignored. We may then consider the probability that $x_i < x_j$ and the complementary probability that $x_i > x_j$. Moreover, if we draw two members $x_i$, $y_i$ and $x_j$, $y_j$ from a bivariate population we may consider the probabilities of *concordance* of type 1:

$$\pi_1 = \text{Prob } (y_i < y_j \mid x_i < x_j), \quad . \quad . \quad . \quad (9.1)$$

that is to say, the probability that $y_i < y_j$ if $x_i < x_j$. We have the complementary probability

$$\chi_1 = 1 - \pi_1 = \text{Prob } (y_i > y_j \mid x_i < x_j) \quad . \quad . \quad (9.2)$$

The number $\pi_1$ represents a property of the population.

**9.4** Now suppose that we draw a sample of $n$ values at random from the population and arrange the $x$'s in ascending order of magnitude. Of the $\frac{1}{2}n(n-1)$ pairs of $x$'s which we may choose for comparison, some have the corresponding $y$'s in ascending order and some do not. The number of those which do divided by $\frac{1}{2}n(n-1)$ is clearly an estimator of $\pi_1$. Moreover it is an unbiassed estimator, as we shall prove in the next chapter. If $p_1$ is this proportion and $q_1 = 1 - p_1$ we see at once that the $\tau$-coefficient for this sample, which we write as $t$, is simply given by

$$t_1 = p_1 - q_1 = 2p_1 - 1 \quad . \quad . \quad . \quad (9.3)$$

We could therefore define $t_1$ (as we have already noticed in **2.14**) in terms of concordance and arrive at a coefficient which has an analogue in the continuous case.

**9.5** Suppose now that we have a triad of values $(x_i, y_i)$, $(x_j, y_j)$, $(x_k, y_k)$, $i \neq j \neq k$. We may consider the probability of concordance of type 2:

$$\pi_2 = \text{Prob }(y_i < y_k \mid x_i < x_j), \quad . \quad . \quad . \quad (9.4)$$

that is to say, the probability that if $x_i < x_j$ then $y_i$ is less than $y_k$. We define a sample quantity $p_2$ as the proportion of concordances of type 2 in the sample divided by the total possible number. Unlike $p_1$, which can vary from 0 to 1, $p_2$ (as we shall show in the next chapter) can only vary from $\frac{1}{3}$ to $\frac{2}{3}$. For reasons which will appear later we do not take $6(p_2 - \frac{1}{2})$, which can vary from $-1$ to $+1$, as another coefficient. Instead, following (2.35) we define a sample value

$$r_s = \frac{3t}{n+1} + \frac{6(n-2)}{n+1}(p_2 - \tfrac{1}{2}) \quad . \quad . \quad (9.5)$$

The coefficient $r_s$ is Spearman's coefficient for the sample, and again it appears that we may define a rank correlation coefficient in terms of concordances. We note that for large $n$ (9.5) becomes

$$\rho_s = 6(\pi_2 - \tfrac{1}{2}), \quad . \quad . \quad . \quad . \quad (9.6)$$

which may be regarded as a definition of Spearman's $\rho$ for a continuous population.

## Relation between ranks and variate values

**9.6** Suppose that we draw a sample from a univariate population of $x$-values and rank them in ascending order of magnitude. It is of some interest to consider the product-moment coefficient of correlation between the $x$-values and the ranks. The coefficient is, in fact, sometimes surprisingly high. The basic results (due to A. Stuart) are as follows :

(*a*) If the correlation for sets of $n$ is $C_n$, and the limiting value as $n$ tends to infinity is $C$, we always have

$$C_n = \left(\frac{n-1}{n+1}\right)^{\frac{1}{2}} C \quad . \quad . \quad . \quad . \quad (9.7)$$

(*b*) If the parent population is a uniform distribution, *i.e.* takes any value in a finite range equally frequently, then $C = 1$ and

$$C_n = \left(\frac{n-1}{n+1}\right)^{\frac{1}{2}} \quad . \quad . \quad . \quad . \quad (9.8)$$

(*c*) If the parent population is normal $C = \sqrt{(3/\pi)}$ and

$$C_n = 0{\cdot}9772\left(\frac{n-1}{n+1}\right)^{\frac{1}{2}} \quad . \quad . \quad . \quad (9.9)$$

(*d*) If the parent population has the so-called $\Gamma$-distribution

$$dF = \frac{1}{\Gamma(m)} e^{-x} x^{m-1}\, dx, \quad 0 \leqslant x \leqslant \infty$$

then

$$C_n = \left(\frac{n-1}{n+1}\right)^{\frac{1}{2}} \left(\frac{3m}{\pi}\right)^{\frac{1}{2}} \frac{\Gamma(m+\frac{1}{2})}{\Gamma(m+1)} \quad . \quad . \quad (9.10)$$

For example, in rankings of 10 from a normal population the product-moment correlation between ranks and variates is

$$0{\cdot}9772 \times \sqrt{\tfrac{9}{11}} = 0{\cdot}884.$$

**9.7** In virtue of this fairly close relationship between ranks and variates we might expect that if we replace variate values by rank-numbers and then operate on the latter as if they were the primary variates we should in many cases draw the same conclusions. This appears to be so in a number of practical cases ; but the procedure has to be followed with a certain amount of caution. By a replacement with ranks we effectively standardise the scale of the variate and fix the mean, a procedure which might in some instances lead us astray.

**9.8** A converse procedure has been recommended by some authors. Given a ranking of $n$ drawn from a normal population, we replace the ranks by variate values $x$ ; the value $x_i$ is the mean value of the $i$th member (in order of magnitude) of a sample of $n$. This, of course, does not obviate the difficulty referred to in **9.7**. It has, however, been shown by Hoeffding (1951) that when tests concerning normal hypotheses are under examination such a procedure has optimum properties.*

## Relation between *t* and parent correlation in the normal case

**9.9** We now require to modify and to extend our notation slightly to avoid confusion.

(1) We shall continue to denote the $\tau$-coefficient in a sample by $t$;

(2) Spearman's $\rho$ in a sample will be denoted by $r_s$ and the corresponding parent parameter given by (9.6) as $\rho_s$.

(3) The parameter of the bivariate normal population expressing the product-moment correlation will be denoted by $\rho$. The product-moment correlation of a sample of variates will be denoted by $r$.

(4) We shall sometimes make estimates of $\rho$ from values of $t$ or $r_s$. These we shall denote by primes on $r$, *e.g.* $r'$.

**9.10** It may be shown that for samples from a normal population

$$E(t) = \frac{2}{\pi} \sin^{-1} \rho \quad . \quad . \quad . \quad . \quad (9.11)$$

For instance, if $\rho = 1/\sqrt{2} = 0{\cdot}707$, $E(t) = 0{\cdot}5$. We may therefore construct an estimator of $\rho$, say $r'$, by putting

$$r' = \sin \tfrac{1}{2} \pi t \quad . \quad . \quad . \quad . \quad (9.12)$$

This is *not* an unbiassed estimator of $\rho$, for we should require that $E(r') = \rho$, which does not follow from (9.11). Nevertheless, the procedure appears reasonable. The relation (9.11) was given for the first time by Greiner (1909) and the expression (9.13) below for its variance by Esscher (1924).

**9.11** In the next chapter we shall show that for normal samples

$$\operatorname{var} t = \frac{2}{n(n-1)}\left[1 - \left(\frac{2}{\pi} \sin^{-1} \rho\right)^2 + 2(n-2)\left\{\tfrac{1}{9} - \left(\frac{2}{\pi} \sin^{-1} \tfrac{1}{2}\rho\right)^2\right\}\right] \quad . \quad (9.13)$$

We know that $t$ is normally distributed for large samples and hence may use this result to test the significance of an observed $t$ by

* The replacement of variates by ranks, from the geometrical viewpoint, is equivalent to approximating to the sample distribution function by a straight line; the replacement by equivalent normal deviates amounts to approximating by the distribution curve of a normal distribution.

reference to the normal integral. But to do so we have to assume some values for the unknown $\rho$. In accordance with the usual practice in the theory of large samples we shall replace by $r'$ of equation (9.12).

If $p$ and $q$ are the proportion of positive and negative scores contributing to $t$ we have

$$t = p - q$$

and hence

$$1 - t^2 = 4pq \quad . \quad . \quad . \quad . \quad (9.14)$$

Thus from (9.13) we have, for large samples

$$\text{var}\, t = \frac{8}{n(n-1)}\left[pq + \tfrac{1}{2}(n-2)\left\{\tfrac{1}{9} - \left(\frac{2}{\pi}\sin^{-1}\tfrac{1}{2}r'\right)^2\right\}\right] \quad . \quad (9.15)$$

It may also be shown that

$$0 \leqslant \tfrac{1}{9} - \left(\frac{2}{\pi}\sin^{-1}\tfrac{1}{2}r'\right)^2 \leqslant \tfrac{4}{9}pq \quad . \quad . \quad (9.16)$$

and, for $n \geqslant 10$

$$\frac{2}{n(n-1)}\{1 + \tfrac{2}{9}(n-2)\} \leqslant \frac{5}{9(n-1)} \quad . \quad (9.17)$$

Substituting in (9.15) we find

$$\begin{aligned} \text{var}\, t &\leqslant \frac{20pq}{9(n-1)} \\ &= \frac{5(1-t^2)}{9(n-1)} \quad . \quad . \quad . \quad (9.18) \end{aligned}$$

The upper limit is, in fact, attained in a number of cases, so that the equality in (9.18) gives us a fairly good estimate of the actual variance.

**9.12** To the degree of approximation with which we are here concerned we may compare this result with (4.9) written in the form

$$\text{var}\, t \leqslant \frac{2(1-t^2)}{n} \quad . \quad . \quad . \quad . \quad (9.19)$$

Apart from the difference in the factors $n$ and $n - 1$, which is not important for large samples, we see on comparing (9.18) with (9.19) that the former gives a limit which is only 0·278 times that of the latter, the standard error being 0·53 or little more than half as great. This is the gain in accuracy which we acquire at the expense of assuming that the population is normal.

**9.13** Since

$$r' = \sin \tfrac{1}{2}\pi t$$

we have, for small variations,

$$\delta r' = \tfrac{1}{2}\pi \cos (\tfrac{1}{2}\pi t)\delta t.$$

Squaring and summing for all such variations we find

$$\operatorname{var} r' = \tfrac{1}{4}\pi^2(1 - r'^2) \operatorname{var} t \quad . \quad . \quad . \quad (9.20)$$

By the use of (9.18) this gives us

$$\operatorname{var} r' \leqslant \frac{5\pi^2}{9} pq \frac{1 - r'^2}{n-1}, \quad n \geqslant 10$$

$$\leqslant (2\cdot34)^2 pq \frac{1 - r'^2}{n - 1} \quad . \quad . \quad . \quad (9.21)$$

If we use $r'$ to estimate $\rho$, (9.16) provides an estimate of the upper limit to the standard error of the estimate. It is interesting to compare this with the standard error of the product-moment sample coefficient $r$, which is given by

$$\operatorname{var} r = \frac{(1 - r^2)^2}{n} \quad . \quad . \quad . \quad . \quad (9.22)$$

Taking the upper limit in (9.21) and ignoring the difference between $n$ and $n - 1$ we have

$$\sqrt{\frac{\operatorname{var} r'}{\operatorname{var} r}} = \frac{2\cdot34\sqrt{(pq)}}{\sqrt{(1 - r^2)}} \quad . \quad . \quad . \quad (9.23)$$

If the parent $\rho$ is zero, $p$ is approximately equal to $q$, so the ratio of standard errors given by (9.23) is approximately 1·17. If $\rho = 0\cdot9$ we may put, approximately,

$$r = 0\cdot9, \quad t = \frac{2}{\pi} \sin^{-1} 0\cdot9 = 0\cdot713, \quad pq = \tfrac{1}{4}(1 - t^2) = 0\cdot123.$$

The ratio of standard errors then becomes approximately 1·88. The product-moment coefficient $r$ is more accurate than $r'$ in the sense that it has a smaller standard error and therefore is more likely to be nearer the true value $\rho$.

### Relation between $\rho_s$ and $\rho$ in the normal case

**9.14** If we define $\tau$ for a continuous population by the expression analogous to (9.3),

$$\tau = 2\pi_1 - 1 \quad . \quad . \quad . \quad . \quad (9.24)$$

then $t$ is an unbiassed estimator of $\tau$. But proceeding likewise from (9.5) gives us

$$E(r_s) = \frac{3\tau}{n+1} + \frac{6(n-2)}{n+1}(\pi_2 - \tfrac{1}{2}),$$

and if we define $\rho_s$ for the population by (9.6) this gives us

$$E(r_s) = \frac{n-2}{n+1}\rho_s + \frac{3\tau}{n+1}$$

$$= \rho_s + \frac{3(\tau - \rho_s)}{n+1} \quad . \quad . \quad . \quad (9.25)$$

This confirms the result of (5.76), that $r_s$ is not an unbiassed estimator of $\rho_s$.

**9.15** Let us now consider the relation between $\rho_s$ and $\rho$ in a normal population. It may be shown that

$$\rho = 2 \sin \tfrac{1}{6}\pi\rho_s,$$

and hence we may take as an estimator of $\rho$ for large samples the quantity $r''$ where

$$r'' = 2 \sin \tfrac{1}{6}\pi r_s \quad . \quad . \quad . \quad (9.26)$$

In virtue of the bias revealed by (9.25), however, it seems better to take

$$r'' = 2 \sin \tfrac{1}{6}\pi\left\{r_s - \frac{3(t - r_s)}{n-2}\right\} \quad . \quad . \quad (9.27)$$

Formula (9.26) is due to K. Pearson (1907) and was arrived at by him in considering grade correlations as follows.

**9.16** We define the *grade* of an individual of variate value $x$ to be the proportional frequency of the population with variate values less than or equal to $x$. The correlation between the grades of variates $x$, $y$ in a bivariate correlation is called the *grade correlation.* This quantity exists for a continuous population and is easily seen to reduce to the Spearman rank correlation when applied to a finite sample. We shall prove in the next chapter by considering concordances that the grade correlation as so defined is in fact the quantity $\rho_s$ as defined by (9.6).

**9.17** It might be expected that there would be some reasonably tractable formula like (9.13) giving the variance of $r_s$ in the normal case. This is not so and, in fact, it has been shown that no such formula can exist in terms of elementary functions.

For large samples we have from (9.26)

$$\delta r'' = \tfrac{1}{3}\pi \cos \tfrac{1}{6}\pi r_s$$

and hence

$$\text{var } r'' = \tfrac{1}{9}\pi^2(1 - \tfrac{1}{4}r^2) \text{ var } r_s \quad . \quad . \quad (9.28)$$

This is only of help to us when we know var $r_s$. In the case when $\rho = 0$ this reduces to $1/(n-1)$ and thus

$$\text{var } r'' = \frac{\pi^2}{9(n-1)} \quad . \quad . \quad . \quad (9.29)$$

$$= \frac{(1{\cdot}047)^2}{n-1}.$$

When $\rho$ is not zero an expression (valid for large $n$) can be derived in the form of an infinite series as follows :

$$\text{var } r_s = \frac{1}{n}(1 - 1{\cdot}5635\rho^2 + 0{\cdot}3047\rho^4 + 0{\cdot}1553\rho^6$$

$$+ 0{\cdot}0616\rho^8 + 0{\cdot}0221\rho^{10} + \ldots) \quad . \quad . \quad (9.30)$$

The values of this for some values of $\rho$ are as follows :

| $\rho$ | var $r_s$ $\frac{1}{n}\times$ |
|---|---|
| 0·0 | 1·0000 |
| 0·1 | 0·9844 |
| 0·2 | 0·9380 |
| 0·3 | 0·8619 |
| 0·4 | 0·7583 |
| 0·5 | 0·6309 |
| 0·6 | 0·4851 |
| 0·7 | 0·3295 |
| 0·8 | 0·1776 |
| 0·9 | 0·0503 |

**9.18** If we compare the standard error of $r''$ with that given by (9.22) we find for $\rho = 0$ a ratio of 1·047 and for $\rho = 0{\cdot}5$ a ratio of 1·137. The balance of precision still lies in favour of product-moment $r$ but not very strongly so, and an estimator of $\rho$ based on $r_s$, all things considered, is quite good. This bears out the remarks of **9.7.** It is, in fact, not an accident, though we cannot enter here into the reasons, that the variance of $r''$ in (9.29) has a factor $\pi^2/9$ whereas the factor $C$ in (9.9) is the reciprocal of the fourth root of this quantity.

**9.18** It is also of some interest to consider the relationship between $t$ and $r_s$ for the normal case. Again no exact expressions are known, but for large samples an expansion similar to that of (9.30) gives

$$\operatorname{cov}(r_s, t) = \frac{2}{3n}(1 - 1{\cdot}2486\rho^2 + 0{\cdot}0683\rho^4 + 0{\cdot}0728\rho^6 + 0{\cdot}0403\rho^8 + 0{\cdot}0164\rho^{10} + \ldots) \quad (9.31)$$

We find, for example, that for $\rho = 0$ the correlation between $r_s$ and $t$ is unity, as we already know from **5.14**; for $\rho = 0{\cdot}2$ it is 0·999,55; for $\rho = 0{\cdot}4$ it is 0·9981; and even for $\rho = 0{\cdot}8$ it is 0·9843 though it tends to zero as $\rho$ approaches unity. For large $n$ the ratio of $r_s$ and $t$ tends to the ratio of their expectations, notwithstanding that the correlation between them may be small for high $\rho$, because their variances tend to zero. This ratio is $3 \sin^{-1} \frac{1}{2}\rho/\sin^{-1} \rho$, which varies from 1·3 in the neighbourhood of $\rho = 0$ through 1·42 when $\rho = 0{\cdot}6$ to unity when $\rho = 1$. This is one contributory reason why, in practice, we often find a value of $r_s$ about 40 per cent or 50 per cent greater than $t$, unless either is near unity.

**9.19** In conclusion let us remove one possible misunderstanding arising from the relative magnitudes of the standard errors of $r'$ and $r''$, namely the estimators of $\rho$ based on $t$ and $r_s$. The fact that they are different indicates a genuine difference of efficiency in the estimation process, the one with the smaller variance being the more efficient.

Now for large samples the variances of $t$ and $r_s$ as given by (9.13) and (9.30) are also different. But this does not mean that $t$ is a better or worse estimator of $\tau$ than $r_s$ is of $\rho_s$. The difference in variances is due to the difference of scales; and it is easy to verify that for $\rho$ not near to unity

$$\frac{E(t)}{\sqrt{\operatorname{var} t}} = \frac{E(r_s)}{\sqrt{\operatorname{var} r_s}}, \quad (9.32)$$

which is in accordance with our general result that the correlation of $t$ and $r_s$ is high, at least for large $n$ and $\rho$ not close to unity.

## References

See Esscher (1924) and Greiner (1909) for the mean and variance of $t$. For the mean of $r_s$ see Hoeffding (1948) and Moran (1948) and for the variance see Kendall (1949) and David and others (1951). For grade correlations see K. Pearson (1907).

For the relationship between ranks and variate values see Stuart (1954). The asymptotic relation for the normal case had previously been obtained but not published by Sir Cyril Burt.

For concordances of the first and second kind see Sundrum (1953).

## CHAPTER 10

# PROOF OF THE RESULTS OF CHAPTER 9

### Correlation between ranks and variate values

**10.1** Let $N$ samples of size $n$ be drawn from a continuous population with mean $\mu$ and variance $\sigma^2$. In each sample the observations are ordered, the $i$th smallest value being given the rank $i$. Let us evaluate, for the set of $Nn$ observations, the covariance of the variate values and ranks ($\mu_{11}$) and the variances of variate values ($\mu_{20}$) and ranks ($\mu_{02}$).

If the $i$th smallest value in the $j$th sample is $x_{(i)j}$ we have

$$\mu_{02} = \tfrac{1}{12}(n^2 - 1) \quad . \quad (10.1)$$

$$\mu_{20} = \frac{1}{Nn}\sum_{i=1}^{n}\sum_{j=1}^{N}\left\{x_{(i)j} - \frac{1}{Nn}\sum_{i=1}^{n}\sum_{j=1}^{N} x_{(i)j}\right\}^2$$

$$= \frac{1}{Nn}\sum_{i}\sum_{j} x_{(i)j}^2 - \left\{\frac{1}{Nn}\sum_{i}\sum_{j} x_{(i)j}\right\}^2 \quad . \quad (10.2)$$

$$\mu_{11} = \frac{1}{Nn}\sum_{i}\sum_{j} \{i - \tfrac{1}{2}(n+1)\}\left\{x_{(i)j} - \frac{1}{Nn}\sum_{i}\sum_{j} x_{(i)j}\right\}. \quad (10.3)$$

Now as $N$ tends to infinity

$$\lim \frac{1}{N}\sum_{j} x_{(i)j}^r = E(x_{(i)}^r)$$

and hence

$$\lim_{N\to\infty} \mu_{20} = \frac{1}{n}\sum_{i} E(x_{(i)}^2) - \left\{\frac{1}{n}\sum_{i} E(x_{(i)})\right\}^2, \quad . \quad (10.4)$$

$$\lim_{N\to\infty} \mu_{11} = \frac{1}{n}\sum_{i} iE(x_{(i)}) - \left\{\frac{1}{n}\sum_{i} E(x_{(i)})\right\}^2 \quad . \quad (10.5)$$

The distribution of $x_{(i)}$, say $G(x)$, in samples of $n$ from a population with distribution function $F(x)$ is given by *

$$dG(x) = n\binom{n-1}{i-1}\{F(x)\}^{i-1}\{1 - F(x)\}^{n-i}\, dF(x) \quad . \quad (10.6)$$

---

* Kendall, *Advanced Theory*, 1, p. 211.

Thus

$$\frac{1}{n}\sum_i E(x_{(i)}^r) = \int_{-\infty}^{\infty}\left\{\sum_i \binom{n-1}{i-1} F^{i-1}(1-F)^{n-i}\right\} x^r \, dF(x) \quad (10.7)$$

But the sum in braces is the binomial expansion of $\{F + (1 - F)\}^{n-1}$ and is therefore unity. Hence

$$\begin{aligned}\frac{1}{n}\sum_i E(x_{(i)}^r) &= \int_{-\infty}^{\infty} x^r \, dF \\ &= \mu \quad (r = 1) \\ &= \sigma^2 + \mu^2 \quad (r = 2)\end{aligned} \quad . \quad (10.8)$$

We shall assume that these moments exist. Similarly we find

$$\frac{1}{n}\sum_i iE\{x_{(i)}\} = (n-1)\int_{-\infty}^{\infty} xF \, dF + \mu \quad . \quad (10.9)$$

Hence from (10.4) and (10.5) we find

$$\lim_{N \to \infty} \mu_{20} = \sigma^2, \quad . \quad . \quad . \quad . \quad (10.10)$$

$$\lim \mu_{11} = (n-1)\left\{\int_{-\infty}^{\infty} xF(x) \, dF(x) - \tfrac{1}{2}\mu\right\} \quad . \quad (10.11)$$

Thus the correlation required is given by

$$\begin{aligned}C_n &= \lim_{N \to \infty} \frac{\mu_{11}}{\sqrt{(\mu_{20}\mu_{02})}} \\ &= \left\{\frac{12(n-1)}{\sigma^2(n+1)}\right\}^{\frac{1}{2}}\left\{\int_{-\infty}^{\infty} xF(x) \, dF - \tfrac{1}{2}\mu\right\}\end{aligned} \quad . \quad (10.12)$$

If we now let $n$ tend to infinity we get

$$C = \lim_{n \to \infty} C_n = \left(\frac{12}{\sigma^2}\right)^{\frac{1}{2}}\left\{\int_{-\infty}^{\infty} xF(x) \, dF - \tfrac{1}{2}\mu\right\}, \quad . \quad (10.13)$$

so that

$$C_n = \left\{\frac{n-1}{n+1}\right\}^{\frac{1}{2}} C \quad . \quad . \quad . \quad . \quad . \quad . \quad (10.14)$$

**10.2** Consider now some particular cases:

If the expression in braces in (10.13) is denoted by $\frac{1}{4}\Delta$ we have

$$\Delta = 4\int_{-\infty}^{\infty} x\{F(x) - \tfrac{1}{2}\} dF(x)$$

which, on an integration by parts, gives

$$\begin{aligned}\Delta &= 2\int_{-\infty}^{\infty} F(x)\{1 - F(x)\} dx \\ &= 2\int_{-\infty}^{\infty}\int_{-\infty}^{\infty} \{|x - y| \, dF(y)\} \, dF(x)\end{aligned} \quad . \quad (10.15)$$

This quantity $\Delta$ is, in fact, the coefficient of dispersion known as Gini's mean difference * and is non-negative. We then obtain Stuart's formula

$$C = \frac{\Delta\sqrt{3}}{2\sigma} \quad . \quad . \quad . \quad . \quad (10.16)$$

**10.3** For the uniform distribution

$$dF = \frac{dx}{k}, \quad 0 \leqslant x \leqslant k, \quad . \quad . \quad . \quad (10.17)$$

we have

$$\sigma^2 = \tfrac{1}{12}k^2,$$
$$\Delta = \tfrac{1}{3}k,$$

and hence

$$C = 1 \quad . \quad . \quad . \quad . \quad . \quad . \quad (10.18)$$

This is as we should expect for a distribution in which all values are equally probable.

**10.4** For the normal distribution, which we may take to have unit variance and zero mean without loss of generality,

$$dF = \frac{1}{\sqrt{(2\pi)}} e^{-\frac{1}{2}x^2}\,dx, \quad -\infty \leqslant x \leqslant \infty, \quad . \quad (10.19)$$

we have

$$\sigma^2 = 1$$

$$\Delta = \frac{2}{\sqrt{\pi}}$$

and hence

$$C = \sqrt{\frac{3}{\pi}} \quad . \quad . \quad . \quad . \quad (10.20)$$

**10.5** For the distribution

$$dF = \frac{1}{\Gamma(m)} e^{-x} x^{m-1}\,dx, \quad 0 \leqslant x \leqslant \infty, \quad . \quad . \quad (10.21)$$

we find

$$\sigma^2 = m$$

$$\Delta = \frac{m\,\Gamma(2m+1)}{2^{2m-1}\{\Gamma(m+1)\}^2}$$

whence, using the formula

$$\pi^{\frac{1}{2}}\,\Gamma(2m+1) = 2^{2m}\,\Gamma(m+\tfrac{1}{2})\Gamma(m+1)$$

---

* Kendall, *Advanced Theory*, **1**, p. 42.

we find

$$C = \sqrt{\frac{3m}{\pi}} \frac{\Gamma(m + \frac{1}{2})}{\Gamma(m + 1)} \quad . \quad . \quad . \quad (10.22)$$

These are the results stated in **9.6**. For $m = \frac{1}{2}$ (the lowest value of any statistical interest), $C = 0{\cdot}78$; for $m = 1$, $C = 0{\cdot}87$; for $m = 4$, $C = 0{\cdot}95$.

## Concordance

**10.6** We now show that $p_1$ and $p_2$, the sample relative-frequencies of concordance, are unbiassed estimators of the parent values $\pi_1$ and $\pi_2$. From one approach to probability theory this is obvious, but perhaps a simple proof is not out of place.

Let us attach to any pair of members a variate which is unity if there is a concordance of type 1 and zero in the contrary case. The expectation of $p_1$ is then the expectation of this variate for any given pair, since the expectation of a sum is the sum of expectations even when the constituent members are dependent. But the expectation of this variate is $\pi_1$ and the result follows. The same line of proof applies to $p_2$ and $\pi_2$.

**10.7** Let the distribution function of $x$, $y$ be $F(x, y)$. The distribution functions of $x$ or $y$ alone are respectively $F(x, \infty)$ and $F(\infty, y)$.

Now for any fixed $x_j$ the probability that $x_i < x_j$ is $F(x_j, \infty)$ and hence the probability that $y_i < y_j$ given $x_i < x_j$ is $F(x_j, y_j)/F(x_j, \infty)$. To obtain $p_1$, the probability that for any two pairs, $(x_i, y_i)$ and $(x_j, y_j)$, $y_i < y_j$ if $x_i < x_j$, we integrate for $x_j$, $y_j$ to obtain

$$\pi_1 = \frac{\iint F(x_j, y_j)\, dF(x_j, y_j)}{\iint F(x_j, \infty)\, dF(x_j, y_j)} \quad . \quad . \quad . \quad (10.23)$$

We may now drop the suffix $j$. Moreover

$$\iint F(x, \infty)\, dF(x, y) = \int F(x, \infty)\, dF(x, \infty)$$

$$= \left[\tfrac{1}{2}F^2(x, \infty)\right]_0^1 = \tfrac{1}{2}$$

and hence

$$\pi_1 = 2\iint F(x, y)\, dF(x, y), \quad . \quad . \quad . \quad (10.24)$$

the integration taking place over the whole range of $x$ and $y$.

Likewise we find, by a similar type of argument,

$$\pi_2 = 2 \iint F(x, \infty)\, F(\infty, y)\, dF(x, y) \quad . \quad . \quad (10.25)$$

**10.8** Consider the case when the variates are perfectly related by a linear relation. The joint distribution of $x$ and $y$ then becomes univariate and without loss of generality we may suppose this distribution to be uniform in the range 0 to 1. $F(x, y)$ is then reducible to a single variate $z$, say, and

$$\begin{aligned}\pi_1 &= 2 \int_0^1 z\, dz \\ &= 1.\end{aligned}$$

In the case of independence $\pi_1 = 0$ and thus $\pi_1$ may vary from 0 to 1. Being a probability it cannot lie outside those limits.

But for $\pi_2$ we have, in the case of complete linear dependence,

$$\begin{aligned}\pi_2 &= 2 \int_0^1 z^2\, dz \\ &= \tfrac{2}{3},\end{aligned}$$

and if there is negative dependence

$$\begin{aligned}\pi_2 &= 2 \int_0^1 z(1 - z)\, dz \\ &= \tfrac{1}{3}.\end{aligned}$$

Hence, $\pi_2$ lies between $\frac{1}{3}$ and $\frac{2}{3}$ and the coefficient $6(\pi_2 - \frac{1}{2})$ accordingly between $-1$ and 1.

**10.9** From (10.25) we see that the covariance of the grades of $x$ and $y$ is

$$\begin{aligned}\text{cov} &= \iint F(x, \infty)\, F(\infty, y)\, dF(x, y) \\ &\qquad - \left\{\int F(x, \infty)\, dF(x, \infty)\right\}\left\{\int F(\infty, y)\, dF(\infty, y)\right\} \\ &= \tfrac{1}{2}\pi_2 - \tfrac{1}{4}\end{aligned}$$

The variance becomes $\frac{1}{3} - \frac{1}{4} = \frac{1}{12}$. Hence the grade correlation is

$$\tfrac{1}{2}(\pi_2 - \tfrac{1}{2})/\tfrac{1}{12} = 6(\pi_2 - \tfrac{1}{2}), \quad . \quad . \quad . \quad (10.26)$$

and is thus the quantity we have defined as $\rho_s$.

**10.10** Now we proceed to the derivation of the expressions for means and variances of $t$ and $r_s$ in the normal case.

Let sgn $\xi$ stand for $+1$ if $\xi$ is positive, zero if $\xi$ is zero and $-1$ if $\xi$ is negative. We shall require the result that for real $\xi$

$$\left.\begin{aligned} \text{sgn}\ \xi &= \frac{1}{\pi}\int_{-\infty}^{\infty} \frac{e^{it\xi}\,dt}{it} \\ &= +1, \quad \xi > 0 \\ &= 0, \quad \xi = 0 \\ &= -1, \quad \xi < 0. \end{aligned}\right\} \quad . \quad . \quad . \ (10.27)$$

The integral is to be understood as a principal value, that is to say

$$\int_{-\infty}^{\infty} = \lim_{\substack{c \to \infty \\ \varepsilon \to 0}} \left\{\int_{-c}^{-\varepsilon} + \int_{\varepsilon}^{c}\right\}$$

Equation (10.27) is equivalent to the real integral

$$\text{sgn}\ \xi = \frac{1}{\pi}\int_{-\infty}^{\infty} \frac{\sin t\xi\,dt}{t} \quad . \quad . \quad . \ (10.28)$$

From the definition as a principal value it is clear that if $\xi = 0$ the integral vanishes in virtue of the symmetry of the integrand. Perhaps the quickest way of establishing (10.27) is to consider the complex integral

$$\int \frac{e^{iz\xi}\,dz}{iz}.$$

If $\xi$ is positive we take this round the contour consisting of the real axis from $-R$ to $-\varepsilon$, the small semicircle of radius $\varepsilon$ above the axis, the real axis from $\varepsilon$ to $R$ and the large semicircle of radius $R$ above the axis. This integral vanishes, for the integrand has no poles inside the contour. The integral along the real axis tends to

$$\int_{-\infty}^{\infty} \frac{e^{it\xi}\,dt}{it}.$$

The integral round the large semicircle tends to zero as $R$ tends to infinity. The integral round the small semicircle is effectively the integral of $dz/iz$ round that semicircle clockwise and is $-\pi$. Thus

$$\int_{-\infty}^{\infty} \frac{e^{it\xi}\,dt}{it} - \pi = 0,$$

whence the result (10.27) for $\xi > 0$ follows. If $\xi < 0$ we consider the integral with the sign of $t$ changed.

**10.11** Consider now a normal population of variates $x$, $y$ with correlation $\rho$. Its equation will be

$$dF = \frac{1}{2\pi\sqrt{(1-\rho^2)}} \exp\left\{-\frac{1}{2(1-\rho^2)}(x^2 - 2\rho xy + y^2)\right\} dx\, dy. \quad (10.29)$$

We lose no generality by taking the variates measured from zero means with unit variances. If we take a pair of values of $x$, say $x_1$ and $x_2$, we may allot a score based on $x_1 - x_2$, and for the calculation of $\tau$ can take this score to be sgn $(x_1 - x_2)$ or some convenient positive numerical multiple of $x_1 - x_2$. The distribution of a pair of independent values $x_1$ and $x_2$, $y_1$ and $y_2$ is

$$dF \propto \exp\left[-\frac{1}{2(1-\rho^2)}\{x_1^2 + x_2^2 - 2\rho(x_1y_1 + x_2y_2) + y_1^2 + y_2^2\}\right]$$
$$\times\, dx_1\, dx_2\, dy_1\, dy_2 \,. \quad . \quad (10.30)$$

Put

$$u_1 = \frac{1}{\sqrt{2}}(x_1 - x_2), \qquad u_2 = \frac{1}{\sqrt{2}}(x_1 + x_2)$$
$$v_1 = \frac{1}{\sqrt{2}}(y_1 - y_2), \qquad v_2 = \frac{1}{\sqrt{2}}(y_1 + y_2)$$

The distribution then becomes

$$dF \propto \exp\left[-\frac{1}{2(1-\rho^2)}(u_1^2 - 2\rho u_1v_1 + v_1^2)\right]du_1\, dv_1$$
$$\times \exp\left[-\frac{1}{2(1-\rho^2)}(u_2^2 - 2\rho u_2v_2 + v_2^2)\right]du_2\, dv_2 \quad . \quad (10.31)$$

Consequently $u_1$ and $v_1$ are also distributed normally with correlation $\rho$ independently of $u_2$ and $v_2$. Dropping the suffixes we have

$$dF \propto \exp\left[-\frac{1}{2(1-\rho^2)}\{u^2 - 2\rho uv + v^2\}\right]du\, dv \quad . \quad (10.32)$$

**10.12** Now if $t$ is a sample value of $\tau$, $E(t)$ is the expectation of the sum of $\frac{1}{2}n(n-1)$ terms each of which may be written sgn $u$ sgn $v$. Thus

$$E(t) = E(\text{sgn}\, u\ \text{sgn}\, v)$$
$$= \int_{-\infty}^{\infty}\int_{-\infty}^{\infty} \text{sgn}\, u\ \text{sgn}\, v\ dF$$

which in consequence of (10.1) becomes

$$\frac{1}{\pi^2}\int_{-\infty}^{\infty}\frac{dt_1}{it_1}\int_{-\infty}^{\infty}\frac{dt_2}{it_2}\left\{\int_{-\infty}^{\infty}\int_{-\infty}^{\infty} e^{iut_1+ivt_2}\, dF\right\} \quad . \quad (10.33)$$

The expression in curly brackets is the characteristic function of $F$ and is equal to *

$$\exp - \tfrac{1}{2}(t_1^2 + 2\rho t_1 t_2 + t_2^2) \quad . \quad . \quad . \quad (10.34)$$

Hence

$$E(t) = \frac{1}{\pi^2}\int_{-\infty}^{\infty}\int_{-\infty}^{\infty}\frac{dt_1}{it_1}\frac{dt_2}{it_2}\exp - \tfrac{1}{2}(t_1^2 + 2\rho t_1 t_2 + t_2^2)$$

Thus

$$\frac{\partial E(t)}{\partial \rho} = \frac{1}{\pi^2}\int_{-\infty}^{\infty}\int_{-\infty}^{\infty} dt_1\, dt_2 \exp - \tfrac{1}{2}(t_1^2 + 2\rho t_1 t_2 + t_2^2)$$

$$= \frac{2}{\pi\sqrt{(1-\rho^2)}} \quad . \quad . \quad . \quad . \quad . \quad . \quad (10.35)$$

Hence, by a simple integration for $\rho$, remembering that $E(t)$ vanishes when $\rho = 0$, we have

$$E(t) = \frac{2}{\pi}\sin^{-1}\rho \quad . \quad . \quad . \quad . \quad (10.36)$$

which is the result given in (9.11).

**10.13** To find the variance of $t$ in all possible samples we require

$$E(t^2) = E(\Sigma \operatorname{sgn} u \operatorname{sgn} v)^2$$

where summation extends over all $\binom{n}{2}$ values of $u$ and $v$. We may write

$$\Sigma (\operatorname{sgn} u \operatorname{sgn} v)^2 = \Sigma \operatorname{sgn} u_{ij} \operatorname{sgn} u_{kl} \operatorname{sgn} v_{ij} \operatorname{sgn} v_{kl}$$

and there are three types of case :

(i) If $i = k$, $j = l$ the term is $+1$ and the expectation of each term is $+1$.

(ii) If $i \neq k$, $j \neq l$, the expectation of the term reduces to

$$E(\operatorname{sgn} u_{ij} \operatorname{sgn} v_{ij})\, E(\operatorname{sgn} u_{kl} \operatorname{sgn} v_{kl})\,;$$

$$= \left(\frac{2}{\pi}\sin^{-1}\rho\right)^2 \quad . \quad . \quad . \quad . \quad (10.37)$$

from (10.36).

---

* Kendall, *Advanced Theory*, Vol. I, Example 3.15, p. 79. The integral is easily evaluated directly.

(iii) If $i = k$ or $j = l$ but not both, we have a type which may be evaluated by considering the case $i = k = 1$, $j = 2$, $k = 3$. Writing a single integral sign for convenience, let

$$M = E(\text{sgn}\, u_{12}\, \text{sgn}\, v_{12}\, \text{sgn}\, u_{13}\, \text{sgn}\, v_{13})$$
$$= \frac{1}{\pi^4}\int \frac{dt_1}{it_1}\frac{dt_2}{it_2}\frac{dt_3}{it_3}\frac{dt_4}{it_4}\int f e^{i\Omega}\, dx_1\, dx_2\, dx_3\, dy_1\, dy_2\, dy_3 \quad . \ (10.38)$$

where we now write (dropping $\sqrt{2}$) $u_{12} = x_1 - x_2$, etc., and thus

$$\Omega = (x_1 - x_2)t_1 + (y_1 - y_2)t_2 + (x_1 - x_3)t_3 + (y_1 - y_3)t_4$$
$$= x_1(t_1 + t_3) - x_2t_1 - x_3t_3 + y_1(t_2 + t_4) - y_2t_2 - y_3t_4 \quad . \ (10.39)$$

For the integration of $f\, e^{i\Omega}$ over the values of $x$ and $y$ we may use the known properties of characteristic functions or integrate directly to find

$$T = \int f e^{i\Omega}\, dx_1 \ldots dy_1 \ldots = \exp\,[-\tfrac{1}{2}(t_1 + t_3)^2 + (t_2 + t_4)^2$$
$$+ t_1^2 + t_2^2 + t_3^2 + t_4^2 + 2\rho'\{(t_1 + t_3)(t_2 + t_4) + t_1t_2 + t_3t_4\}]$$

and thus

$$\frac{\partial T}{\partial \rho'} = -T\{2t_1t_2 + 2t_3t_4 + t_1t_4 + t_2t_3\}\,. \quad . \ (10.40)$$

If we differentiate $M$ of (10.38) with respect to $\rho$ and substitute from (10.40) we have an expression

$$\frac{\partial M}{\partial \rho} = \frac{2}{\pi^4}\int dt_1\, dt_2 \frac{dt_3}{it_3}\frac{dt_4}{it_4}T + \frac{2}{\pi^4}\int dt_3\, dt_4 \frac{dt_1}{it_1}\frac{dt_2}{it_2}T$$
$$+ \frac{1}{\pi_4}\int dt_1 dt_4 \frac{dt_2}{it_2}\frac{dt_3}{it_3}T + \frac{1}{\pi^4}\int dt_2\, dt_3 \frac{dt_1}{it_1}\frac{dt_4}{it_4}T$$

Because of the symmetry of $T$ in $t_1$ and $t_3$, $t_2$ and $t_4$, this may be reduced to

$$\frac{\partial M}{\partial \rho} = \frac{4}{\pi^4}\int dt_1\, dt_2 \frac{dt_2}{it_3}\frac{dt_4}{it_4}T + \frac{2}{\pi^4}\int dt_1\, dt_4 \frac{dt_2}{it_2}\frac{dt_3}{it_3}T \quad . \ (10.41)$$

We now carry out the integration in the first part with respect to $t_1$ and $t_2$, obtaining

$$\int dt_1\, dt_2\, T = \frac{\pi}{\sqrt{(1 - \rho^2)}} \exp - \tfrac{3}{4}(t_3^2 + 2\rho t_3t_4 + t_4^2)$$

The remaining part of the integration can now be completed in the manner which led to the evaluation of (10.33).

Similarly the second integral in (10.41) may be evaluated. We arrive at

$$\frac{\partial M}{\partial \rho} = \frac{8 \sin^{-1} \rho}{\pi^2 \sqrt{(1-\rho^2)}} - \frac{4}{\pi^2} \frac{\sin^{-1} \frac{1}{2}\rho}{\sqrt{\{1-(\frac{1}{2}\rho)^2\}}} \quad . \quad (10.42)$$

When $\rho = 1$, $M = 1$, and by a further integration we find

$$M = \left(\frac{2}{\pi} \sin^{-1} \rho\right)^2 - \left(\frac{2}{\pi} \sin^{-1} \tfrac{1}{2}\rho\right)^2 + \frac{1}{9} \quad . \quad . \quad (10.43)$$

There are $\binom{n}{2}$ cases of type (i), $\binom{n}{2}\binom{n-2}{2}$ cases of type (ii), and $6\binom{n}{3}$ cases of type (iii). Thus

$$E(t^2) = \frac{1}{\binom{n}{2}^2}\left[\binom{n}{2} + \binom{n}{2}\binom{n-2}{2}\left(\frac{2}{\pi} \sin^{-1} \rho\right)^2 + 6\binom{n}{3}\left\{\frac{1}{9} + \left(\frac{2}{\pi} \sin^{-1} \rho\right)^2 - \left(\frac{2}{\pi} \sin^{-1} \frac{1}{2}\rho\right)^2\right\}\right] \quad . \quad (10.44)$$

Subtracting the square of $E(t)$, we find, after a little rearrangement,

$$\text{var } t = \frac{1}{\binom{n}{2}}\left[1 - \left(\frac{2}{\pi} \sin^{-1} \rho\right)^2 + 2(n-2)\left\{\frac{1}{9} - \left(\frac{2}{\pi} \sin^{-1} \frac{1}{2}\rho\right)^2\right\}\right] \quad . \quad . \quad (10.45)$$

which is the result given in (9.13).

**10.14** We may approximate to this formula as follows:

If

$$\sin^{-1} \tfrac{1}{2}\rho = \alpha$$
$$\tfrac{1}{3} \sin^{-1} \rho = \beta$$

then

$$2 \sin \alpha = \sin 3\beta$$
$$= 3 \sin \beta(1 - \tfrac{4}{3} \sin^2 \beta)$$

But

$$|\beta| \leqslant \frac{\pi}{6}$$

and hence

$$1 - \tfrac{4}{3} \sin^2 \beta \geqslant \tfrac{2}{3}$$

Thus

$$|\alpha| \geqslant |\beta|$$

and hence

$$0 \leqslant \frac{1}{9} - \left(\frac{2}{\pi} \sin^{-1} \tfrac{1}{2}\rho\right)^2 \leqslant \frac{1}{9}\left\{1 - \left(\frac{2}{\pi} \sin^{-1} \rho\right)^2\right\} \leqslant \frac{4}{9}pq \quad . \quad (10.46)$$

where $p$, $q$ are defined in **9.11**. Furthermore,

$$\frac{2}{n(n-1)}\left\{1+\frac{2}{9}(n-2)\right\} \leqslant \frac{5}{9(n-1)},\ n \geqslant 10 \quad . \quad (10.47)$$

Using these results in (10.45) we find

$$\left.\begin{aligned}\text{var}\, t &\leqslant \frac{20pq}{9(n-1)} \\ &= \frac{5(1-t^2)}{9(n-1)}\end{aligned}\right\}, \quad . \quad . \quad . \quad (10.48)$$

as given in (9.18).

**10.15** The remaining results we require are proved by the same method as the one used to derive $E(t)$ and var $t$; but the detailed working rapidly becomes more complicated.

Consider first of all $E(r_s)$. As in (2.35) we have

$$E(r_s) = \frac{3}{n^3-n} E\{\Sigma\, a_{ij} b_{ij} + \Sigma\, a_{ij} b_{ik}\},\quad j \neq k$$

$$= \frac{3}{n^3-n}\{n(n-1)\,E(a_{ij}\, b_{ij}) + n(n-1)(n-2)\,E(a_{ij}\, b_{ik})\}$$

$$= \frac{3}{n+1}E(a_{ij}\, b_{ij}) + \frac{n-2}{n+1}E(a_{ij}\, b_{ik}) \quad . \quad . \quad . \quad (10.49)$$

We have already found that

$$E(a_{ij}\, b_{ij}) = \frac{2}{\pi}\sin^{-1}\rho.$$

To evaluate $E(a_{ij}\, b_{ik})$ consider the case $i = 1, j = 2, k = 3$. In the manner of **10.11** we find

$$E(a_{12}b_{13}) = \frac{1}{\pi^2}\int_{-\infty}^{\infty}\int_{-\infty}^{\infty}\frac{dt_1}{it_1}\frac{dt_2}{it_2}E\left[\exp\{it(x_1-x_2)+it_2(y_1-y_2)\}\right]$$

$$= \frac{1}{\pi^2}\int_{-\infty}^{\infty}\int_{-\infty}^{\infty}\frac{dt_1}{it_1}\frac{dt_2}{it_2}\exp\{-\tfrac{1}{2}(t_1^2+\rho t_1 t_2+t_2^2)\} \quad . \quad (10.50)$$

This is like the integral of **10.12** with $\rho$ instead of $2\rho$ and is therefore $\frac{2}{\pi}\sin^{-1}\tfrac{1}{2}\rho$.

Hence we find

$$E(r_s) = \frac{6}{\pi(n+1)}\{\sin^{-1}\rho + (n-2)\sin^{-1}\tfrac{1}{2}\rho\} \quad . \quad (10.51)$$

**10.16** The detailed evaluation of var $r_s$ and cov $(r_s, t)$ proceeds in the same manner, but in the former we arrive at integrals of the elliptic type. Recourse must then be had to expansions in powers of $\rho$, and this leads to equations (9.30) and (9.31). Reference may be made to Kendall (1949) and David and others (1951) for the details.

## References

See references to the previous chapter. Kendall (1949) considered the relationship between rank coefficients and parent parameters in non-normal populations expressed as a Gram-Charlier series. Sundrum (1953*a*) has obtained the third and fourth moments of $t$ and considered their evaluation in the normal case.

CHAPTER 11

# PAIRED COMPARISONS

**11.1** Up to this stage we have considered rankings as given by the circumstances of the problem, and have not concerned ourselves with the question whether the data do properly lend themselves to a ranking treatment. Cases often arise, particularly in psychological work, where there is some doubt on this point. Suppose we ask an observer to rank $n$ men in order of intelligence. He may attempt to do so, and may even succeed in producing a ranking, although the nature of "intelligence" is so obscure that we cannot assume the possibility of ordering individuals by reference to it. To some extent we are begging the question by assuming that intelligence is a linear variable. Again, we may ask an observer to rank a number of districts according to his preference for living in them; but his preferences will depend on a number of factors such as cost, availability of transport, height above sea level, or nearness to shopping centres, and it by no means follows that he is capable of expressing a final preference on a linear scale. If we insist on his carrying out a ranking, and even if he complies under the impression that he is doing something within his powers, we may be forcing the data, so to speak, into an over-narrow framework which will distort the true situation. The method we shall discuss in this section is designed to overcome such difficulties.

**11.2** We shall suppose that of $n$ objects each of the possible $\frac{1}{2}n(n-1)$ pairs is presented to an observer, one pair at a time, and that he records his preference for one member of the pair. If $A$ is preferred to $B$ we may write $A \rightarrow B$ or $B \leftarrow A$.

*Example 11.1*

In some experiments on a dog, six different kinds of food were prepared. Each of the $\binom{6}{2} = 15$ possible pairs was offered to the dog and a note was made of which member he took first. (These data are for illustrative purposes and were not a serious attempt to investigate canine preferences for food.) Denoting the six foods by the letters $A$ to $F$ we may record the results as follows:

TABLE 11.1

PREFERENCES OF A DOG FOR SIX FOODS

| | $A$ | $B$ | $C$ | $D$ | $E$ | $F$ |
|---|---|---|---|---|---|---|
| $A$ | — | 1 | 1 | 0 | 1 | 1 |
| $B$ | 0 | — | 0 | 1 | 1 | 0 |
| $C$ | 0 | 1 | — | 1 | 1 | 1 |
| $D$ | 1 | 0 | 0 | — | 0 | 0 |
| $E$ | 0 | 0 | 0 | 1 | — | 1 |
| $F$ | 0 | 1 | 0 | 1 | 0 | — |

For instance an entry 1 in column $Y$ and row $X$ means $X \rightarrow Y$ and, of course, corresponds to 0 in row $Y$ and column $X$. Thus, in the above table, $A \rightarrow B$, $A \rightarrow C$, $A \leftarrow D$, etc. The diagonals are blocked out.

The arrangement of the objects in rows and columns is arbitrary, but it is clearly convenient to have the orders in row and column the same.

The complex of preferences may also be represented diagram-

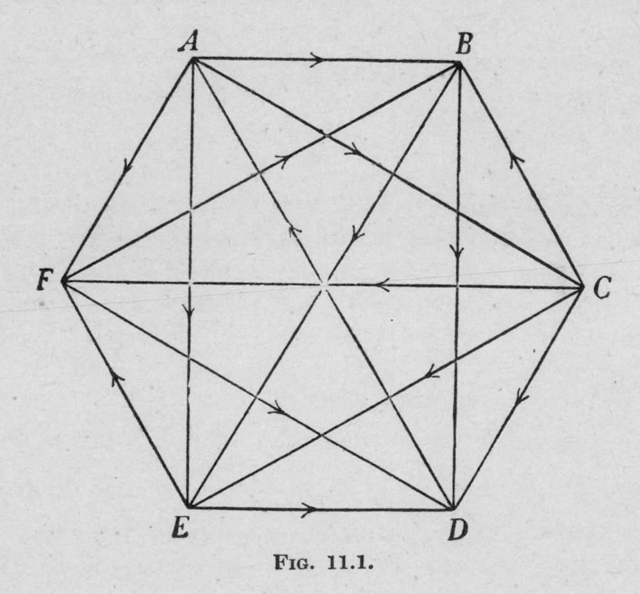


FIG. 11.1.

matically. We represent the six objects $A$ to $F$ by the vertices of a regular polygon as in Fig. 11.1. The vertices are joined in all possible ways by straight lines and if $X \rightarrow Y$ we draw an arrow on the join $XY$ pointing from $X$ to $Y$.

**11.3** If an observer expresses preferences for three objects $X$, $Y$, $Z$ as $X \rightarrow Y \rightarrow Z \rightarrow X$ or $X \leftarrow Y \leftarrow Z \leftarrow X$ we shall say that the triad is "circular" or "inconsistent". In the triangle $XYZ$ all the arrows in the diagram of type 11.1 go round the same way. In Fig. 11.1 the triads $ACD$, $BEF$ and three others are circular.

Clearly circular triads cannot arise in ordinary ranking for if $X \rightarrow Y$ and $Y \rightarrow Z$ then $X \rightarrow Z$. It is then a necessary and sufficient condition for the possibility of expressing the preferences as a ranking that no circular triads be present. The more circular triads there are, so to speak, the further we depart from the ranking situation towards a position of inconsistency under which $X$ may be preferred to $Y$ and $Y$ to $Z$ but nevertheless $Z$ is preferred to $X$.

**11.4** It is possible to have circular polyads of extent greater than three. For instance if $A \rightarrow B \rightarrow C \rightarrow D \rightarrow A$ the tetrad $ABCD$ is circular. A circular $n$-ad must, however, contain $n - 2$ circular triads but it may contain more; and the fact that it contains circular triads does not imply that it is itself circular. Suppose, for instance, that $ABCD$ is circular. Then either $A \rightarrow C$ or $C \rightarrow A$. In the first case $ACD$ is circular, in the second $ABC$. Similarly either $ABD$ or $BCD$ is circular. Thus the tetrad must contain at least two circular triads. On the other hand, the scheme expressed by $A \rightarrow B \rightarrow C \leftarrow D \rightarrow A$, $B \rightarrow D$, $C \rightarrow A$ contains the circular triads $ABC$ and $ABD$, but $ABCD$ is not circular.

We shall therefore concentrate on circular triads which compose the elementary inconsistencies of the situation, and shall ignore the more ambiguous criteria based on polyads of greater extent.

**11.5** It will be shown in the next chapter that if $n$ is odd the maximum number of circular triads is $\frac{1}{24}(n^3 - n)$, and if $n$ is even the maximum number is $\frac{1}{24}(n^3 - 4n)$. The minimum number is zero. We may therefore define a *coefficient of consistence* by the equations

$$\left.\begin{aligned} \zeta &= 1 - \frac{24d}{n^3 - n}, \quad n \text{ odd} \\ &= 1 - \frac{24d}{n^3 - 4n}, \quad n \text{ even} \end{aligned}\right\} \qquad . \qquad . \quad (11.1)$$

where $d$ is the observed number of circular triads. If and only if $\zeta$ is unity there are no circular triads, and the data may be ranked.

For example, in the data of Example 11.1 there are 5 circular triads. The maximum number is 8, so $\zeta = 0{\cdot}375$.

**11.6** We may, in a certain sense, test the significance of a value of $\zeta$ by considering the distribution it would have if all the preferences were allotted at random. This will tell us whether the observed $\zeta$ could have arisen by chance if the observer was completely incompetent, or, alternatively, whether there is some degree of consistence in his preferences notwithstanding a lack of perfection.

Appendix Table 9 gives the probabilities that certain values of $d$ will be attained or exceeded for $n = 2$ to 7, on the assumption that preferences are allotted purely at random so that any preference scheme is as probable as any other. These distributions are rather troublesome to obtain, and in practice are not often required for higher values of $n$; but when a test is required it may be derived from the $\chi^2$-distribution, to which that of $d$ tends as $n$ increases. In fact, writing

$$\left.\begin{aligned} \nu &= \frac{n(n-1)(n-2)}{(n-4)^2} \\ \chi^2 &= \frac{8}{n-4}\left\{\frac{1}{4}\binom{n}{3} - d + \tfrac{1}{2}\right\} + \nu \end{aligned}\right\} \quad . \quad . \quad (11.2)$$

we have the result that $\chi^2$ is distributed approximately in the usual form with $\nu$ degrees of freedom. The distribution is, however, measured from higher to lower values of $d$, so that the probability that $d$ will be attained or exceeded is the complement of the probability for $\chi^2$. The following example illustrates the point.

*Example 11.2*

In a set of 7 a value of $d$ equal to 13 is observed. From (11.2) we have

$$\nu = \frac{7 \times 6 \times 5}{9} = 23{\cdot}33$$

$$\chi^2 = \tfrac{8}{3}(8{\cdot}75 - 13 + \tfrac{1}{2}) + 23{\cdot}33 = 13{\cdot}33.$$

From Appendix Table 8 we see that these values correspond approximately to a significance level of about 0·95. The appropriate significance level for $d$ is thus $1 - 0{\cdot}95 = 0{\cdot}05$. The exact value of the probability, from Appendix Table 9, is 0·036. The approximation is fair for such a low value of $n$ as 7.

**11.7** In a table of the type of **11.1** it is possible to ascertain the number of circular triads $d$ without counting them directly. Suppose the row totals are $a_1 \ldots a_n$. Then

$$d = \tfrac{1}{6}n(n-1)(n-2) - \tfrac{1}{2}\sum_{i=1}^{n} a_i(a_i - 1) \quad . \quad (11.3)$$

For example, in Table **11.1** the row totals are 4, 2, 4, 1, 2, 2, totalling $15 = \binom{6}{2}$. Thus

$$\begin{aligned} \tfrac{1}{2}\Sigma\, a(a-1) &= \tfrac{1}{2}\Sigma\, a^2 - \tfrac{1}{2}\Sigma\, a \\ &= \tfrac{1}{2}(45 - 15) = 15 \end{aligned}$$

giving

$$d = 20 - 15 = 5.$$

The same formula applies to column totals, say $b_1 \ldots b_n$. For we have, in virtue of the method of construction of the tables,

$$b_i = (n-1) - a_i$$

Thus

$$\begin{aligned} \Sigma\, b_i &= \Sigma\, a_i \\ \Sigma\, b_i^2 &= n(n-1)^2 - 2(n-1)\,\Sigma\, a + \Sigma\, a^2 \\ &= \Sigma\, a_i^2 \end{aligned}$$

and hence

$$\Sigma\, b(b-1) = \Sigma\, a(a-1).$$

We can also write (11.3) in the form

$$d = \tfrac{1}{12}n(n-1)(2n-1) - \tfrac{1}{2}\Sigma\, a_i^2 \quad . \quad (11.4)$$

which is probably the simplest for calculation.

## Coefficient of agreement

**11.8** Suppose now that we have $m$ observers each of which provides $\binom{n}{2}$ preferences between pairs of $n$ objects. Suppose that in a table of form **11.1** we enter a unit in the cell in row $X$ and column $Y$ whenever $X \rightarrow Y$ and count the units in each cell. A cell may then contain any number from 0 to $m$. If the observers are in complete agreement there will be $\binom{n}{2}$ cells containing $m$, the remaining cells being zero. The agreement may be complete even if there are inconsistencies present.

Suppose that the number in row $X$ and column $Y$ contains the number $\gamma$. Let

$$\Sigma = \Sigma\binom{\gamma}{2} \quad . \quad . \quad . \quad . \quad . \quad (11.5)$$

the summation extending over the $n(n-1)$ cells of the table (the diagonal cells being ignored). Then $\Sigma$ is the sum of the number of agreements between pairs of judges. Put

$$u = \frac{2\,\Sigma}{\binom{m}{2}\binom{n}{2}} - 1$$

$$= \frac{8\,\Sigma}{m(m-1)\,n(n-1)} - 1 \quad . \quad . \quad (11.6)$$

We shall call $u$ the *coefficient of agreement*. If there is complete agreement, and only in this case, $u = 1$. The further we depart from this case, as measured by agreements between pairs of observers, the smaller $u$ becomes. The minimum number of agreements in each cell is $\frac{1}{2}m$ if $m$ is even or $\frac{1}{2}(m \pm 1)$ if $m$ is odd. In the first case the value of $u$ is $-1/(m-1)$, in the second $-1/m$.

This minimum value is not $-1$ unless $m = 2$. In such a case, with two observers, we have

$$u = \frac{2\,\Sigma}{\frac{1}{2}n(n-1)} - 1 \quad . \quad . \quad . \quad (11.7)$$

so that $u$ may be regarded as a generalisation of the coefficient $\tau$ in this case.

*Example 11.3*

A class of boys (ages 11 to 13 inclusive) were asked to state their preferences with respect to certain school subjects. Each child was given a sheet on which were written the possible pairs of subjects and asked to underline the one preferred in each case. The results were as follows:

21 boys, 13 school subjects. The preferences are shown in Table 11.2.

TABLE 11.2

PREFERENCES OF 21 BOYS IN 13 SUBJECTS

| | 1 | 2 | 3 | 4 | 5 | 6 | 7 | 8 | 9 | 10 | 11 | 12 | 13 | TOTALS |
|---|---|---|---|---|---|---|---|---|---|---|---|---|---|---|
| 1. Woodwork | — | 14 | 20 | 15 | 15 | 16 | 16 | 18 | 18 | 18 | 20 | 21 | 20 | 211 |
| 2. Gymnastics | 7 | — | 14 | 12 | 13 | 18 | 14 | 16 | 16 | 20 | 16 | 18 | 19 | 183 |
| 3. Art | 1 | 7 | — | 10 | 14 | 10 | 16 | 18 | 16 | 16 | 17 | 16 | 19 | 160 |
| 4. Science | 6 | 9 | 11 | — | 11 | 12 | 15 | 14 | 13 | 13 | 17 | 17 | 16 | 154 |
| 5. History | 6 | 8 | 7 | 10 | — | 14 | 11 | 12 | 14 | 15 | 13 | 14 | 16 | 140 |
| 6. Geography | 5 | 3 | 11 | 9 | 7 | — | 14 | 14 | 13 | 13 | 16 | 15 | 17 | 137 |
| 7. Arithmetic | 5 | 7 | 5 | 6 | 10 | 7 | — | 9 | 11 | 13 | 15 | 13 | 15 | 116 |
| 8. Religion | 3 | 5 | 3 | 7 | 9 | 7 | 12 | — | 12 | 14 | 14 | 16 | 14 | 116 |
| 9. English Literature | 3 | 5 | 5 | 8 | 7 | 8 | 10 | 9 | — | 10 | 13 | 13 | 15 | 106 |
| 10. Commercial subjects | 3 | 1 | 5 | 8 | 6 | 8 | 8 | 7 | 11 | — | 10 | 10 | 14 | 91 |
| 11. Algebra | 1 | 5 | 4 | 4 | 8 | 5 | 6 | 7 | 8 | 11 | — | 10 | 13 | 82 |
| 12. English Grammar | 0 | 3 | 5 | 4 | 7 | 6 | 8 | 5 | 8 | 11 | 11 | — | 13 | 81 |
| 13. Geometry | 1 | 2 | 2 | 5 | 5 | 4 | 6 | 7 | 6 | 7 | 8 | 8 | — | 61 |
| | | | | | | | | | | | | | TOTAL | 1,638 |

The calculation of $\Sigma$ for this table, in which the objects are arranged in order of total number of preferences, may be shortened by noting that $\Sigma$, as given by equation (11.5), may be transformed into the form

$$\Sigma = \Sigma(\gamma)^2 - m\,\Sigma(\gamma) + \binom{m}{2}\binom{n}{2},$$

where the summation now takes place over the half of the table below the diagonal. Since the numbers in this half are smaller than those in the other half there is a considerable saving in arithmetic.

We find $$\Sigma = 9718$$

and hence $$u = \frac{2 \times 9718}{\binom{21}{2}\binom{13}{2}} - 1 = 0{\cdot}186.$$

There is thus a certain amount of agreement among the children, indicated by the positive value of $u$.

The distribution of circular triads was as follows:

| No. of Triads | Frequency | No. of Triads | Frequency |
|---|---|---|---|
| 0 | 1 | 12 | 1 |
| 1 | 1 | 17 | 3 |
| 4 | 5 | 21 | 1 |
| 6 | 2 | 25 | 1 |
| 7 | 2 | 29 | 1 |
| 8 | 1 | 39 | 1 |
| 10 | 1 | | |
| | | TOTAL | 21 |

The total number of circular triads was 242 with a mean of 11·5. Only one boy was entirely consistent. On the other hand, for $n = 13$ the maximum number of circular triads is 91, with a mean value of 71·5. It is thus clear that, except perhaps for one boy, we cannot suppose that any boy allotted preferences at random. We are again led to conclude that the boys are genuinely capable of making distinctions, and that consistently, on the whole, half the boys have coefficients $\zeta$ greater than 0·92.

*Example 11.4*

It frequently happens in practice that observers decline to express a preference between some pairs of objects. We then arrive at difficulties similar to those arising from tied ranks. We shall deal with them in the table of type 11.1 by putting $\frac{1}{2}$ in each of the cells row $X$, column $Y$ and row $Y$, column $X$ where no preference is expressed between $X$ and $Y$. The following will illustrate the method. I am indebted for the data to Mr. J. W. Whitfield.

46 workers in a department were asked to say which of a pair they considered more important in the 66 possible pairs from the following items:

| | |
|---|---|
| Ventilation | Good opportunities for promotion |
| Canteen facilities | Lavatories and Cloakrooms |
| Responsibility | Work which requires no thought |
| Pension fund | Lighting |
| Interesting work | Hours of work |

Security of employment (*i.e.* of work in general)
Tenure of employment (*i.e.* at this particular factory)

The following table shows the results:

| | V | C | R | P | Op | L&C | WNT | Li | IW | HW | SE | TE | Totals |
|---|---|---|---|---|---|---|---|---|---|---|---|---|---|
| V | — | 14 | 10 | 10 | 20 | 16 | 3 | 20 | 20 | 24 | 28½ | 27 | 192½ |
| C | 32 | — | 24½ | 26½ | 30½ | 25 | 0 | 35 | 28 | 30 | 34 | 32½ | 298 |
| R | 36 | 21½ | — | 21 | 40 | 33 | 0 | 35½ | 36 | 32 | 37 | 28 | 320 |
| P | 36 | 19½ | 25 | — | 31½ | 26 | 2 | 32 | 32 | 29 | 32 | 29½ | 294½ |
| Op | 26 | 15½ | 6 | 14½ | — | 23 | 1 | 27 | 28½ | 26 | 25½ | 23 | 216 |
| L&C | 30 | 21 | 13 | 20 | 23 | — | 0 | 18 | 22½ | 22 | 24 | 30½ | 224 |
| WNT | 43 | 46 | 46 | 44 | 45 | 46 | — | 46 | 46 | 44 | 46 | 44½ | 496½ |
| Li | 26 | 11 | 10½ | 14 | 19 | 28 | 0 | — | 26 | 25 | 27½ | 20 | 207 |
| IW | 26 | 18 | 10 | 14 | 17½ | 23½ | 0 | 20 | — | 14 | 33 | 23 | 199 |
| HW | 22 | 16 | 14 | 17 | 20 | 24 | 2 | 21 | 32 | — | 32 | 18½ | 218½ |
| SE | 17½ | 12 | 9 | 14 | 20½ | 22 | 0 | 18½ | 13 | 14 | — | 26½ | 167 |
| TE | 19 | 13½ | 18 | 16½ | 23 | 15½ | 1½ | 26 | 23 | 27½ | 19½ | — | 203 |
| Totals | 313½ | 208 | 186 | 211½ | 290 | 282 | 9½ | 299 | 307 | 287½ | 339 | 303 | 3,036 |

We find from the sums of squares of items in the table

$$\Sigma \gamma^2 = 86{,}392, \qquad \Sigma \gamma = 3036.$$

Thus

$$\tfrac{1}{2} \Sigma \gamma(\gamma - 1) = 41{,}678.$$

Hence, if we use formula (11.6) without regard to fractional $\gamma$'s,

$$u = \frac{2 \times 41{,}678}{\binom{46}{2}\binom{12}{2}} - 1$$

$$= 0{\cdot}220.$$

Consider now a score such as that in row $C$ column $R$, $24\frac{1}{2}$, with the complementary score in column $C$ row $R$ of $21\frac{1}{2}$. As we have just calculated the score, the contributions of these two are

$$\binom{24\frac{1}{2}}{2} + \binom{21\frac{1}{2}}{2} = \frac{1}{2}\left\{\binom{25}{2} + \binom{24}{2}\right\} + \frac{1}{2}\left\{\binom{22}{2} + \binom{21}{2}\right\} - \frac{1}{4}$$

Thus our crude method is equivalent to taking an average of the undetermined preference, first by assuming $R \rightarrow C$ so that the scores are 25 and 21, secondly by assuming $R \leftarrow C$ so that the scores are 24 and 22 ; except for the factor $\frac{1}{4}$ which is negligible. This is in accordance with our treatment of ties in the ranking case.

In the above table the score shown for row $R$ column $P$, 21, was in fact $20\frac{2}{2}$, *i.e.* comprised two halves, and similarly that in column $R$ row $P$ was $24\frac{2}{2}$. If we were to average the possible scores we should have

$$\tfrac{1}{4}(20, 26) + \tfrac{1}{2}(21, 25) + \tfrac{1}{4}(22, 24)$$

and the difference from our actual count of (21, 25) is thus

$$\frac{1}{8}\left\{\binom{20}{2} + \binom{26}{2} + \binom{22}{2} + \binom{24}{2} - 2\binom{21}{2} - 2\binom{25}{2}\right\} = \frac{1}{2}$$

Again the difference is negligible.

**11.9** A test of significance of $u$ can be obtained by considering what the distribution would be if all the preferences were allotted at random. These distributions have been worked out for values of $m = 3$, $n = 2$ to $8$ ; $m = 4$, $n = 2$ to $6$ ; $m = 5$, $n = 2$ to $5$ ; $m = 6$, $n = 2$ to $4$, and form the basis of Appendix Tables 10.

For higher values of $m$ and $n$ a sufficient approximation is given by the $\chi^2$-distribution. We write

$$\chi^2 = \frac{4}{m-2}\left\{\Sigma - \frac{1}{2}\binom{n}{2}\binom{m}{2}\frac{m-3}{m-2}\right\} \quad . \quad . \quad (11.8)$$

$$\nu = \binom{n}{2}\frac{m(m-1)}{(m-2)^2} \quad . \quad . \quad . \quad . \quad . \quad (11.9)$$

and test in the $\chi^2$-distribution with $\nu$ degrees of freedom. A continuity correction may be applied by deducting unity from $\Sigma$.

For example, with $m = 3$, $n = 8$, we have

$$\chi^2 = 4\,\Sigma, \qquad \nu = 168$$

From Appendix Table 10A we have, exactly,

$$\text{for } \Sigma = 54, \qquad P = 0{\cdot}011$$
$$\text{for } \Sigma = 58, \qquad P = 0{\cdot}0011$$

For these values of $\Sigma$ (with continuity corrections) the corresponding values of $\chi^2$ are 212 and 228. For $\nu = 168$ we can take $\sqrt{(2\chi^2)}$ to be distributed normally with unit variance about $\sqrt{(2\nu - 1)} = 18{\cdot}30$, so that our deviates are

$$\sqrt{(2 \times 212) - 18{\cdot}30} = 2{\cdot}29$$

and

$$\sqrt{(2 \times 228) - 18{\cdot}30} = 3{\cdot}05.$$

These are seen from Appendix Table 3 to correspond to probabilities 0·011 and 0·00114, very close to the exact values.

Similarly, with $m = 6$, $n = 4$ we find from (11.8) and (11.9) that $\Sigma - 33{\cdot}75$ is distributed with 11·25 degrees of freedom. From Appendix Table 10D we see that the 1 per cent point lies between $\Sigma = 59$ and $\Sigma = 60$. The corresponding $\chi^2$ values are then (with continuity corrections) 24·25 and 25·25. From Appendix Table 8 we see that these values do in fact fall very close to the 1 per cent point for $\nu = 11{\cdot}25$, which is somewhere between 24·725 ($\nu = 11$) and 26·217 ($\nu = 12$).

*Example 11.5*

In Example 11.3, for $n = 13$, $m = 21$ we found $\Sigma = 9718$ and $u = 0{\cdot}186$. This indicates some community of preference but not a very large amount. Is the value significant?

From (11.8) and (11.9) we find

$$\chi^2 = \frac{4}{21}\left\{9718 - \frac{1}{2}.\frac{18}{19}\binom{13}{2}\binom{21}{2}\right\} = 421{\cdot}4$$

$$\nu = \binom{13}{2}\frac{21 \times 20}{19^2} = 90{\cdot}7$$

$$\sqrt{(2\chi^2)} - \sqrt{(2\nu - 1)} = 15{\cdot}3.$$

This is far beyond any ordinary significance point, and we conclude that the observed $u$ could not have arisen by chance from a population in which all the boys allotted preferences at random. This confirms our conclusion reached in Example **11.3.**

Again, in Example 11.4 we find

$$\chi^2 = 754{\cdot}5, \qquad \nu = 70{\cdot}6$$
$$\sqrt{(2\chi^2)} - \sqrt{(2\nu - 1)} = 27{\cdot}02,$$

again an extremely improbable result if the preference were allotted at random. We may conclude that the observed value of $u$ is significant.

## References

See Kendall and Babington Smith (1940) and Moran (1947). For paired comparisons in the non-null case see Babington Smith (1950) and Ehrenberg (1952).

Ehrenberg also corrects a result of Kendall and Babington Smith concerning a test of significance of $u$ when the data are ranked. If $M = \binom{m}{2}$ and $N = \binom{n}{2}$ $u$ may be tested in the $\chi^2$ distribution with

$$\chi^2 = \frac{6(2n + 5)MN}{(m - 2)(2n^2 + 6n + 17)}u + \nu$$

with

$$\nu = \frac{2(2n + 5)^3MN}{(m - 2)^2(2n^2 + 6n + 7)^2} \text{ degrees of freedom.}$$

## CHAPTER 12

# PROOF OF THE RESULTS OF CHAPTER 11

**12.1** We will first establish the result that in a complex of paired comparisons the maximum number of circular triads is $\frac{1}{24}(n^3 - n)$ for $n$ odd and $\frac{1}{24}(n^3 - 4n)$ for $n$ even.

Consider a polygon of the type of Fig. 11.1 with $n$ vertices. There will be $n - 1$ lines emanating from each vertex. Let $a_1 \ldots a_n$ be the number of arrows which *leave* the vertices. Then

$$\sum_{j=1}^{n} a_j = \binom{n}{2} \quad . \quad . \quad . \quad . \qquad (12.1)$$

and the mean value of $a$ is $\frac{1}{2}(n - 1)$. Consider the function

$$T = \sum_{j=1}^{n} \{a_j - \tfrac{1}{2}(n - 1)\}^2 \quad . \quad . \quad . \qquad (12.2)$$

that is to say, $n$ times the variance of the $a$-numbers. We have at once

$$T = \Sigma\, a_j^2 - \tfrac{1}{4}n(n - 1)^2 \quad . \quad . \quad . \qquad (12.3)$$

**12.2** We now show that if the direction of a preference is altered and the effect is to increase the number of circular triads by $p$, $T$ is reduced by $2p$ and vice versa. Consider the preference $A \rightarrow B$. The only triads affected by reversing to $B \rightarrow A$ are those containing the line $AB$. Suppose there are $\alpha$ preferences of type $A \rightarrow X$ (including $A \rightarrow B$) and $\beta$ of type $B \rightarrow X$. Then there are four possible types of triads:

$A \rightarrow X \leftarrow B$, say $x$ in number
$A \leftarrow X \rightarrow B$,
$A \rightarrow X \rightarrow B$, which must number $\alpha - x - 1$
$A \leftarrow X \leftarrow B$, ,, ,, ,, $\beta - x$

When the preference $A \rightarrow B$ is reversed the first two remain non-circular. The third becomes circular, the fourth ceases to be so. The increase in the number of circular triads is

$$(\alpha - x - 1) - (\beta - x) = \alpha - \beta - 1 = p.$$

The reduction in $T$ is

$$\alpha^2 - (\alpha - 1)^2 + \beta^2 - (\beta + 1)^2 = 2(\alpha - \beta - 1) = 2p.$$

Our result follows; for the effect of altering individual preferences is cumulative on $T$ and $d$.

**12.3** From the definition of $T$ it is clear that the maximum value is given when the data are ranked, and thus max $T = \frac{1}{12}(n^3 - n)$. For the minimum value consider a polygon with vertices $A_1 \ldots A_n$. Set up the preferences $A_1 \to A_2 \to \ldots \to A_n$. Next set up the preferences $A_1 \to A_3 \to A_5 \to$. If this does not provide a closed tour of all the points of the polygon proceed to the next unvisited vertex, $A_k$, and set up the preferences $A_k \to A_{k+2} \to$ etc., and so on. Then set up the preferences $A_1 \to A_4 \to A_7$, etc., and so on until the whole preference schema is completed.

If $n$ is odd the preferences described will consist of circular tours of the polygon, and each $a$ will be $\frac{1}{2}(n - 1)$ so that $T = 0$; and this is obviously a minimum. If $n$ is even the last preference $A_1 \to A_{\frac{1}{2}n+1}$ will not be a tour but will consist of a single line joining one vertex with the symmetrically opposite vertex. Thus there will be $\frac{1}{2}n$ vertices with $a = \frac{1}{2}n$ and $\frac{1}{2}n$ with $a = \frac{1}{2}n - 1$. In this case $T = \frac{1}{4}n$ and again this is a minimum.

Thus $T$ can range from 0 or $\frac{1}{4}n$ to $\frac{1}{12}(n^3 - n)$ and since an increase of two in $T$ corresponds to a decrease of unity in $d$, there are the following maximum values of $d$:

$$\frac{1}{24}(n^3 - n), \quad n \text{ odd}$$

$$\frac{1}{24}(n^3 - 4n), \quad n \text{ even.}$$

**12.4** The numbers $a$ are the totals of rows in the table of type 11.1, and from what has been said it follows that the number of circular triads is given by

$$\begin{aligned} d &= \tfrac{1}{2}\{\tfrac{1}{12}(n^3 - n) - T\} \\ &= \tfrac{1}{2}\{\tfrac{1}{12}(n^3 - n) + \tfrac{1}{4}n(n - 1)^2 - \Sigma a_j^2\} \\ &= \tfrac{1}{12}n(n - 1)(2n - 1) - \tfrac{1}{2}\Sigma a_j^2 \\ &= \tfrac{1}{6}n(n - 1)(n - 2) - \tfrac{1}{2}\Sigma a_j(a_j - 1) \end{aligned}$$

as given in (11.3) and (11.4).

**12.5** We now establish the $\chi^2$-approximation to the distribution of $d$ as $n$ becomes large.

Let the objects be numbered from 1 to $n$. Write $P_{ijk} = 1$ if the triad $(i, j, k)$ is circular and $P_{ijk} = 0$ if it is not. Then

$$d = \Sigma P_{ijk} \quad . \quad . \quad . \quad . \quad (12.4)$$

the summation taking place over all triads. Thus—

$$E(d) = \binom{n}{3} E(P_{ijk}).$$

By enumerating the possible cases for preferences in a given triad we see that $E(P_{ijk}) = \frac{1}{4}$. Hence, for the mean value of $d$,

$$E(d) = \tfrac{1}{4}\binom{n}{3} \quad . \quad . \quad . \quad . \quad (12.5)$$

Now consider $E(\Sigma P_{ijk})^2$. When we expand this there will be $\binom{n}{3}$ terms of type $P^2_{ijk}$; $3\binom{n}{3}\binom{n-3}{2}$ terms of type $P_{ijk} P_{ilm}$ where $j \neq l$, $k \neq m$; $3\binom{n}{3}(n-3)$ terms of type $P_{ijk} P_{ijl}$ where $k \neq l$; and $\binom{n}{3}\binom{n-3}{3}$ terms of type $P_{ijk} P_{lmn}$ with different suffixes. By examining particular configurations we see that the expectation of the first is $\frac{1}{4}$ and of each of the others is $\frac{1}{16}$. Thus

$$E(\Sigma P_{ijk})^2 = \frac{1}{16}\binom{n}{3}\left\{4 + \frac{3}{2}(n-3)(n-4) + 3(n-3) + \binom{n-3}{3}\right\}$$

$$= \frac{1}{16}\binom{n}{3}\left\{\binom{n}{3} + 3\right\}$$

Hence

$$\mu_2(d) = E(d - \bar{d})^2 = \frac{3}{16}\binom{n}{3} \quad . \quad . \quad . \quad . \quad (12.6)$$

The calculation of the third and fourth moments is much more complicated, but is the same in principle. We find

$$\mu_3 = -\frac{3}{32}\binom{n}{3}(n-4) \quad . \quad . \quad . \quad . \quad . \quad . \quad (12.7)$$

$$\mu_4 = \frac{1}{55{,}296}\binom{n}{3}\{972n^3 + 972n^2 - 36{,}936n + 80{,}352\} \quad . \quad . \quad (12.8)$$

**12.6** The moments of the $\chi^2$-distribution,

$$dF \propto e^{-\frac{1}{2}\chi^2} \chi^{\nu-1}\, d\chi,$$

are given by

$$\begin{aligned} \mu_1' \text{ (about zero)} &= \nu \\ \mu_2 &= 2\nu \\ \mu_3 &= 8\nu \end{aligned}$$

We note that $\mu_3(d)$ is negative whereas $\mu_3(\chi^2)$ is positive. We shall therefore measure $d$ from the other end of its distribution so as to bring the distributions into accord. Applying a correction for continuity, we see that

$$x = k\left\{\frac{1}{4}\binom{n}{3} - d + \tfrac{1}{2}\right\} + \nu \quad . \quad . \quad (12.9)$$

has mean value $\nu$, the mean of $\chi^2$. We will choose $k$ so that the distributions have the same variance, which is obviously so when

$$k = \sqrt{\frac{\mu_2(\chi^2)}{\mu_2(d)}} = \sqrt{\frac{2\nu}{\frac{3}{16}\binom{n}{3}}} \quad . \quad . \quad (12.10)$$

For the third moments to be equal we must have

$$\frac{\frac{3}{32}\binom{n}{3}(n-4)}{\left\{\frac{3}{16}\binom{n}{3}\right\}^{\frac{3}{2}}} = \frac{8\nu}{(2\nu)^{\frac{3}{2}}}$$

leading to

$$\nu = \frac{n(n-1)(n-2)}{(n-4)^2} \quad . \quad . \quad . \quad (12.11)$$

Using this value of $\nu$ in (12.10) we find that

$$\frac{8}{n-4}\left\{\frac{1}{4}\binom{n}{3} - d + \tfrac{1}{2}\right\} + \nu \quad . \quad . \quad (12.12)$$

has the first three moments the same as those of $\chi^2$.

**12.7** It may be shown that the distribution of $d$ tends to normality as $n$ tends to infinity. The proof—for details of which see Moran (1947)—follows the lines of those given in Chapter 5. We show that moments of odd order are of lower order in $n$ than those of even order. In an expansion

$$(\Sigma Q_{ijk})^{2m}$$

where $Q_{ijk} = P_{ijk} - \frac{1}{4}$, the dominant term is of type $Q^2_{ijk}\, Q^2_{lmn} \ldots$ occurring in $m$ factors with expectation $\frac{3}{32}$ and frequency $\dfrac{(2m)!}{2^m m!}$.

Thus the dominant term gives

$$\mu_{2m} \sim \frac{(2m)!}{2^m m!}\left(\frac{3}{32}\right)^m n^{3m}$$

$$\sim \frac{(2m)!}{2^m m!}(\mu_2)^m$$

and the tendency to normality follows.

**12.8** Finally, we derive the $\chi^2$-approximation for testing the coefficient of agreement, $u$, when all preferences are allotted at random.

The contribution to $\Sigma$ from two cells (row $X$, column $Y$) and (row $Y$, column $X$) is typified by

$$\binom{\gamma}{2} + \binom{m-\gamma}{2} \quad . \quad . \quad . \quad (12.13)$$

Of the $2^m$ total ways in which the $m$ preferences can be allotted to the cells there will be $\binom{m}{\gamma}$ in which $\gamma$ units occur. Consequently the frequency of the contribution to $\Sigma$ is the corresponding coefficient of $t$ in the array

$$f = t^{\binom{m}{2}} + \binom{m}{1}t^{\binom{m-1}{2}} + \ldots + \binom{m}{\gamma}t^{\binom{m-\gamma}{2}+\binom{\gamma}{2}} + \ldots + t^{\binom{m}{2}} \quad (12.14)$$

Now if the preferences are allotted at random the contributions to $\Sigma$ for the $\binom{n}{2}$ cells are independent; and hence the distribution of $\Sigma$ is given by

$$f^{\binom{n}{2}} \quad . \quad . \quad . \quad . \quad . \quad (12.15)$$

the frequency of $\Sigma$ being the coefficient of $t^{\Sigma}$ in this array.

For instance, with $m = 3, n = 4$,

$$f = t^3 + 3t + 3t + t^3 = 2t(3 + t^2)$$

and the distribution is arrayed by

$$\{2t(3 + t^2)\}^6 = 2^6 t^6 (729 + 1458t^2 + 1215t^4 + 540t^6 + 135t^8 + 18t^{10} + t^{12})$$

with a total frequency of $2^6 \times 4^6$. These and similar values form the basis of Appendix Tables 10.

**12.9** For constant $m$ the distribution of $\chi^2$ tends to normality with increasing $n$, for it is the mean of $\binom{n}{2}$ constituents with finite equal moments.* For constant $n$ the distribution tends with increasing $m$ to a form of the $\chi^2$-distribution; for each of the $\binom{n}{2}$ cells contributes a variate $\binom{\gamma}{2} + \binom{m-\gamma}{2}$ which is effectively like $\gamma^2$, and the distribution of $\gamma$ tends to normality.

The $r$th moment of $\Sigma$ about the origin is given by

$$2^m \mu_r' = \left[\left(t\frac{\partial}{\partial t}\right)^r f^{\binom{n}{2}}\right]_{t=1} \quad . \quad . \quad . \quad (12.16)$$

The differentiation, in fact, multiplies a term containing $t^\Sigma$ by $\Sigma^r$, and when we put $t = 1$ the array becomes the sum of frequencies each multiplied by $\Sigma^r$ which provides the $r$th moment. Thus, for the first moment,

$$2^m \mu_1' = \binom{n}{2}\sum_{j=0}^{m}\binom{m}{j}\{j^2 - mj + \tfrac{1}{2}(m^2 - m)\}$$

$$= \binom{n}{2}\left\{2^m\binom{m}{2} + \Sigma\binom{m}{j}(j^2 - jr)\right\}$$

giving

$$\mu_1' = \frac{1}{2}\binom{m}{2}\binom{n}{2} \quad . \quad . \quad . \quad . \quad . \quad . \quad (12.17)$$

In a similar way—we omit the algebra—we find

$$\mu_2 = \frac{1}{4}\binom{n}{2}\binom{m}{2} \quad . \quad . \quad . \quad . \quad . \quad . \quad . \quad (12.18)$$

$$\mu_3 = \frac{3}{4}\binom{n}{2}\binom{m}{3} \quad . \quad . \quad . \quad . \quad . \quad . \quad . \quad (12.19)$$

$$\mu_4 = \binom{m}{2}\binom{n}{2}\left\{\frac{3m^2 - 15m + 17}{8} + \frac{3}{32}\binom{n}{2}m(m-1)\right\}$$

$$. \quad . \quad . \quad (12.20)$$

Proceeding in the manner of **12.6** we see that

$$\chi^2 = \frac{4}{m-2}\left\{\Sigma - \frac{1}{2}\binom{n}{2}\binom{m}{2}\frac{m-3}{m-2}\right\} \quad . \quad . \quad (12.21)$$

---

* This is a particular case of the Central Limit Theorem—see Kendall, *Advanced Theory*, Vol. I, 7.32.

is distributed in the usual form with

$$\nu = \binom{n}{2}\frac{m(m-1)}{(m-2)^2} \quad . \quad . \quad . \quad (12.22)$$

degrees of freedom.

**References**

**See references to the previous chapter.**

## CHAPTER 13

# SOME FURTHER APPLICATIONS

**13.1** In this final chapter I shall sketch briefly a number of recent advances in ranking theory. Some of the ideas and methods we shall touch upon are new and have not been fully worked out. The development of others is hampered by the intractability of the mathematical problems involved. This chapter, therefore, unlike its predecessors, is not a systematic introduction to a section of statistical theory which has been investigated to the point where it can be applied to practical cases as a routine. Rather is it a review of recent developments and a guide to further reading.

### Models of ranking situations

**13.2** In the foregoing we have been mainly concerned either with ranking situations in which there is no parental correlation—the so-called null case; or with one particular model (**5.17**) in which our observations were regarded as an extract from a larger parent ranking. In some situations neither of these is appropriate. We may know, for example, that there is some parental correlation present and be more interested in its magnitude than its existence; or we may have a parent population of rankings all of the same extent, of which several are presented for scrutiny in the sample.

**13.3** Some progress has been made in two situations of fairly common occurrence.

(a) *Stuart's model*

Stuart (1951) has discussed the problem of sampling from a population of rankers. Suppose each member of a population arranges a number $n$ of objects in order of preference; for example, a set of occupations may be arranged according to the social prestige attached to them. If $m$ members are drawn at random from a population of $M$, we have $m$ sets of rankings of $n$; but our problem is not now primarily to test independence (as in Chapter 6), although that also arises, but to see how far such community of preference as exists among the $m$ observed members can be taken to be representative of preference in the population of $M$.

**13.4** Stuart uses the ranking concordance coefficient $W$ to discuss this problem. In the non-null case the distribution of this function is very complicated, and even its first four moments require extensive algebra to evaluate. The labour is not, however, prohibitive, and the results were successfully applied to a practical problem concerned with social stratification. A sample of about 1000 people were asked to rank 30 selected occupations in terms of an undefined quality "social class". The mean rank allotted to each occupation was calculated and the problem then arose: how far were differences in the sample mean-ranks significant of real differences in the population? Reference may be made to Stuart's paper for details.

**13.5** In this connection, mention may be made of an important outstanding problem in concordance theory. Suppose we have two sets of rankings $m_1$ and $m_2$ in number. The tests of Chapter 6 may show that the concordance coefficients of each, say $W_1$ and $W_2$, are significant. How do we test whether $W_1 - W_2$ is significant; or, more generally, can any method be devised of testing whether the agreement among the $m_1$ rankings differs appreciably from the degree among the $m_2$ rankings? Nothing seems to have been done on this problem.

(b) *The Thurstone–Mosteller–Daniels model*

**13.6** Suppose that one ranking is determined by an objective criterion, *e.g.* the objects might be ordered in time or space according to some measurable variable. An individual ranker, not knowing the true order, judges the objects and assigns an order to them. The population of values which now concerns us is the (infinite) set of rankings which such an observer might produce on repeated trials, the members of the set differing because he makes mistakes or misjudgements; or, more generally, the rankings which a number of different observers might produce. The model considered by Daniels (1950) supposes a continuous variable $y$ as the source of variation from a true value $m$, the frequency function of ratings $y_1, \dots y_n$ being

$$f(y_1 - m_1)f(y_2 - m_2) \dots f(y_n - m_n) \quad . \quad . \quad (13.1)$$

and the problem being to estimate the $m$'s, or at least their order, from the observations. Effectively, this becomes a problem in regression, and Daniels makes considerably more progress than might be expected from its unpromising nature.

## Paired-comparison models

**13.7** In the paired-comparison case, models of considerable generality can be written down, although their practical application is not easy to make. For instance, suppose that we have $n$ objects and the probability of ranking the $i$th higher than the $j$th is $\pi_{ij}$. This model would be appropriate to a situation where an individual made preferences which were subject to error, as in the ranking model of **13.6**, or to the case where a number of individuals differed in their preferences. Such a model was proposed by Babington Smith (1950) and discussed by Ehrenberg (1952). The coefficient of agreement $u$ (**11.8**) then has a mean value given by

$$E(u) = 1 - \frac{4}{m(m-1)} \sum_{i<j}^{n} \pi_{ij}(1 - \pi_{ij}) \quad . \quad (13.2)$$

and a variance

$$\text{var}\, u = \frac{64}{m(m-1)n^2(n-1)^2} \sum_{i<j} [(m-1)\{\pi_{ij}(1-\pi_{ij})\} - 4\pi_{ij}^2(1-\pi_{ij})^2] \quad . \quad (13.3)$$

The difficulty in applying the result resides in our ignorance of the $\pi$'s.

**13.8** An approach of a different kind has been developed by Bradley and Terry (1952). We suppose that $n$ objects have " true " ratings, expressed by the numbers $\pi_1, \ldots \pi_n \left(\sum_{j=1}^{n} \pi_j = 1\right)$ such that, when the $i$th and $j$th objects are compared, the probability that the $i$th is preferred to the $j$th is $\pi_i/(\pi_i + \pi_j)$. This model, which has a certain prior plausibility for much paired comparison work, is simpler than the previous one, since it depends on $n$ parameters $\pi_i$ instead of $\frac{1}{2}n(n-1)$ parameters $\pi_{ij}$. Bradley and Terry have developed methods of estimating the $\pi$'s from observation and of testing the significance of a set of results. The tables required for the practical application of the method have been published (Bradley and Terry, 1952, and Bradley, 1954).

## Ranking tests of standard statistical situations

**13.9** The ideas underlying the formation of ranking coefficients, especially the coefficient $\tau$, can be applied to a number of situations which often occur in statistical analysis. We may notice five of them.

(a) *Tests of independence.* Given $n$ pairs of observations $(x_1, y_1) \ldots (x_n, y_n)$ it may be desired to test whether the distribution of $x$'s is independent of that of the $y$'s. Simple tests based on $\tau$ or

$\rho_s$ themselves may be used. A more sophisticated test has been given by Hoeffding (1948).

(b) *Tests of homogeneity in two samples.* The test of **3.12** has been developed from a different point of view by Wilcoxon (1945) and by Mann and Whitney (1947) and is usually known as Wilcoxon's test. Effectively it tests the homogeneity of two samples by considering the proportion of cases in which members of one exceed members of the other, and is formally reducible to the test of $\tau$ for a two-fold classification.

(c) *Tests of homogeneity in k samples.* The tests for two samples are not easily extensible to more than two samples. Terpstra (1952) and Jonckheere (1953) have generalised Wilcoxon's test in certain ways, the test again being fundamentally one of $\tau$ with ties in one ranking. Kruskal and Wallis (1952) also discussed the case and have reviewed the earlier literature.

(d) *Tests of trend in time-series.* A set of observations which are ordered in time can be tested for trend by considering the correlation between the rank order of the observed values and the time-order, as in Example 1.1. Mann (1945) has discussed two possibilities and their relative merits, and Stuart (1954) has considered others. See also Cox and Stuart (1955).

(e) *Fitting of functional relationships.* One of the most difficult problems of statistics arises in the fitting of functional relationships to variables all of which are subject to error. The classical methods of dealing with the problem involve making certain assumptions about the error variances. Theil (1950) has recently shown that the problem may also be tackled successfully without such assumptions by the use of methods based on order properties.

## Reduction of paired comparisons to ranks

**13.10** In some situations where extensive paired comparisons are obtained, it is necessary to summarise the final results in ranking form; as, for example, in taste testing, where it may be desired ultimately to rank a set of objects in order of general preference. Wei (1952) and I (1955) have discussed a method of dealing with the situation; and I have also considered the problem of reducing the number of paired comparisons required by the use of balanced experimental designs.

## The efficiency and power of ranking methods

**13.11** The scope of this book did not permit us to enlarge on the efficiency and power of ranking methods in the sense of the modern theory of testing hypotheses, except that we have incidentally touched on the relative efficiencies of $\tau$ and $\rho_s$ for estimating the correlation parameter in bivariate normal populations. A good deal of work has been done on these matters in recent years. Broadly speaking, a method of estimation or test which uses ranks gains in generality by not being dependent on the distributional form of the parent populations, but it may suffer a corresponding loss of efficiency or power. This is only natural; a tool which has many purposes is not usually as efficient for any one of them as a specialized tool developed solely for a single purpose. On the other hand, there are situations where the power of rank-order tests is surprisingly high and little seems to be lost by employing ranking methods. For some results in this field see Stuart (1954*b*).

**13.12** The references which follow cover the ground fairly completely, but the student who wishes to go fully into the subject may also like to consult the bibliographies by van Dantzig and Hemelrijk (1955) and by I. R. Savage (1954).

# REFERENCES


Benard, A., and van Elteren, Ph. (1953). A generalization of the method of $m$ rankings. *Kon. Ned. Ak. Wet.*, A, 56, No. 4 and *Indag. Math.*, **15**, No. 4.

Bradley, R. A., and Terry, M. E. (1952). The rank analysis of incomplete block designs. I. The method of paired comparisons. *Biometrika*, **39**, 324.

Bradley, R. A. (1954). The rank analysis of incomplete block designs. II. Additional tables for the method of paired comparisons. *Biometrika*, **41**, 502.

Chambers, E. G. (1946). Statistical techniques in applied psychology. *Biometrika*, **33**, 269.

Cox, D. R., and Stuart, A. (1955). Some quick sign tests for trend in location and dispersion. *Biometrika*, **42**.

Daniels, H. E. (1944). The relation between measures of correlation in the universe of sample permutations. *Biometrika*, **33**, 129.

Daniels, H. E. (1948). A property of rank correlations. *Biometrika*, **35**, 416.

Daniels, H. E. (1950). Rank correlation and population models. *J. Roy. Statist. Soc.*, B, **12**, 171.

Daniels, H. E. (1951). Note on Durbin and Stuart's formula for $E(r_s)$. *J. Roy. Statist. Soc.*, B, **13**, 310.

Daniels, H. E., and Kendall, M. G. (1947). The significance of rank correlations where parental correlation exists. *Biometrika*, **34**, 197.

Dantzig, G. B. (1939). On a class of distributions that approach the normal distribution function. *Ann. Math. Statist.*, **10**, 247.

David, S. T., and others (1951). Some questions of distribution in the theory of rank correlation. *Biometrika*, **38**, 131.

Dixon, W. J. (1953). Power functions of the sign test and power efficiency for normal alternatives. *Ann. Math. Statist.*, **24**, 467.

Dubois, P. (1939). Formulas and tables for rank correlation. *Psych. Rec.*, **3**, 46.

Durbin, J. (1951). Incomplete blocks in ranking experiments. *Brit. J. Psych.* (Stat. Section), **4**, 85.

Durbin, J., and Stuart, A. (1951). Inversions and rank correlation coefficients. *J. Roy. Statist. Soc.*, B, **13**, 303.

Eells, W. C. (1929). Formulas for probable errors of coefficients of correlation. *J. Am. Stat. Ass.*, **24**, 170.

Ehrenberg, A. S. C. (1952). On sampling from a population of rankers. *Biometrika*, **39**, 82.

Esscher, F. (1924). On a method of determining correlation from the ranks of variates. *Skand. Akt.* **7**, 201.

Feller, W. (1945). Limit theorems in probability. *Bull. Am. Math. Soc.*, **51**, 800.

Friedman, M. (1937). The use of ranks to avoid the assumption of normality implicit in the analysis of variance. *J. Am. Stat. Ass.*, **32**, 675.

Friedman, M. (1940). A comparison of alternative tests of significance for the problem of $m$ rankings. *Ann. Math. Statist.*, **11**, 86.

Greiner, R. (1909). Über das Fehlersystem der Kollektivmasslehre. *Zeitschrift für Mathematik und Physik*, **57**, 121, 225 and 337.

Guttman, L. (1946). An approach for quantifying paired comparisons and rank order. *Ann. Math. Statist.*, **17**, 144.

Haden, H. G. (1947). A note on the distribution of the different orderings of $n$ objects. *Proc. Camb. Phil. Soc.*, **43**, 1.

Hoeffding, W. (1947). On the distribution of the rank correlation coefficient $\tau$ when the variates are not independent. *Biometrika*, **34**, 183.

Hoeffding, W. (1948). A class of statistics with asymptotically normal distribution. *Ann. Math. Statist.*, **19**, 293.

Hoeffding, W. (1948). A non-parametric test of independence. *Ann. Math. Statist.*, **19**, 546.

Hoeffding, W. (1951). Optimum non-parametric tests. *Second Berkeley Symposium*, University of California Press.

Hoeffding, W. (1952). The large sample power of tests based on permutations of observations. *Ann. Math. Statist.*, **23**, 169.

Hotelling, H., and Pabst, M. R. (1936). Rank correlation and tests of significance involving no assumptions of normality. *Ann. Math. Statist.*, **7**, 29.

Irwin, J. O. (1925). The further theory of Francis Galton's individual difference problem. *Biometrika*, **17**, 100.

Jonkheere, A. R. (1954). A distribution-free $k$-sample test against ordered alternatives. *Biometrika*, **41**, 133.

Kaarsemaker, L., and Van Wijngaarden, A. (1952). *Tables for use in rank correlation.* Report R 73, Computation Mathematical Centre, Amsterdam.

Kendall, M. G. (1938). A new measure of rank correlation. *Biometrika*, **30**, 81.

Kendall, M. G. (1942*a*). Partial rank correlation. *Biometrika*, **32**, 277.

Kendall, M. G. (1942*b*). Note on the estimation of a ranking. *J. Roy. Statist. Soc.*, **105**, 119.

Kendall, M. G. (1943). *The Advanced Theory of Statistics*, Vol. 1 (5th edition, 1954). Vol. 2 (3rd edition, 1955). London : Charles Griffin & Co.

Kendall, M. G. (1945). The treatment of ties in ranking problems. *Biometrika*, **33**, 239.

Kendall, M. G. (1947). The variance of $\tau$ when both rankings contain ties. *Biometrika*, **34**, 297.

Kendall, M. G. (1949). Rank and product-moment correlation. *Biometrika*, **36**, 177.

Kendall, M. G., and others (1939). The distribution of Spearman's coefficient of rank correlation, etc. *Biometrika*, **30**, 251.

Kendall, M. G., and Babington Smith, B. (1939). The problem of $m$ rankings. *Ann. Math. Statist.*, **10**, 275.

Kendall, M. G., and Babington Smith, B. (1940). On the method of paired comparisons. *Biometrika*, **31**, 324.

Kendall, M. G. (1955). Further contributions to the theory of paired comparisons. *Biometrics.*, **11**, 43.

Kruskal, W. H. (1952). A non-parametric test for the several sample problem. *Ann. Math. Statist.*, **23**, 525.

Kruskal, W. H., and Wallis, W. A. (1952). Use of ranks in one-criterion variance-analysis. *J. Am. Stat. Ass.*, **47**, 583.

Lehmann, E. L. (1951). Consistency and unbiasedness of certain non-parametric tests. *Ann. Math. Statist.*, **22**, 155.

Lehmann, E. L. (1953). The power of rank tests. *Ann. Math. Statist.*, **24**, 23.

Mann, H. B. (1945). Non-parametric tests against trend. *Econometrica*, **13**, 245.

Mann, H. B., and Whitney, D. R. (1947). On a test of whether one of two random variables is larger than the other. *Ann. Math. Statist.*, **15**, 50.

MORAN, P. A. P. (1947). On the method of paired comparisons. *Biometrika*, **34**, 363.

MORAN, P. A. P. (1948). Rank correlation and permutation distributions. *Proc. Camb. Phil. Soc.*, **44**, 142.

MORAN, P. A. P. (1948). Rank correlations and product-moment correlation. *Biometrika*, **35**, 203.

MORAN, P. A. P. (1950*a*). Recent developments in ranking theory. *J. Roy. Statist. Soc.*, B, **12**, 153.

MORAN, P. A. P. (1950*b*). A curvilinear ranking test. *J. Roy. Statist. Soc.*, **12**, 292.

MORAN, P. A. P. (1951). Partial and multiple rank correlation. *Biometrika*, **38**, 26.

MOSTELLER, F. (1951*a*, *b*, *c*). Remarks on the method of paired comparisons. *Psychometrika*, **15**, 3 ; **16**, 203 ; **16**, 207.

MUHSAM, H. V. (1954). A probability approach to ties in rank correlation. *Bull. Res. Council of Israel*, **3**, 321.

OLDS, E. G. (1938). Distribution of sums of squares of rank differences for small numbers of individuals. *Ann. Math. Statist.*, **9**, 133.

PEARSON, K. (1907). Mathematical contributions to the theory of evolution. XVI. On further methods of determining correlation. *Drapers' Co. Res. Mem., Biometric Series IV*. Cambridge University Press.

PEARSON, K. (1914, 1921). On an extension of the method of correlation by grades or ranks. *Biometrika*, **10**, 416, and Second note, *ibid.*, **13**, 302.

PEARSON, K., and PEARSON, M. V. (1931, 1932). On the mean character and variance of a ranked individual, and on the mean and variance of the intervals between ranked individuals. *Biometrika*, **23**, 364, and **24**, 203.

PITMAN, E. J. G. (1937, 1938). Significance tests which may be applied to samples from any populations. *Supp. J. R. Stat. Soc.*, **4**, 119. II. The correlation coefficient test. *Supp. J. R. Stat. Soc.*, **4**, 225. III. The analysis of variance test. *Biometrika*, **29**, 332.

SAVAGE, I. R. (1952). Bibliography of non-parametric statistics and related topics. *National Bureau of Standards, Washington D.C., Report 182.*

SAVAGE, I. R. (1954). Contributions to the theory of rank order statistics. *Memorandum for private circulation.*

SILLITTO, G. P. (1947). The distribution of Kendall's $\tau$ coefficient of rank correlation in rankings containing ties. *Biometrika*, **34**, 36.

SILVERSTONE, H. (1950). A note on the cumulants of Kendall's S-distribution. *Biometrika*, **37**, 231.

SMITH, B. BABINGTON (1950). Discussion of Professor Ross's paper. *J. Roy. Statist. Soc.*, B, **12**, 54.

SPEARMAN, C. (1904). The proof and measurement of association between two things. *Am. J. Psych.*, **15**, 88.

SPEARMAN, C. (1906). A footrule for measuring correlation. *Brit. J. Psych.*, **2**, 89.

SPEARMAN, C. (1910). Correlation calculated from faulty data. *Brit. J. Psych.*, **3**, 271.

STUART, A. (1951). An application of the distribution of the ranking concordance coefficient. *Biometrika*, **38**, 33.

STUART, A. (1953). The estimation and comparison of strengths of association in contingency tables. *Biometrika*, **40**, 105.

STUART, A. (1954*a*). The correlation between variate-values and ranks in samples from a continuous distribution. *Brit. J. Psych.* (Stat. Section), **7**, 37.

STUART, A. (1954*b*). The asymptotic relative efficiency of distribution-free tests of randomness against normal alternatives. *J. Am. Stat. Ass.*, **49**, 147.

"STUDENT" (1921). An experimental determination of the probable error of Dr. Spearman's correlation coefficient. *Biometrika*, **13**, 263.

SUNDRUM, R. M. (1953). *Theory and Applications of Distribution-Free Methods in Statistics*, Ph.D. Thesis, London University.

SUNDRUM, R. M. (1953*a*). Moments of the rank correlation coefficient $\tau$ in the general case. *Biometrika*, **40**, 409.

SUNDRUM, R. M. (1953*b*). A method of systematic sampling based on order properties. *Biometrika*, **40**, 452.

SUNDRUM, R. M. (1953*c*). The power of Wilcoxon's two-sample test. *J. Roy. Soc.*, B, **15**, 246.

TERPSTRA, T. J. (1952). The asymptotic normality and consistency of Kendall's test against trend when ties are present in one ranking. *Proc. Kon. Ned. Ak. Wet.*, A, 55, *Indag. Math.*, **14**, 327.

TERRY, M. E. (1952). Some rank order tests which are most powerful against specific alternatives. *Ann. Math. Statist.*, **23**, 346.

THEIL, H. (1950). A rank invariant method of linear and polynomial regression analysis. *Proc. Kon. Ned. Ak. v. Wet.*, **53**, 386, 521, 1397.

VAN DANTZIG, D. (1951). On the consistency and the power of Wilcoxon's two-sample test. *Proc. Kon. Ned. Ak. v. Wet.*, **54**, 172.

VAN DANTZIG, D. and HEMELRIJK, J. (1954). Statistical methods based on few assumptions. *Bull. Int. Stat. Inst.*, **34**, 2$^{me}$ livraison, 239.

VAN DER VAART, H. R. (1950). Some remarks on the power function of Wilcoxon's test for the problem of two samples. *Proc. Kon. Ned. Ak. v. Wet.*, **53**, 494 and 507.

VAN DER WAERDEN, B. L. (1952). Order tests for the two-sample problem and their power. *Proc. Kon. Ned. Ak. v. Wet*, **55**, 453 (Corrigenda, **56**, 80).

WALLIS, W. A. (1939). The correlation ratio for ranked data. *J. Am. Stat. Ass.*, **34**, 533.

WATKINS, G. P. (1933). An ordinal index of correlation. *J. Am. Stat. Ass.*, **28**, 139.

WEI, T. H. (1952). The Algebraic Foundations of Ranking Theory. Ph.D. thesis. Cambridge University.

WELCH, B. L. (1937). On the *z*-test in randomised blocks and Latin Squares. *Biometrika*, **29**, 21.

WHITFIELD, J. W. (1947). Rank correlation between two variables, one of which is ranked, the other dichotomous. *Biometrika*, **34**, 292.

WHITFIELD, J. W. (1950). Uses of the ranking method in psychology. *J. Roy. Statist. Soc.*, **12**, 163.

WILCOXON, F. (1945). Individual comparisons by ranking methods. *Biometrics*, **1**, 80.

WOODBURY, M. A. (1940). Rank correlation when there are equal variates. *Ann. Math. Stats.*, **11**, 358.

# APPENDIX TABLE 1

PROBABILITY THAT $S$ (FOR $\tau$) ATTAINS OR EXCEEDS A SPECIFIED VALUE. (SHOWN ONLY FOR POSITIVE VALUES. NEGATIVE VALUES OBTAINABLE BY SYMMETRY)

| $S$ | Values of $n$ | | | | $S$ | Values of $n$ | | |
|---|---|---|---|---|---|---|---|---|
| | 4 | 5 | 8 | 9 | | 6 | 7 | 10 |
| 0 | 0·625 | 0·592 | 0·548 | 0·540 | 1 | 0·500 | 0·500 | 0·500 |
| 2 | 0·375 | 0·408 | 0·452 | 0·460 | 3 | 0·360 | 0·386 | 0·431 |
| 4 | 0·167 | 0·242 | 0·360 | 0·381 | 5 | 0·235 | 0·281 | 0·364 |
| 6 | 0·042 | 0·117 | 0·274 | 0·306 | 7 | 0·136 | 0·191 | 0·300 |
| 8 | | 0·042 | 0·199 | 0·238 | 9 | 0·068 | 0·119 | 0·242 |
| 10 | | $0{\cdot}0^{2}83$ | 0·138 | 0·179 | 11 | 0·028 | 0·068 | 0·190 |
| 12 | | | 0·089 | 0·130 | 13 | $0{\cdot}0^{2}83$ | 0·035 | 0·146 |
| 14 | | | 0·054 | 0·090 | 15 | $0{\cdot}0^{2}14$ | 0·015 | 0·108 |
| 16 | | | 0·031 | 0·060 | 17 | | $0{\cdot}0^{2}54$ | 0·078 |
| 18 | | | 0·016 | 0·038 | 19 | | $0{\cdot}0^{2}14$ | 0·054 |
| 20 | | | $0{\cdot}0^{2}71$ | 0·022 | 21 | | $0{\cdot}0^{3}20$ | 0·036 |
| 22 | | | $0{\cdot}0^{2}28$ | 0·012 | 23 | | | 0·023 |
| 24 | | | $0{\cdot}0^{3}87$ | $0{\cdot}0^{2}63$ | 25 | | | 0·014 |
| 26 | | | $0{\cdot}0^{3}19$ | $0{\cdot}0^{2}29$ | 27 | | | $0{\cdot}0^{2}83$ |
| 28 | | | $0{\cdot}0^{4}25$ | $0{\cdot}0^{2}12$ | 29 | | | $0{\cdot}0^{2}46$ |
| 30 | | | | $0{\cdot}0^{3}43$ | 31 | | | $0{\cdot}0^{2}23$ |
| 32 | | | | $0{\cdot}0^{3}12$ | 33 | | | $0{\cdot}0^{2}11$ |
| 34 | | | | $0{\cdot}0^{4}25$ | 35 | | | $0{\cdot}0^{3}47$ |
| 36 | | | | $0{\cdot}0^{5}28$ | 37 | | | $0{\cdot}0^{3}18$ |
| | | | | | 39 | | | $0{\cdot}0^{4}58$ |
| | | | | | 41 | | | $0{\cdot}0^{4}15$ |
| | | | | | 43 | | | $0{\cdot}0^{5}28$ |
| | | | | | 45 | | | $0{\cdot}0^{6}28$ |

*Note.*—Repeated zeros are indicated by powers, *e.g.* $0{\cdot}0^{3}47$ stands for 0·00047.

# APPENDIX TABLE 2

PROBABILITY FUNCTION OF $S(d^2)$ (FOR $\rho$)

| $n = 4$ | | $n = 5$ | | $n = 6$ | | $n = 7$ | | $n = 8$ | | $n = 9$ | | $n = 10$ | |
|---|---|---|---|---|---|---|---|---|---|---|---|---|---|
| $S$ | $P$ | $S$ | $P$ | $S$ | $P$ | $S$ | $P$ | $S$ | $P$ | $S$ | $P$ | $S$ | $P$ |
| 12 | 458 | 22 | 475 | 36 | 500 | 58 | 482 | 86 | 488 | 122 | 491 | 166 | 500 |
| 14 | 375 | 24 | 392 | 38 | 460 | 60 | 453 | 88 | 467 | 124 | 474 | 168 | 486 |
| 16 | 208 | 26 | 342 | 40 | 401 | 62 | 420 | 90 | 441 | 126 | 456 | 170 | 473 |
| 18 | 167 | 28 | 258 | 42 | 357 | 64 | 391 | 92 | 420 | 128 | 440 | 172 | 459 |
| 20 | 042 | 30 | 225 | 44 | 320 | 66 | 357 | 94 | 397 | 130 | 422 | 174 | 446 |
| | | 32 | 175 | 46 | 282 | 68 | 331 | 96 | 376 | 132 | 405 | 176 | 433 |
| | | 34 | 117 | 48 | 249 | 70 | 297 | 98 | 352 | 134 | 388 | 178 | 419 |
| | | 36 | 067 | 50 | 210 | 72 | 278 | 100 | 332 | 136 | 372 | 180 | 406 |
| | | 38 | 042 | 52 | 178 | 74 | 249 | 102 | 310 | 138 | 354 | 182 | 393 |
| | | 40 | $0^{2}83$ | 54 | 149 | 76 | 222 | 104 | 291 | 140 | 339 | 184 | 379 |
| | | | | 56 | 121 | 78 | 198 | 106 | 268 | 142 | 322 | 186 | 367 |
| | | | | 58 | 088 | 80 | 177 | 108 | 250 | 144 | 307 | 188 | 354 |
| | | | | 60 | 068 | 82 | 151 | 110 | 231 | 146 | 290 | 190 | 341 |
| | | | | 62 | 051 | 84 | 133 | 112 | 214 | 148 | 276 | 192 | 328 |
| | | | | 64 | 029 | 86 | 118 | 114 | 195 | 150 | 260 | 194 | 316 |
| | | | | 66 | 017 | 88 | 100 | 116 | 180 | 152 | 247 | 196 | 304 |
| | | | | 68 | $0^{2}83$ | 90 | 083 | 118 | 163 | 154 | 231 | 198 | 292 |
| | | | | 70 | $0^{2}14$ | 92 | 069 | 120 | 150 | 156 | 218 | 200 | 280 |
| | | | | | | 94 | 055 | 122 | 134 | 158 | 205 | 202 | 268 |
| | | | | | | 96 | 044 | 124 | 122 | 160 | 193 | 204 | 257 |
| | | | | | | 98 | 033 | 126 | 108 | 162 | 179 | 206 | 246 |
| | | | | | | 100 | 024 | 128 | 098 | 164 | 168 | 208 | 235 |
| | | | | | | 102 | 017 | 130 | 085 | 166 | 156 | 210 | 224 |
| | | | | | | 104 | 012 | 132 | 076 | 168 | 146 | 212 | 214 |
| | | | | | | 106 | $0^{2}62$ | 134 | 066 | 170 | 135 | 214 | 203 |
| | | | | | | 108 | $0^{2}34$ | 136 | 057 | 172 | 125 | 216 | 193 |
| | | | | | | 110 | $0^{2}14$ | 138 | 048 | 174 | 115 | 218 | 184 |
| | | | | | | 112 | $0^{3}20$ | 140 | 042 | 176 | 106 | 220 | 174 |
| | | | | | | | | 142 | 035 | 178 | 097 | 222 | 165 |
| | | | | | | | | 144 | 029 | 180 | 089 | 224 | 156 |
| | | | | | | | | 146 | 023 | 182 | 081 | 226 | 148 |

*Notes.*—Decimal points are omitted from the values of $P$, *e.g.* for $n = 4$, $S = 20$ the value of $P$ is 0·042.

As the distribution of $S(d^2)$ is symmetrical, only values of $P \geqslant \frac{1}{2}$ are shown. For values of $S(d^2)$ lower than those shown enter the table with $22 - S(d^2)$ for $n = 4$, $42 - S(d^2)$ for $n = 5$, $72 - S(d^2)$ for $n = 6$, $114 - S(d^2)$ for $n = 7$, $170 - S(d^2)$ for $n = 8$, $242 - S(d^2)$ for $n = 9$ and $332 - S(d^2)$ for $n = 10$. For example, with $n = 7$, $S(d^2) = 24$ the value of $P$ is $1 - 0{\cdot}083 = 0{\cdot}917$.

APPENDIX TABLE 2—*continued*

| $n = 8$ | | $n = 9$ | | $n = 10$ | | $n = 10$ | |
|---|---|---|---|---|---|---|---|
| *S* | *P* | *S* | *P* | *S* | *P* | *S* | *P* |
| 148 | 018 | 184 | 074 | 228 | 139 | 286 | 010 |
| 150 | 014 | 186 | 066 | 230 | 132 | 288 | $0^{2}87$ |
| 152 | 011 | 188 | 060 | 232 | 124 | 290 | $0^{2}75$ |
| 154 | $0^{2}77$ | 190 | 054 | 234 | 116 | 292 | $0^{2}73$ |
| 156 | $0^{2}54$ | 192 | 048 | 236 | 109 | 294 | $0^{2}53$ |
| 158 | $0^{2}36$ | 194 | 043 | 238 | 102 | 296 | $0^{2}44$ |
| 160 | $0^{2}23$ | 196 | 038 | 240 | 096 | 298 | $0^{2}36$ |
| 162 | $0^{2}11$ | 198 | 033 | 242 | 089 | 300 | $0^{2}29$ |
| 164 | $0^{3}57$ | 200 | 029 | 244 | 083 | 302 | $0^{2}24$ |
| 166 | $0^{3}20$ | 202 | 025 | 246 | 077 | 304 | $0^{2}19$ |
| 168 | $0^{4}25$ | 204 | 022 | 248 | 072 | 306 | $0^{2}14$ |
| | | 206 | 018 | 250 | 067 | 308 | $0^{2}11$ |
| | | 208 | 016 | 252 | 062 | 310 | $0^{3}80$ |
| | | 210 | 013 | 254 | 057 | 312 | $0^{3}57$ |
| | | 212 | 011 | 256 | 052 | 314 | $0^{3}40$ |
| | | 214 | $0^{2}86$ | 258 | 048 | 316 | $0^{3}27$ |
| | | 216 | $0^{2}69$ | 260 | 044 | 318 | $0^{3}17$ |
| | | 218 | $0^{2}54$ | 262 | 040 | 320 | $0^{3}10$ |
| | | 220 | $0^{2}41$ | 264 | 037 | 322 | $0^{4}54$ |
| | | 222 | $0^{2}30$ | 266 | 033 | 324 | $0^{4}25$ |
| | | 224 | $0^{2}22$ | 268 | 030 | 326 | $0^{4}10$ |
| | | 226 | $0^{2}15$ | 270 | 027 | 328 | $0^{5}28$ |
| | | 228 | $0^{2}10$ | 272 | 025 | 330 | $0^{6}28$ |
| | | 230 | $0^{3}66$ | 274 | 022 | | |
| | | 232 | $0^{3}37$ | 276 | 019 | | |
| | | 234 | $0^{3}18$ | 278 | 017 | | |
| | | 236 | $0^{4}83$ | 280 | 015 | | |
| | | 238 | $0^{4}25$ | 282 | 013 | | |
| | | 240 | $0^{5}28$ | 284 | 012 | | |

# APPENDIX TABLE 3

## Areas under the Normal Curve (Probability Function of the Normal Distribution)

The table shows the area of the curve $y = \frac{1}{\sqrt{(2\pi)}}e^{-\frac{1}{2}x^2}$ lying to the left of specified deviates $x$; *e.g.* the area corresponding to a deviate 1·86 (= 1·5 + 0·36) is 0·9686.

| Deviate | 0· + | 0·5 + | 1·0 + | 1·5 + | 2·0 + | 2·5 + | 3·0 + | 3·5 + |
|---|---|---|---|---|---|---|---|---|
| 0·00 | 5000 | 6915 | 8413 | 9332 | 9772 | $9^{2}379$ | $9^{2}865$ | $9^{3}77$ |
| 0·01 | 5040 | 6950 | 8438 | 9345 | 9778 | $9^{2}396$ | $9^{2}869$ | $9^{3}78$ |
| 0·02 | 5080 | 6985 | 8461 | 9357 | 9783 | $9^{2}413$ | $9^{2}874$ | $9^{3}78$ |
| 0·03 | 5120 | 7019 | 8485 | 9370 | 9788 | $9^{2}430$ | $9^{2}878$ | $9^{3}79$ |
| 0·04 | 5160 | 7054 | 8508 | 9382 | 9793 | $9^{2}446$ | $9^{2}882$ | $9^{3}80$ |
| 0·05 | 5199 | 7088 | 8531 | 9394 | 9798 | $9^{2}461$ | $9^{2}886$ | $9^{3}81$ |
| 0·06 | 5239 | 7123 | 8554 | 9406 | 9803 | $9^{2}477$ | $9^{2}889$ | $9^{3}81$ |
| 0·07 | 5279 | 7157 | 8577 | 9418 | 9808 | $9^{2}492$ | $9^{2}893$ | $9^{3}82$ |
| 0·08 | 5319 | 7190 | 8599 | 9429 | 9812 | $9^{2}506$ | $9^{2}897$ | $9^{3}83$ |
| 0·09 | 5359 | 7224 | 8621 | 9441 | 9817 | $9^{2}520$ | $9^{2}900$ | $9^{3}83$ |
| 0·10 | 5398 | 7257 | 8643 | 9452 | 9821 | $9^{2}534$ | $9^{3}03$ | $9^{3}84$ |
| 0·11 | 5438 | 7291 | 8665 | 9463 | 9826 | $9^{2}547$ | $9^{3}06$ | $9^{3}85$ |
| 0·12 | 5478 | 7324 | 8686 | 9474 | 9830 | $9^{2}560$ | $9^{3}10$ | $9^{3}85$ |
| 0·13 | 5517 | 7357 | 8708 | 9484 | 9834 | $9^{2}573$ | $9^{3}13$ | $9^{3}86$ |
| 0·14 | 5557 | 7389 | 8729 | 9495 | 9838 | $9^{2}585$ | $9^{3}16$ | $9^{3}86$ |
| 0·15 | 5596 | 7422 | 8749 | 9505 | 9842 | $9^{2}598$ | $9^{3}18$ | $9^{3}87$ |
| 0·16 | 5636 | 7454 | 8770 | 9515 | 9846 | $9^{2}609$ | $9^{3}21$ | $9^{3}87$ |
| 0·17 | 5675 | 7486 | 8790 | 9525 | 9850 | $9^{2}621$ | $9^{3}24$ | $9^{3}88$ |
| 0·18 | 5714 | 7517 | 8810 | 9535 | 9854 | $9^{2}632$ | $9^{3}26$ | $9^{3}88$ |
| 0·19 | 5753 | 7549 | 8830 | 9545 | 9857 | $9^{2}643$ | $9^{3}29$ | $9^{3}89$ |
| 0·20 | 5793 | 7580 | 8849 | 9554 | 9861 | $9^{2}653$ | $9^{3}31$ | $9^{3}89$ |
| 0·21 | 5832 | 7611 | 8869 | 9564 | 9864 | $9^{2}664$ | $9^{3}34$ | $9^{3}90$ |
| 0·22 | 5871 | 7642 | 8888 | 9573 | 9868 | $9^{2}674$ | $9^{3}36$ | $9^{3}90$ |
| 0·23 | 5910 | 7673 | 8907 | 9582 | 9871 | $9^{2}683$ | $9^{3}38$ | $9^{4}04$ |
| 0·24 | 5948 | 7704 | 8925 | 9591 | 9875 | $9^{2}693$ | $9^{3}40$ | $9^{4}08$ |
| 0·25 | 5987 | 7738 | 8944 | 9599 | 9878 | $9^{2}702$ | $9^{3}42$ | $9^{4}12$ |
| 0·26 | 6026 | 7764 | 8962 | 9608 | 9881 | $9^{2}711$ | $9^{3}44$ | $9^{4}15$ |
| 0·27 | 6064 | 7794 | 8980 | 9616 | 9884 | $9^{2}720$ | $9^{3}46$ | $9^{4}18$ |
| 0·28 | 6103 | 7823 | 8997 | 9625 | 9887 | $9^{2}728$ | $9^{3}48$ | $9^{4}22$ |
| 0·29 | 6141 | 7852 | 9015 | 9633 | 9890 | $9^{2}736$ | $9^{3}50$ | $9^{4}25$ |
| 0·30 | 6179 | 7881 | 9032 | 9641 | 9893 | $9^{2}744$ | $9^{3}52$ | $9^{4}28$ |
| 0·31 | 6217 | 7910 | 9049 | 9649 | 9896 | $9^{2}752$ | $9^{3}53$ | $9^{4}31$ |
| 0·32 | 6255 | 7939 | 9066 | 9656 | 9898 | $9^{2}760$ | $9^{3}55$ | $9^{4}33$ |
| 0·33 | 6293 | 7967 | 9082 | 9664 | 9901 | $9^{2}767$ | $9^{3}57$ | $9^{4}36$ |
| 0·34 | 6331 | 7995 | 9099 | 9671 | 9904 | $9^{2}774$ | $9^{3}58$ | $9^{4}39$ |
| 0·35 | 6368 | 8023 | 9115 | 9678 | 9906 | $9^{2}781$ | $9^{3}60$ | $9^{4}41$ |
| 0·36 | 6406 | 8051 | 9131 | 9686 | 9909 | $9^{2}788$ | $9^{3}61$ | $9^{4}43$ |
| 0·37 | 6443 | 8078 | 9147 | 9693 | 9911 | $9^{2}795$ | $9^{3}62$ | $9^{4}46$ |
| 0·38 | 6480 | 8106 | 9162 | 9699 | 9913 | $9^{2}801$ | $9^{3}64$ | $9^{4}48$ |
| 0·39 | 6517 | 8133 | 9177 | 9706 | 9916 | $9^{2}807$ | $9^{3}65$ | $9^{4}50$ |
| 0·40 | 6554 | 8159 | 9192 | 9713 | 9918 | $9^{2}813$ | $9^{3}66$ | $9^{4}52$ |
| 0·41 | 6591 | 8186 | 9207 | 9719 | 9920 | $9^{2}819$ | $9^{3}68$ | $9^{4}54$ |
| 0·42 | 6628 | 8212 | 9222 | 9726 | 9922 | $9^{2}825$ | $9^{3}69$ | $9^{4}56$ |
| 0·43 | 6664 | 8238 | 9236 | 9732 | 9925 | $9^{2}831$ | $9^{3}70$ | $9^{4}58$ |
| 0·44 | 6700 | 8264 | 9251 | 9738 | 9927 | $9^{2}836$ | $9^{3}71$ | $9^{4}59$ |
| 0·45 | 6736 | 8289 | 9265 | 9744 | 9929 | $9^{2}841$ | $9^{3}72$ | $9^{4}61$ |
| 0·46 | 6772 | 8315 | 9279 | 9750 | 9931 | $9^{2}846$ | $9^{3}73$ | $9^{4}63$ |
| 0·47 | 6808 | 8340 | 9292 | 9756 | 9932 | $9^{2}851$ | $9^{3}74$ | $9^{4}64$ |
| 0·48 | 6844 | 8365 | 9306 | 9761 | 9934 | $9^{2}856$ | $9^{3}75$ | $9^{4}66$ |
| 0·49 | 6879 | 8389 | 9319 | 9767 | 9936 | $9^{2}861$ | $9^{3}76$ | $9^{4}67$ |

*Note.*—Decimal points in the body of the table are omitted. Repeated 9's are indicated by powers, *e.g.* $9^{3}71$ stands for 0·99971.

# APPENDIX TABLE 4

RANDOM RANKINGS OF 20 (RANDOM PERMUTATIONS OF THE FIRST TWENTY NATURAL NUMBERS)

| | | | | | | | | | | | | | | | | | | | |
|---|---|---|---|---|---|---|---|---|---|---|---|---|---|---|---|---|---|---|---|
| 4 | 19 | 15 | 10 | 13 | 3 | 11 | 18 | 1 | 8 | 7 | 2 | 14 | 17 | 12 | 9 | 6 | 20 | 5 | 16 |
| 16 | 14 | 2 | 17 | 8 | 11 | 12 | 13 | 4 | 3 | 7 | 10 | 5 | 15 | 1 | 6 | 20 | 18 | 10 | 9 |
| 6 | 5 | 10 | 12 | 17 | 7 | 9 | 2 | 1 | 15 | 10 | 11 | 13 | 14 | 16 | 3 | 20 | 4 | 18 | 8 |
| 18 | 9 | 10 | 19 | 6 | 12 | 4 | 1 | 20 | 11 | 13 | 16 | 15 | 3 | 2 | 5 | 14 | 17 | 8 | 7 |
| 11 | 12 | 8 | 9 | 1 | 15 | 13 | 2 | 14 | 17 | 3 | 19 | 6 | 7 | 16 | 4 | 5 | 20 | 18 | 10 |
| | | | | | | | | | | | | | | | | | | | |
| 1 | 15 | 18 | 4 | 8 | 20 | 19 | 9 | 11 | 3 | 17 | 10 | 13 | 14 | 6 | 7 | 5 | 2 | 12 | 16 |
| 18 | 2 | 16 | 12 | 8 | 5 | 11 | 17 | 4 | 10 | 3 | 9 | 7 | 13 | 1 | 14 | 6 | 19 | 20 | 15 |
| 2 | 3 | 18 | 19 | 11 | 1 | 7 | 12 | 20 | 8 | 15 | 5 | 14 | 4 | 13 | 6 | 9 | 17 | 16 | 10 |
| 15 | 16 | 12 | 13 | 17 | 19 | 1 | 2 | 20 | 7 | 4 | 11 | 10 | 9 | 6 | 8 | 5 | 18 | 14 | 3 |
| 8 | 18 | 3 | 4 | 10 | 7 | 16 | 17 | 9 | 6 | 11 | 15 | 19 | 2 | 13 | 12 | 14 | 1 | 20 | 5 |
| | | | | | | | | | | | | | | | | | | | |
| 8 | 6 | 13 | 1 | 10 | 11 | 15 | 20 | 7 | 14 | 3 | 18 | 2 | 12 | 16 | 17 | 4 | 19 | 5 | 9 |
| 10 | 5 | 17 | 2 | 15 | 9 | 16 | 3 | 14 | 1 | 6 | 12 | 19 | 13 | 20 | 4 | 11 | 8 | 7 | 18 |
| 16 | 1 | 18 | 11 | 2 | 14 | 13 | 15 | 20 | 7 | 9 | 3 | 19 | 17 | 5 | 12 | 6 | 10 | 4 | 8 |
| 12 | 7 | 5 | 20 | 15 | 19 | 13 | 10 | 18 | 1 | 8 | 16 | 9 | 2 | 6 | 11 | 4 | 3 | 17 | 14 |
| 20 | 1 | 19 | 5 | 9 | 6 | 11 | 10 | 7 | 3 | 2 | 18 | 4 | 14 | 8 | 17 | 15 | 12 | 13 | 16 |
| | | | | | | | | | | | | | | | | | | | |
| 9 | 6 | 17 | 15 | 10 | 12 | 18 | 13 | 1 | 19 | 4 | 5 | 14 | 3 | 2 | 16 | 7 | 11 | 20 | 8 |
| 4 | 2 | 3 | 19 | 11 | 10 | 7 | 16 | 13 | 18 | 15 | 1 | 12 | 17 | 9 | 8 | 6 | 5 | 20 | 14 |
| 9 | 18 | 19 | 14 | 10 | 12 | 4 | 16 | 5 | 2 | 6 | 17 | 1 | 8 | 20 | 11 | 13 | 7 | 3 | 15 |
| 13 | 12 | 8 | 7 | 18 | 4 | 16 | 10 | 17 | 19 | 5 | 1 | 20 | 3 | 14 | 11 | 2 | 6 | 9 | 15 |
| 6 | 1 | 4 | 5 | 8 | 9 | 10 | 18 | 15 | 20 | 13 | 7 | 12 | 2 | 3 | 19 | 17 | 16 | 11 | 14 |
| | | | | | | | | | | | | | | | | | | | |
| 8 | 20 | 4 | 5 | 15 | 10 | 11 | 6 | 16 | 18 | 19 | 9 | 7 | 14 | 17 | 1 | 12 | 3 | 2 | 13 |
| 19 | 16 | 3 | 4 | 7 | 6 | 12 | 1 | 13 | 2 | 10 | 17 | 8 | 20 | 11 | 9 | 18 | 5 | 15 | 14 |
| 19 | 18 | 13 | 8 | 15 | 9 | 10 | 2 | 17 | 14 | 16 | 7 | 5 | 1 | 20 | 4 | 11 | 3 | 0 | 12 |
| 2 | 11 | 13 | 5 | 7 | 18 | 20 | 6 | 16 | 14 | 1 | 3 | 15 | 8 | 19 | 9 | 12 | 17 | 4 | 10 |
| 2 | 12 | 10 | 10 | 17 | 13 | 20 | 11 | 3 | 4 | 8 | 14 | 15 | 19 | 7 | 9 | 5 | 6 | 18 | 1 |
| | | | | | | | | | | | | | | | | | | | |
| 13 | 11 | 4 | 3 | 7 | 5 | 20 | 15 | 1 | 12 | 9 | 6 | 14 | 17 | 16 | 2 | 18 | 19 | 10 | 8 |
| 15 | 1 | 16 | 7 | 3 | 14 | 8 | 11 | 2 | 13 | 10 | 6 | 18 | 5 | 9 | 12 | 19 | 4 | 17 | 20 |
| 3 | 20 | 1 | 11 | 17 | 16 | 4 | 14 | 6 | 2 | 9 | 19 | 15 | 12 | 10 | 8 | 5 | 13 | 7 | 18 |
| 18 | 16 | 3 | 2 | 12 | 19 | 4 | 20 | 14 | 11 | 8 | 10 | 7 | 17 | 1 | 5 | 15 | 13 | 9 | 6 |
| 3 | 4 | 12 | 5 | 10 | 14 | 15 | 1 | 7 | 2 | 13 | 19 | 17 | 18 | 6 | 11 | 20 | 16 | 9 | 8 |
| | | | | | | | | | | | | | | | | | | | |
| 13 | 20 | 11 | 14 | 3 | 9 | 4 | 5 | 10 | 17 | 18 | 1 | 16 | 15 | 8 | 10 | 6 | 7 | 12 | 2 |
| 17 | 16 | 13 | 18 | 7 | 2 | 9 | 15 | 10 | 6 | 11 | 4 | 12 | 19 | 14 | 3 | 20 | 5 | 1 | 8 |
| 13 | 7 | 3 | 4 | 8 | 6 | 15 | 2 | 18 | 16 | 5 | 19 | 9 | 12 | 10 | 20 | 11 | 1 | 14 | 17 |
| 2 | 19 | 17 | 7 | 18 | 20 | 15 | 5 | 9 | 11 | 3 | 16 | 13 | 6 | 12 | 1 | 4 | 10 | 14 | 8 |
| 4 | 6 | 7 | 10 | 20 | 18 | 3 | 5 | 11 | 12 | 2 | 1 | 14 | 9 | 19 | 13 | 15 | 17 | 8 | 16 |
| | | | | | | | | | | | | | | | | | | | |
| 19 | 3 | 15 | 12 | 10 | 17 | 16 | 1 | 8 | 7 | 2 | 6 | 14 | 9 | 11 | 18 | 4 | 5 | 20 | 13 |
| 18 | 14 | 9 | 2 | 8 | 6 | 7 | 1 | 3 | 10 | 5 | 17 | 20 | 4 | 13 | 15. | 11 | 12 | 16 | 19 |
| 18 | 5 | 17 | 1 | 4 | 7 | 11 | 20 | 9 | 10 | 15 | 3 | 19 | 14 | 16 | 13 | 6 | 12 | 8 | 2 |
| 5 | 1 | 10 | 6 | 19 | 7 | 15 | 11 | 2 | 4 | 3 | 9 | 20 | 18 | 14 | 17 | 13 | 16 | 8 | 12 |
| 19 | 17 | 1 | 16 | 10 | 9 | 8 | 18 | 13 | 15 | 5 | 2 | 7 | 20 | 14 | 12 | 11 | 4 | 3 | 6 |
| | | | | | | | | | | | | | | | | | | | |
| 13 | 6 | 14 | 4 | 9 | 17 | 19 | 7 | 12 | 8 | 18 | 16 | 11 | 1 | 3 | 5 | 20 | 10 | 2 | 15 |
| 10 | 16 | 9 | 6 | 12 | 17 | 4 | 19 | 11 | 1 | 20 | 13 | 14 | 18 | 15 | 7 | 2 | 3 | 8 | 5 |
| 14 | 8 | 7 | 16 | 18 | 6 | 17 | 19 | 11 | 20 | 4 | 13 | 2 | 10 | 1 | 15 | 9 | 3 | 5 | 12 |
| 16 | 2 | 8 | 14 | 4 | 10 | 19 | 11 | 7 | 6 | 12 | 17 | 5 | 20 | 13 | 15 | 1 | 9 | 3 | 18 |
| 14 | 5 | 9 | 8 | 17 | 10 | 6 | 12 | 19 | 13 | 3 | 20 | 2 | 18 | 4 | 7 | 1 | 11 | 15 | 16 |
| | | | | | | | | | | | | | | | | | | | |
| 12 | 18 | 15 | 4 | 1 | 13 | 5 | 17 | 9 | 7 | 14 | 20 | 19 | 6 | 10 | 11 | 2 | 3 | 8 | 16 |
| 8 | 17 | 5 | 3 | 4 | 12 | 10 | 14 | 9 | 18 | 15 | 6 | 13 | 2 | 20 | 16 | 19 | 1 | 7 | 11 |
| 11 | 19 | 8 | 9 | 16 | 10 | 13 | 17 | 15 | 4 | 5 | 20 | 14 | 2 | 1 | 3 | 7 | 18 | 6 | 12 |
| 14 | 1 | 5 | 2 | 3 | 15 | 11 | 9 | 18 | 19 | 7 | 10 | 16 | 13 | 6 | 8 | 4 | 17 | 12 | 20 |
| 9 | 17 | 5 | 20 | 2 | 7 | 4 | 19 | 18 | 15 | 1 | 10 | 8 | 16 | 14 | 3 | 11 | 13 | 12 | 6 |

*Note.*—Random rankings of fewer than 20 can be derived merely by omitting unwanted ranks.

| | | | | | | | | | | | | | | | | | | | |
|---|---|---|---|---|---|---|---|---|---|---|---|---|---|---|---|---|---|---|---|
| 10 | 14 | 17 | 19 | 20 | 1 | 13 | 18 | 5 | 11 | 7 | 8 | 16 | 3 | 9 | 12 | 15 | 6 | 2 | 4 |
| 20 | 5 | 9 | 14 | 1 | 8 | 4 | 12 | 13 | 3 | 15 | 7 | 2 | 19 | 10 | 6 | 17 | 16 | 11 | 18 |
| 5 | 15 | 1 | 17 | 2 | 11 | 9 | 10 | 13 | 18 | 19 | 16 | 3 | 14 | 4 | 20 | 12 | 8 | 6 | 7 |
| 2 | 13 | 14 | 3 | 9 | 19 | 15 | 8 | 20 | 17 | 18 | 4 | 11 | 10 | 6 | 1 | 5 | 7 | 12 | 16 |
| 18 | 12 | 14 | 10 | 1 | 13 | 9 | 3 | 8 | 7 | 5 | 17 | 16 | 2 | 4 | 20 | 15 | 19 | 6 | 11 |
| | | | | | | | | | | | | | | | | | | | |
| 3 | 16 | 11 | 6 | 12 | 13 | 15 | 5 | 7 | 20 | 19 | 18 | 4 | 10 | 9 | 14 | 8 | 2 | 17 | 1 |
| 2 | 11 | 4 | 16 | 13 | 20 | 14 | 18 | 6 | 15 | 8 | 10 | 1 | 3 | 19 | 7 | 5 | 9 | 17 | 12 |
| 14 | 12 | 20 | 10 | 15 | 2 | 9 | 3 | 16 | 13 | 6 | 5 | 7 | 11 | 8 | 1 | 17 | 19 | 4 | 18 |
| 12 | 10 | 18 | 5 | 4 | 20 | 17 | 16 | 13 | 15 | 9 | 7 | 14 | 2 | 6 | 11 | 1 | 19 | 8 | 3 |
| 1 | 18 | 5 | 16 | 12 | 7 | 19 | 15 | 14 | 2 | 10 | 9 | 13 | 3 | 20 | 4 | 17 | 11 | 6 | 8 |
| | | | | | | | | | | | | | | | | | | | |
| 10 | 8 | 14 | 18 | 16 | 3 | 2 | 4 | 9 | 19 | 15 | 5 | 11 | 12 | 13 | 17 | 6 | 1 | 20 | 7 |
| 18 | 4 | 1 | 9 | 12 | 14 | 15 | 19 | 2 | 6 | 3 | 10 | 17 | 13 | 7 | 16 | 8 | 20 | 11 | 5 |
| 1 | 15 | 18 | 9 | 13 | 16 | 7 | 8 | 5 | 11 | 3 | 4 | 12 | 20 | 14 | 10 | 19 | 6 | 2 | 17 |
| 13 | 20 | 11 | 10 | 6 | 12 | 18 | 9 | 15 | 17 | 19 | 1 | 7 | 16 | 8 | 2 | 3 | 5 | 14 | 4 |
| 6 | 16 | 9 | 7 | 10 | 2 | 8 | 20 | 13 | 1 | 11 | 15 | 17 | 3 | 19 | 4 | 14 | 12 | 18 | 5 |
| | | | | | | | | | | | | | | | | | | | |
| 20 | 7 | 10 | 5 | 15 | 19 | 16 | 1 | 13 | 12 | 11 | 18 | 4 | 3 | 6 | 2 | 14 | 17 | 9 | 8 |
| 17 | 12 | 19 | 4 | 2 | 6 | 1 | 15 | 7 | 18 | 3 | 13 | 10 | 20 | 11 | 8 | 14 | 5 | 16 | 9 |
| 18 | 1 | 7 | 8 | 15 | 14 | 6 | 19 | 11 | 20 | 9 | 4 | 17 | 2 | 16 | 3 | 10 | 13 | 12 | 5 |
| 14 | 19 | 9 | 7 | 17 | 18 | 4 | 11 | 12 | 8 | 6 | 10 | 3 | 16 | 13 | 1 | 20 | 2 | 5 | 15 |
| 9 | 11 | 18 | 1 | 8 | 4 | 16 | 10 | 7 | 13 | 19 | 12 | 5 | 17 | 6 | 20 | 2 | 3 | 14 | 15 |
| | | | | | | | | | | | | | | | | | | | |
| 14 | 10 | 8 | 9 | 4 | 20 | 6 | 11 | 17 | 1 | 16 | 3 | 18 | 13 | 7 | 15 | 19 | 12 | 2 | 5 |
| 17 | 15 | 18 | 16 | 6 | 14 | 8 | 9 | 7 | 11 | 2 | 10 | 19 | 3 | 5 | 20 | 4 | 1 | 13 | 12 |
| 5 | 7 | 2 | 20 | 12 | 13 | 6 | 19 | 3 | 1 | 15 | 8 | 17 | 18 | 10 | 11 | 16 | 4 | 14 | 9 |
| 12 | 4 | 10 | 8 | 14 | 16 | 11 | 1 | 19 | 13 | 18 | 15 | 9 | 17 | 6 | 3 | 2 | 7 | 20 | 5 |
| 5 | 14 | 8 | 11 | 9 | 4 | 12 | 20 | 2 | 1 | 15 | 6 | 10 | 17 | 13 | 3 | 7 | 18 | 19 | 16 |
| | | | | | | | | | | | | | | | | | | | |
| 6 | 3 | 12 | 19 | 14 | 15 | 13 | 2 | 17 | 1 | 5 | 16 | 18 | 4 | 11 | 20 | 9 | 8 | 7 | 10 |
| 18 | 11 | 6 | 10 | 16 | 1 | 8 | 12 | 15 | 3 | 14 | 20 | 4 | 2 | 9 | 13 | 5 | 19 | 17 | 7 |
| 18 | 12 | 4 | 7 | 11 | 13 | 5 | 9 | 2 | 14 | 19 | 3 | 1 | 17 | 8 | 16 | 6 | 15 | 20 | 10 |
| 16 | 5 | 20 | 11 | 2 | 9 | 15 | 1 | 19 | 3 | 10 | 14 | 12 | 6 | 7 | 17 | 8 | 4 | 13 | 18 |
| 6 | 20 | 11 | 13 | 18 | 14 | 17 | 8 | 12 | 7 | 5 | 4 | 2 | 16 | 9 | 10 | 15 | 3 | 19 | 1 |
| | | | | | | | | | | | | | | | | | | | |
| 8 | 6 | 20 | 16 | 11 | 12 | 15 | 3 | 9 | 7 | 13 | 1 | 5 | 14 | 4 | 18 | 2 | 10 | 17 | 19 |
| 18 | 12 | 5 | 16 | 1 | 9 | 7 | 6 | 8 | 4 | 13 | 14 | 19 | 2 | 15 | 10 | 3 | 11 | 17 | 20 |
| 4 | 15 | 9 | 20 | 2 | 10 | 5 | 13 | 6 | 3 | 7 | 16 | 1 | 8 | 18 | 14 | 17 | 19 | 12 | 11 |
| 16 | 19 | 17 | 13 | 15 | 12 | 11 | 18 | 8 | 2 | 5 | 10 | 20 | 7 | 3 | 1 | 14 | 6 | 9 | 4 |
| 12 | 4 | 2 | 18 | 5 | 11 | 1 | 7 | 17 | 6 | 14 | 8 | 9 | 3 | 16 | 10 | 15 | 13 | 20 | 19 |
| | | | | | | | | | | | | | | | | | | | |
| 13 | 20 | 9 | 5 | 1 | 6 | 8 | 4 | 7 | 19 | 16 | 15 | 10 | 2 | 12 | 17 | 11 | 18 | 14 | 3 |
| 6 | 7 | 11 | 8 | 10 | 1 | 20 | 16 | 12 | 9 | 13 | 15 | 14 | 18 | 3 | 17 | 2 | 5 | 4 | 19 |
| 17 | 8 | 11 | 10 | 4 | 5 | 12 | 9 | 7 | 1 | 19 | 14 | 20 | 6 | 2 | 18 | 15 | 3 | 16 | 13 |
| 5 | 16 | 9 | 18 | 6 | 15 | 19 | 3 | 4 | 20 | 14 | 1 | 2 | 12 | 7 | 17 | 10 | 13 | 8 | 11 |
| 8 | 11 | 15 | 16 | 1 | 18 | 12 | 10 | 5 | 13 | 20 | 2 | 14 | 17 | 9 | 6 | 4 | 7 | 3 | 19 |
| | | | | | | | | | | | | | | | | | | | |
| 17 | 6 | 10 | 12 | 2 | 4 | 9 | 18 | 5 | 13 | 8 | 15 | 11 | 1 | 16 | 3 | 20 | 7 | 14 | 19 |
| 20 | 17 | 5 | 2 | 9 | 7 | 10 | 11 | 8 | 1 | 4 | 19 | 14 | 16 | 12 | 3 | 13 | 15 | 6 | 18 |
| 9 | 12 | 8 | 20 | 15 | 5 | 10 | 2 | 16 | 17 | 11 | 18 | 6 | 3 | 4 | 1 | 14 | 7 | 13 | 19 |
| 19 | 15 | 14 | 11 | 5 | 18 | 16 | 9 | 17 | 2 | 20 | 7 | 12 | 4 | 13 | 6 | 1 | 8 | 3 | 10 |
| 1 | 10 | 8 | 17 | 6 | 19 | 18 | 7 | 12 | 11 | 13 | 5 | 14 | 2 | 20 | 4 | 9 | 16 | 3 | 15 |
| | | | | | | | | | | | | | | | | | | | |
| 4 | 3 | 13 | 19 | 6 | 1 | 5 | 12 | 17 | 8 | 11 | 2 | 16 | 20 | 10 | 18 | 9 | 15 | 14 | 7 |
| 11 | 7 | 12 | 10 | 16 | 5 | 18 | 4 | 1 | 13 | 19 | 2 | 3 | 14 | 6 | 8 | 9 | 20 | 17 | 15 |
| 7 | 14 | 13 | 3 | 15 | 19 | 16 | 8 | 5 | 20 | 11 | 6 | 12 | 17 | 1 | 10 | 18 | 9 | 2 | 4 |
| 14 | 6 | 4 | 10 | 2 | 8 | 19 | 5 | 20 | 15 | 9 | 3 | 17 | 12 | 16 | 1 | 18 | 13 | 7 | 11 |
| 13 | 12 | 17 | 7 | 4 | 5 | 2 | 19 | 9 | 20 | 15 | 11 | 6 | 3 | 1 | 14 | 16 | 18 | 8 | 10 |
| | | | | | | | | | | | | | | | | | | | |
| 17 | 12 | 10 | 15 | 18 | 4 | 14 | 6 | 16 | 3 | 13 | 11 | 1 | 5 | 19 | 8 | 20 | 9 | 2 | 7 |
| 16 | 20 | 11 | 2 | 8 | 18 | 4 | 14 | 7 | 12 | 3 | 5 | 15 | 19 | 13 | 10 | 6 | 17 | 9 | 1 |
| 14 | 6 | 8 | 17 | 4 | 13 | 7 | 5 | 9 | 20 | 12 | 10 | 11 | 19 | 1 | 15 | 16 | 2 | 18 | 3 |
| 20 | 18 | 2 | 1 | 3 | 12 | 14 | 7 | 10 | 11 | 6 | 17 | 15 | 16 | 5 | 9 | 8 | 13 | 4 | 19 |
| 19 | 3 | 1 | 17 | 4 | 5 | 13 | 10 | 7 | 9 | 11 | 18 | 2 | 12 | 8 | 20 | 15 | 6 | 14 | 16 |
| | | | | | | | | | | | | | | | | | | | |
| 7 | 20 | 1 | 15 | 19 | 16 | 12 | 3 | 5 | 11 | 4 | 13 | 6 | 10 | 8 | 9 | 17 | 2 | 14 | 18 |
| 9 | 7 | 12 | 4 | 5 | 19 | 18 | 15 | 2 | 11 | 1 | 17 | 8 | 16 | 20 | 13 | 3 | 6 | 14 | 10 |
| 12 | 10 | 5 | 3 | 19 | 1 | 2 | 14 | 6 | 16 | 9 | 8 | 15 | 11 | 13 | 4 | 20 | 17 | 18 | 7 |
| 8 | 15 | 13 | 4 | 9 | 11 | 17 | 18 | 7 | 6 | 12 | 16 | 14 | 5 | 2 | 3 | 1 | 20 | 10 | 19 |
| 10 | 6 | 1 | 3 | 16 | 12 | 14 | 11 | 17 | 4 | 8 | 9 | 5 | 19 | 2 | 7 | 18 | 15 | 13 | 20 |

Appendix Table 4—*continued*

| | | | | | | | | | | | | | | | | | | | |
|---|---|---|---|---|---|---|---|---|---|---|---|---|---|---|---|---|---|---|---|
| 16 | 14 | 8 | 12 | 1 | 10 | 19 | 5 | 2 | 17 | 11 | 15 | 7 | 3 | 4 | 13 | 18 | 20 | 9 | 6 |
| 9 | 12 | 19 | 18 | 16 | 5 | 14 | 20 | 15 | 8 | 13 | 11 | 10 | 7 | 3 | 2 | 6 | 1 | 17 | 4 |
| 5 | 10 | 8 | 12 | 9 | 18 | 17 | 6 | 13 | 2 | 1 | 3 | 15 | 20 | 7 | 16 | 19 | 11 | 4 | 14 |
| 12 | 9 | 4 | 1 | 3 | 8 | 10 | 18 | 13 | 14 | 2 | 6 | 15 | 7 | 20 | 19 | 17 | 16 | 5 | 11 |
| 7 | 18 | 2 | 10 | 15 | 5 | 9 | 17 | 3 | 20 | 16 | 6 | 12 | 14 | 8 | 1 | 11 | 19 | 4 | 13 |
| 17 | 2 | 5 | 12 | 8 | 10 | 14 | 16 | 7 | 3 | 20 | 11 | 4 | 1 | 9 | 19 | 18 | 15 | 6 | 13 |
| 8 | 20 | 13 | 10 | 9 | 19 | 15 | 2 | 7 | 17 | 14 | 16 | 6 | 11 | 4 | 12 | 1 | 5 | 3 | 18 |
| 13 | 15 | 4 | 7 | 1 | 8 | 14 | 12 | 2 | 6 | 20 | 9 | 16 | 5 | 18 | 19 | 3 | 10 | 11 | 17 |
| 16 | 6 | 13 | 4 | 2 | 19 | 8 | 7 | 1 | 9 | 14 | 11 | 15 | 18 | 12 | 5 | 20 | 10 | 3 | 17 |
| 5 | 15 | 7 | 16 | 13 | 20 | 2 | 14 | 8 | 19 | 10 | 6 | 9 | 3 | 11 | 12 | 17 | 18 | 1 | 4 |
| 10 | 14 | 8 | 5 | 6 | 16 | 2 | 7 | 11 | 9 | 18 | 3 | 1 | 13 | 15 | 12 | 17 | 19 | 20 | 4 |
| 5 | 2 | 16 | 11 | 6 | 3 | 17 | 10 | 19 | 9 | 14 | 8 | 20 | 13 | 15 | 1 | 12 | 7 | 18 | 4 |
| 9 | 16 | 4 | 10 | 7 | 17 | 11 | 15 | 8 | 18 | 19 | 3 | 14 | 1 | 5 | 20 | 6 | 2 | 12 | 13 |
| 4 | 9 | 11 | 10 | 5 | 19 | 20 | 6 | 7 | 3 | 13 | 8 | 15 | 17 | 1 | 14 | 16 | 18 | 2 | 12 |
| 16 | 14 | 15 | 2 | 18 | 5 | 12 | 3 | 17 | 1 | 6 | 9 | 7 | 8 | 20 | 10 | 11 | 13 | 4 | 19 |
| 4 | 16 | 6 | 11 | 17 | 18 | 1 | 14 | 2 | 15 | 20 | 12 | 7 | 19 | 8 | 9 | 13 | 10 | 5 | 3 |
| 19 | 14 | 2 | 17 | 3 | 12 | 1 | 18 | 6 | 10 | 13 | 7 | 5 | 4 | 8 | 11 | 9 | 15 | 16 | 20 |
| 10 | 7 | 1 | 9 | 19 | 18 | 15 | 12 | 3 | 20 | 4 | 6 | 17 | 5 | 8 | 14 | 11 | 16 | 13 | 2 |
| 11 | 7 | 16 | 3 | 15 | 9 | 19 | 20 | 12 | 6 | 4 | 10 | 13 | 2 | 18 | 1 | 8 | 14 | 17 | 5 |
| 18 | 9 | 10 | 11 | 14 | 12 | 6 | 19 | 5 | 4 | 2 | 13 | 15 | 20 | 8 | 1 | 16 | 3 | 7 | 17 |
| 2 | 17 | 12 | 9 | 18 | 20 | 11 | 7 | 8 | 3 | 19 | 1 | 16 | 15 | 4 | 6 | 5 | 14 | 13 | 10 |
| 9 | 4 | 2 | 10 | 14 | 5 | 7 | 17 | 8 | 18 | 20 | 6 | 16 | 15 | 19 | 13 | 1 | 12 | 11 | 3 |
| 6 | 13 | 18 | 9 | 20 | 2 | 17 | 3 | 10 | 12 | 19 | 5 | 7 | 4 | 8 | 1 | 15 | 14 | 11 | 16 |
| 14 | 4 | 16 | 13 | 10 | 5 | 7 | 17 | 20 | 12 | 1 | 6 | 2 | 11 | 15 | 19 | 3 | 18 | 9 | 8 |
| 9 | 15 | 19 | 3 | 5 | 8 | 14 | 11 | 1 | 4 | 18 | 20 | 16 | 7 | 10 | 17 | 12 | 2 | 6 | 13 |
| 7 | 20 | 10 | 2 | 19 | 15 | 5 | 6 | 18 | 1 | 9 | 11 | 14 | 4 | 3 | 13 | 16 | 12 | 17 | 8 |
| 17 | 4 | 10 | 19 | 12 | 8 | 5 | 16 | 6 | 18 | 15 | 2 | 11 | 7 | 13 | 9 | 20 | 3 | 14 | 1 |
| 16 | 14 | 19 | 15 | 9 | 18 | 8 | 13 | 3 | 11 | 2 | 20 | 4 | 12 | 10 | 6 | 17 | 7 | 1 | 5 |
| 6 | 18 | 15 | 13 | 11 | 8 | 10 | 12 | 1 | 19 | 14 | 17 | 2 | 9 | 16 | 3 | 20 | 4 | 7 | 5 |
| 16 | 15 | 13 | 1 | 19 | 12 | 10 | 18 | 7 | 3 | 6 | 20 | 2 | 4 | 9 | 11 | 14 | 17 | 8 | 5 |
| 1 | 9 | 20 | 8 | 4 | 2 | 7 | 5 | 16 | 17 | 18 | 6 | 14 | 11 | 19 | 12 | 15 | 10 | 13 | 3 |
| 13 | 4 | 1 | 9 | 6 | 8 | 3 | 2 | 18 | 19 | 17 | 20 | 10 | 15 | 14 | 11 | 7 | 5 | 12 | 16 |
| 6 | 15 | 3 | 1 | 16 | 19 | 13 | 2 | 17 | 10 | 11 | 5 | 20 | 7 | 4 | 14 | 8 | 9 | 12 | 18 |
| 16 | 1 | 10 | 11 | 15 | 5 | 14 | 18 | 12 | 3 | 19 | 7 | 8 | 9 | 4 | 6 | 17 | 20 | 2 | 13 |
| 1 | 14 | 10 | 7 | 2 | 8 | 15 | 5 | 20 | 11 | 17 | 9 | 19 | 18 | 6 | 16 | 4 | 3 | 12 | 13 |
| 2 | 19 | 11 | 16 | 1 | 5 | 18 | 9 | 3 | 20 | 12 | 17 | 15 | 10 | 4 | 6 | 7 | 8 | 13 | 14 |
| 18 | 15 | 13 | 17 | 2 | 4 | 11 | 1 | 14 | 6 | 16 | 20 | 7 | 12 | 3 | 8 | 10 | 19 | 9 | 5 |
| 10 | 14 | 9 | 7 | 12 | 8 | 1 | 2 | 19 | 20 | 13 | 4 | 17 | 16 | 6 | 18 | 3 | 11 | 15 | 5 |
| 5 | 13 | 6 | 3 | 19 | 20 | 16 | 12 | 4 | 18 | 9 | 10 | 15 | 17 | 1 | 8 | 7 | 14 | 11 | 2 |
| 6 | 13 | 20 | 11 | 2 | 16 | 18 | 12 | 3 | 5 | 8 | 10 | 19 | 9 | 15 | 14 | 1 | 7 | 4 | 17 |
| 10 | 6 | 1 | 2 | 5 | 12 | 8 | 3 | 7 | 9 | 11 | 19 | 16 | 18 | 4 | 14 | 13 | 20 | 17 | 15 |
| 7 | 2 | 20 | 18 | 10 | 3 | 5 | 4 | 9 | 14 | 16 | 17 | 6 | 13 | 12 | 19 | 15 | 1 | 8 | 11 |
| 15 | 11 | 17 | 19 | 2 | 9 | 16 | 7 | 4 | 20 | 18 | 6 | 1 | 12 | 5 | 8 | 10 | 3 | 13 | 14 |
| 20 | 5 | 4 | 9 | 15 | 11 | 2 | 17 | 13 | 6 | 12 | 1 | 14 | 8 | 16 | 10 | 19 | 7 | 3 | 18 |
| 5 | 13 | 19 | 12 | 15 | 20 | 4 | 2 | 17 | 9 | 7 | 10 | 14 | 6 | 16 | 8 | 3 | 11 | 18 | 1 |
| 12 | 13 | 5 | 6 | 8 | 9 | 7 | 15 | 2 | 18 | 20 | 4 | 14 | 3 | 11 | 16 | 17 | 19 | 1 | 10 |
| 6 | 2 | 10 | 18 | 9 | 16 | 20 | 13 | 17 | 5 | 4 | 12 | 1 | 11 | 7 | 19 | 15 | 8 | 3 | 14 |
| 15 | 11 | 10 | 8 | 20 | 6 | 7 | 1 | 9 | 4 | 2 | 14 | 18 | 19 | 3 | 16 | 13 | 12 | 5 | 17 |
| 17 | 15 | 19 | 13 | 7 | 12 | 20 | 8 | 14 | 16 | 9 | 11 | 6 | 2 | 3 | 1 | 4 | 18 | 5 | 10 |
| 7 | 2 | 9 | 19 | 3 | 18 | 6 | 13 | 10 | 20 | 11 | 12 | 4 | 17 | 16 | 8 | 1 | 5 | 14 | 15 |
| 2 | 16 | 4 | 6 | 17 | 18 | 14 | 9 | 12 | 3 | 1 | 5 | 15 | 8 | 19 | 10 | 11 | 20 | 13 | 7 |
| 17 | 3 | 2 | 20 | 12 | 18 | 19 | 13 | 6 | 10 | 14 | 16 | 1 | 4 | 11 | 7 | 9 | 8 | 5 | 15 |
| 8 | 5 | 2 | 17 | 10 | 15 | 12 | 18 | 1 | 20 | 14 | 3 | 13 | 11 | 19 | 4 | 6 | 9 | 16 | 7 |
| 11 | 19 | 20 | 1 | 6 | 13 | 2 | 7 | 3 | 17 | 4 | 8 | 12 | 16 | 15 | 10 | 18 | 9 | 5 | 14 |
| 17 | 7 | 6 | 1 | 8 | 15 | 18 | 20 | 5 | 10 | 12 | 4 | 3 | 9 | 16 | 19 | 2 | 13 | 14 | 11 |
| 12 | 6 | 9 | 14 | 2 | 17 | 4 | 20 | 16 | 10 | 7 | 15 | 1 | 8 | 19 | 13 | 5 | 18 | 3 | 11 |
| 11 | 17 | 9 | 19 | 2 | 5 | 15 | 20 | 6 | 16 | 4 | 1 | 10 | 7 | 8 | 3 | 13 | 18 | 12 | 14 |
| 20 | 11 | 5 | 1 | 9 | 17 | 10 | 19 | 7 | 2 | 4 | 15 | 16 | 14 | 6 | 12 | 13 | 3 | 18 | 8 |
| 11 | 17 | 20 | 1 | 10 | 2 | 12 | 18 | 3 | 6 | 4 | 13 | 16 | 19 | 7 | 9 | 14 | 15 | 8 | 5 |
| 6 | 3 | 10 | 15 | 11 | 4 | 20 | 2 | 5 | 18 | 9 | 19 | 12 | 7 | 1 | 16 | 17 | 8 | 14 | 13 |

## Appendix Table 4—*continued*

| | | | | | | | | | | | | | | | | | | | |
|---|---|---|---|---|---|---|---|---|---|---|---|---|---|---|---|---|---|---|---|
| 2 | 4 | 12 | 16 | 3 | 15 | 6 | 5 | 11 | 10 | 17 | 19 | 13 | 9 | 7 | 18 | 14 | 1 | 20 | 8 |
| 14 | 8 | 16 | 4 | 13 | 19 | 6 | 11 | 3 | 9 | 1 | 7 | 2 | 10 | 17 | 15 | 5 | 20 | 18 | 12 |
| 17 | 1 | 8 | 12 | 15 | 5 | 4 | 16 | 20 | 19 | 6 | 2 | 7 | 14 | 9 | 11 | 3 | 18 | 10 | 13 |
| 5 | 6 | 13 | 9 | 4 | 19 | 16 | 17 | 15 | 11 | 2 | 10 | 7 | 8 | 12 | 3 | 1 | 20 | 14 | 18 |
| 13 | 19 | 20 | 2 | 7 | 9 | 15 | 18 | 4 | 6 | 8 | 1 | 5 | 14 | 16 | 3 | 11 | 17 | 12 | 10 |
| | | | | | | | | | | | | | | | | | | | |
| 2 | 4 | 14 | 10 | 13 | 18 | 11 | 19 | 15 | 16 | 7 | 9 | 3 | 8 | 6 | 17 | 12 | 5 | 20 | 1 |
| 9 | 1 | 13 | 18 | 16 | 8 | 15 | 17 | 4 | 6 | 7 | 20 | 14 | 5 | 10 | 12 | 3 | 11 | 2 | 19 |
| 5 | 2 | 11 | 7 | 1 | 16 | 20 | 14 | 3 | 4 | 15 | 13 | 9 | 8 | 12 | 17 | 19 | 6 | 10 | 18 |
| 8 | 16 | 18 | 4 | 10 | 20 | 2 | 19 | 5 | 7 | 13 | 1 | 11 | 17 | 15 | 12 | 6 | 9 | 14 | 3 |
| 9 | 6 | 16 | 12 | 18 | 19 | 17 | 8 | 10 | 5 | 3 | 4 | 13 | 20 | 1 | 15 | 2 | 11 | 14 | 7 |
| | | | | | | | | | | | | | | | | | | | |
| 2 | 13 | 4 | 9 | 14 | 8 | 10 | 3 | 16 | 17 | 5 | 20 | 1 | 7 | 19 | 11 | 6 | 18 | 15 | 12 |
| 20 | 15 | 8 | 11 | 12 | 18 | 5 | 19 | 3 | 4 | 9 | 13 | 17 | 1 | 2 | 10 | 6 | 16 | 7 | 14 |
| 13 | 16 | 19 | 20 | 15 | 5 | 3 | 4 | 11 | 2 | 17 | 12 | 14 | 7 | 8 | 1 | 10 | 9 | 6 | 18 |
| 15 | 7 | 20 | 16 | 1 | 14 | 5 | 3 | 12 | 17 | 19 | 4 | 9 | 2 | 11 | 8 | 10 | 18 | 6 | 13 |
| 7 | 15 | 16 | 5 | 6 | 14 | 11 | 4 | 20 | 10 | 12 | 1 | 18 | 19 | 9 | 17 | 8 | 3 | 2 | 13 |
| | | | | | | | | | | | | | | | | | | | |
| 14 | 18 | 13 | 1 | 8 | 3 | 11 | 7 | 20 | 15 | 16 | 5 | 19 | 9 | 12 | 10 | 4 | 2 | 17 | 6 |
| 8 | 12 | 7 | 9 | 6 | 14 | 10 | 5 | 16 | 13 | 4 | 19 | 20 | 17 | 11 | 1 | 18 | 2 | 15 | 3 |
| 14 | 6 | 9 | 3 | 2 | 18 | 8 | 16 | 13 | 12 | 10 | 4 | 15 | 5 | 17 | 1 | 20 | 7 | 19 | 11 |
| 6 | 3 | 15 | 13 | 2 | 1 | 4 | 18 | 10 | 7 | 19 | 11 | 12 | 16 | 5 | 17 | 8 | 20 | 9 | 14 |
| 7 | 14 | 3 | 8 | 13 | 2 | 15 | 6 | 16 | 19 | 20 | 1 | 18 | 5 | 4 | 12 | 17 | 11 | 10 | 9 |
| | | | | | | | | | | | | | | | | | | | |
| 11 | 12 | 6 | 5 | 9 | 10 | 3 | 20 | 4 | 16 | 1 | 18 | 15 | 19 | 7 | 8 | 17 | 2 | 13 | 14 |
| 4 | 20 | 17 | 7 | 10 | 9 | 1 | 3 | 16 | 8 | 6 | 2 | 18 | 14 | 19 | 12 | 15 | 5 | 11 | 13 |
| 2 | 18 | 20 | 6 | 4 | 3 | 7 | 16 | 17 | 13 | 12 | 5 | 14 | 15 | 19 | 11 | 9 | 10 | 1 | 8 |
| 8 | 3 | 13 | 18 | 11 | 9 | 4 | 20 | 1 | 14 | 7 | 16 | 12 | 17 | 6 | 15 | 10 | 5 | 19 | 2 |
| 20 | 18 | 11 | 1 | 15 | 7 | 12 | 2 | 10 | 6 | 17 | 14 | 8 | 19 | 9 | 13 | 16 | 5 | 3 | 4 |
| | | | | | | | | | | | | | | | | | | | |
| 5 | 7 | 2 | 8 | 6 | 10 | 11 | 17 | 12 | 16 | 18 | 15 | 4 | 19 | 20 | 9 | 13 | 1 | 14 | 3 |
| 13 | 20 | 16 | 17 | 9 | 19 | 4 | 15 | 7 | 10 | 14 | 3 | 2 | 11 | 12 | 18 | 6 | 8 | 5 | 1 |
| 14 | 3 | 13 | 16 | 5 | 2 | 15 | 9 | 17 | 19 | 12 | 6 | 18 | 7 | 11 | 20 | 10 | 8 | 1 | 4 |
| 13 | 9 | 11 | 6 | 3 | 2 | 14 | 16 | 18 | 15 | 10 | 20 | 4 | 1 | 7 | 8 | 12 | 17 | 5 | 19 |
| 4 | 7 | 1 | 11 | 5 | 18 | 15 | 6 | 10 | 13 | 9 | 14 | 3 | 19 | 2 | 16 | 20 | 17 | 12 | 8 |
| | | | | | | | | | | | | | | | | | | | |
| 6 | 18 | 2 | 9 | 19 | 3 | 17 | 1 | 13 | 4 | 12 | 20 | 15 | 14 | 7 | 11 | 8 | 16 | 5 | 10 |
| 20 | 7 | 12 | 13 | 2 | 1 | 6 | 11 | 14 | 5 | 19 | 9 | 4 | 15 | 18 | 8 | 10 | 16 | 3 | 17 |
| 5 | 12 | 4 | 20 | 13 | 3 | 8 | 17 | 19 | 16 | 18 | 14 | 2 | 10 | 15 | 9 | 1 | 11 | 7 | 6 |
| 1 | 8 | 2 | 17 | 7 | 11 | 12 | 20 | 14 | 5 | 10 | 16 | 15 | 3 | 9 | 4 | 19 | 18 | 13 | 6 |
| 10 | 2 | 18 | 11 | 13 | 12 | 8 | 4 | 14 | 16 | 17 | 3 | 20 | 5 | 15 | 9 | 6 | 1 | 7 | 19 |
| | | | | | | | | | | | | | | | | | | | |
| 5 | 16 | 9 | 3 | 13 | 14 | 2 | 15 | 17 | 8 | 4 | 6 | 10 | 18 | 11 | 1 | 19 | 12 | 20 | 7 |
| 7 | 19 | 12 | 18 | 15 | 2 | 8 | 16 | 4 | 17 | 11 | 20 | 3 | 5 | 14 | 9 | 10 | 6 | 13 | 1 |
| 18 | 12 | 2 | 19 | 1 | 16 | 3 | 5 | 6 | 15 | 17 | 11 | 10 | 20 | 8 | 4 | 7 | 14 | 9 | 13 |
| 3 | 14 | 11 | 18 | 7 | 8 | 6 | 12 | 1 | 2 | 5 | 19 | 4 | 15 | 20 | 9 | 17 | 13 | 10 | 16 |
| 16 | 11 | 8 | 18 | 4 | 7 | 6 | 14 | 12 | 17 | 5 | 9 | 19 | 10 | 15 | 13 | 2 | 1 | 3 | 20 |
| | | | | | | | | | | | | | | | | | | | |
| 17 | 11 | 15 | 13 | 1 | 14 | 12 | 6 | 9 | 18 | 4 | 19 | 7 | 16 | 3 | 20 | 5 | 2 | 10 | 8 |
| 1 | 20 | 8 | 15 | 14 | 10 | 13 | 9 | 12 | 19 | 17 | 18 | 11 | 6 | 4 | 3 | 5 | 2 | 7 | 16 |
| 17 | 7 | 15 | 2 | 18 | 12 | 5 | 11 | 9 | 1 | 16 | 6 | 4 | 20 | 13 | 3 | 19 | 14 | 10 | 8 |
| 4 | 16 | 1 | 11 | 15 | 9 | 13 | 3 | 6 | 7 | 10 | 20 | 12 | 19 | 8 | 18 | 2 | 14 | 17 | 5 |
| 1 | 16 | 8 | 13 | 10 | 19 | 12 | 15 | 11 | 17 | 18 | 5 | 2 | 4 | 20 | 9 | 3 | 7 | 6 | 14 |
| | | | | | | | | | | | | | | | | | | | |
| 4 | 16 | 12 | 9 | 11 | 7 | 5 | 2 | 13 | 14 | 1 | 19 | 3 | 15 | 20 | 18 | 6 | 10 | 8 | 17 |
| 1 | 14 | 15 | 18 | 19 | 13 | 3 | 12 | 11 | 16 | 10 | 9 | 7 | 4 | 8 | 20 | 5 | 17 | 2 | 6 |
| 7 | 1 | 15 | 14 | 6 | 11 | 3 | 2 | 12 | 4 | 10 | 19 | 9 | 5 | 18 | 17 | 20 | 16 | 13 | 8 |
| 7 | 20 | 8 | 18 | 17 | 2 | 16 | 9 | 12 | 1 | 4 | 13 | 3 | 15 | 11 | 14 | 19 | 6 | 10 | 5 |
| 10 | 1 | 16 | 6 | 18 | 2 | 4 | 15 | 3 | 9 | 11 | 17 | 12 | 5 | 7 | 19 | 8 | 13 | 14 | 20 |
| | | | | | | | | | | | | | | | | | | | |
| 6 | 8 | 16 | 17 | 11 | 13 | 4 | 1 | 20 | 2 | 12 | 9 | 7 | 18 | 5 | 10 | 19 | 15 | 14 | 3 |
| 8 | 5 | 7 | 2 | 20 | 1 | 11 | 19 | 12 | 16 | 10 | 13 | 17 | 4 | 3 | 15 | 18 | 6 | 14 | 9 |
| 20 | 14 | 4 | 7 | 18 | 13 | 12 | 11 | 17 | 16 | 19 | 5 | 3 | 9 | 10 | 8 | 2 | 1 | 6 | 15 |
| 8 | 16 | 11 | 15 | 3 | 20 | 9 | 6 | 13 | 14 | 17 | 12 | 7 | 5 | 2 | 4 | 19 | 1 | 18 | 10 |
| 4 | 3 | 17 | 18 | 12 | 5 | 9 | 2 | 8 | 14 | 7 | 6 | 16 | 15 | 10 | 19 | 11 | 20 | 13 | 1 |
| | | | | | | | | | | | | | | | | | | | |
| 5 | 16 | 10 | 11 | 19 | 4 | 12 | 1 | 3 | 9 | 2 | 20 | 6 | 14 | 18 | 8 | 13 | 17 | 15 | 7 |
| 10 | 5 | 15 | 17 | 9 | 14 | 7 | 16 | 11 | 12 | 19 | 3 | 8 | 20 | 4 | 13 | 6 | 1 | 2 | 18 |
| 11 | 15 | 8 | 14 | 9 | 5 | 13 | 18 | 7 | 17 | 4 | 6 | 3 | 10 | 16 | 12 | 20 | 1 | 2 | 19 |
| 1 | 13 | 19 | 17 | 2 | 11 | 16 | 6 | 9 | 18 | 4 | 3 | 8 | 12 | 5 | 10 | 7 | 15 | 14 | 20 |
| 9 | 10 | 2 | 13 | 18 | 8 | 4 | 5 | 3 | 16 | 15 | 7 | 14 | 19 | 17 | 20 | 11 | 12 | 6 | 1 |

## Appendix Table 4—*continued*

| | | | | | | | | | | | | | | | | | | | |
|---|---|---|---|---|---|---|---|---|---|---|---|---|---|---|---|---|---|---|---|
| 20 | 4 | 12 | 13 | 3 | 5 | 14 | 17 | 10 | 15 | 2 | 9 | 16 | 1 | 18 | 19 | 11 | 7 | 6 | 8 |
| 18 | 8 | 14 | 17 | 9 | 1 | 11 | 10 | 12 | 4 | 13 | 6 | 3 | 16 | 7 | 19 | 20 | 5 | 2 | 15 |
| 5 | 20 | 9 | 13 | 17 | 14 | 19 | 2 | 8 | 7 | 1 | 6 | 12 | 4 | 18 | 15 | 10 | 3 | 11 | 16 |
| 18 | 8 | 2 | 12 | 1 | 7 | 16 | 19 | 5 | 9 | 13 | 3 | 20 | 4 | 6 | 11 | 15 | 10 | 17 | 14 |
| 12 | 4 | 1 | 15 | 10 | 11 | 18 | 19 | 7 | 13 | 17 | 9 | 16 | 8 | 14 | 20 | 2 | 5 | 3 | 6 |
| 6 | 20 | 3 | 10 | 13 | 19 | 14 | 12 | 4 | 7 | 2 | 1 | 9 | 18 | 11 | 5 | 15 | 16 | 8 | 17 |
| 7 | 9 | 16 | 15 | 17 | 1 | 11 | 13 | 14 | 5 | 6 | 2 | 19 | 18 | 4 | 3 | 8 | 12 | 20 | 10 |
| 13 | 5 | 19 | 3 | 10 | 8 | 20 | 9 | 1 | 2 | 6 | 18 | 7 | 14 | 15 | 17 | 4 | 12 | 11 | 16 |
| 15 | 2 | 7 | 6 | 4 | 17 | 8 | 1 | 13 | 11 | 10 | 18 | 20 | 5 | 12 | 19 | 3 | 9 | 14 | 16 |
| 18 | 7 | 16 | 6 | 2 | 12 | 3 | 13 | 9 | 15 | 8 | 11 | 5 | 1 | 19 | 20 | 10 | 14 | 4 | 17 |
| 19 | 5 | 15 | 7 | 10 | 2 | 16 | 11 | 8 | 4 | 14 | 1 | 9 | 12 | 20 | 17 | 18 | 13 | 6 | 3 |
| 3 | 11 | 1 | 2 | 10 | 12 | 5 | 19 | 8 | 18 | 16 | 14 | 13 | 9 | 15 | 17 | 4 | 6 | 20 | 7 |
| 18 | 7 | 14 | 5 | 13 | 2 | 1 | 8 | 20 | 9 | 19 | 17 | 4 | 3 | 11 | 16 | 6 | 15 | 12 | 10 |
| 11 | 15 | 16 | 17 | 7 | 4 | 9 | 19 | 5 | 3 | 8 | 18 | 10 | 20 | 14 | 6 | 2 | 12 | 13 | 1 |
| 6 | 17 | 20 | 9 | 14 | 12 | 1 | 10 | 15 | 19 | 5 | 11 | 16 | 13 | 3 | 7 | 4 | 2 | 18 | 8 |
| 1 | 16 | 6 | 3 | 15 | 13 | 17 | 14 | 12 | 20 | 11 | 10 | 4 | 9 | 19 | 18 | 7 | 8 | 5 | 2 |
| 2 | 1 | 13 | 17 | 14 | 15 | 3 | 20 | 11 | 18 | 6 | 12 | 19 | 16 | 7 | 4 | 5 | 10 | 8 | 9 |
| 20 | 8 | 14 | 2 | 18 | 11 | 16 | 1 | 13 | 12 | 6 | 4 | 15 | 7 | 3 | 19 | 9 | 10 | 5 | 17 |
| 3 | 9 | 4 | 8 | 12 | 5 | 19 | 6 | 15 | 17 | 10 | 2 | 20 | 16 | 13 | 18 | 14 | 11 | 7 | 1 |
| 12 | 9 | 18 | 1 | 10 | 4 | 16 | 8 | 7 | 20 | 17 | 2 | 11 | 6 | 13 | 14 | 3 | 15 | 5 | 19 |
| 18 | 13 | 11 | 10 | 3 | 17 | 19 | 20 | 8 | 15 | 16 | 1 | 5 | 7 | 6 | 12 | 9 | 4 | 14 | 2 |
| 18 | 9 | 4 | 14 | 11 | 17 | 2 | 1 | 8 | 5 | 15 | 16 | 20 | 7 | 6 | 10 | 13 | 12 | 19 | 3 |
| 9 | 11 | 5 | 4 | 12 | 7 | 1 | 19 | 16 | 18 | 20 | 13 | 10 | 2 | 3 | 6 | 14 | 15 | 8 | 17 |
| 14 | 15 | 6 | 20 | 7 | 8 | 19 | 13 | 1 | 5 | 4 | 16 | 9 | 3 | 10 | 11 | 18 | 17 | 12 | 2 |
| 19 | 15 | 10 | 1 | 12 | 16 | 9 | 8 | 13 | 2 | 3 | 6 | 20 | 11 | 7 | 5 | 4 | 17 | 14 | 18 |
| 20 | 5 | 17 | 7 | 14 | 1 | 6 | 16 | 4 | 2 | 13 | 9 | 3 | 10 | 8 | 12 | 15 | 19 | 11 | 18 |
| 7 | 9 | 12 | 8 | 20 | 11 | 6 | 16 | 2 | 3 | 4 | 15 | 1 | 17 | 19 | 5 | 14 | 13 | 18 | 10 |
| 11 | 15 | 9 | 6 | 18 | 3 | 2 | 19 | 13 | 20 | 12 | 16 | 14 | 4 | 17 | 5 | 7 | 10 | 8 | 1 |
| 4 | 3 | 17 | 14 | 2 | 18 | 7 | 12 | 16 | 10 | 11 | 15 | 5 | 20 | 13 | 1 | 8 | 9 | 19 | 6 |
| 8 | 6 | 17 | 4 | 10 | 5 | 9 | 3 | 18 | 20 | 15 | 16 | 13 | 1 | 11 | 12 | 14 | 7 | 19 | 2 |
| 11 | 5 | 15 | 9 | 1 | 12 | 6 | 16 | 17 | 3 | 20 | 13 | 14 | 18 | 8 | 7 | 19 | 10 | 4 | 2 |
| 4 | 12 | 13 | 9 | 1 | 7 | 15 | 3 | 6 | 19 | 2 | 8 | 16 | 11 | 17 | 18 | 5 | 20 | 10 | 14 |
| 8 | 15 | 5 | 4 | 13 | 7 | 19 | 10 | 20 | 12 | 17 | 2 | 11 | 6 | 9 | 16 | 3 | 18 | 1 | 14 |
| 3 | 12 | 11 | 18 | 2 | 15 | 13 | 14 | 8 | 19 | 7 | 20 | 10 | 16 | 9 | 6 | 1 | 17 | 4 | 5 |
| 19 | 1 | 10 | 6 | 9 | 2 | 20 | 5 | 18 | 17 | 11 | 16 | 8 | 14 | 4 | 12 | 15 | 13 | 7 | 3 |
| 5 | 2 | 1 | 7 | 14 | 17 | 4 | 16 | 9 | 3 | 13 | 19 | 15 | 18 | 10 | 12 | 20 | 8 | 11 | 6 |
| 2 | 12 | 18 | 13 | 4 | 10 | 5 | 6 | 14 | 16 | 15 | 19 | 9 | 7 | 3 | 17 | 1 | 11 | 20 | 8 |
| 15 | 13 | 2 | 18 | 6 | 19 | 7 | 10 | 11 | 16 | 20 | 1 | 12 | 3 | 14 | 9 | 17 | 4 | 8 | 5 |
| 4 | 12 | 17 | 1 | 7 | 9 | 16 | 8 | 14 | 20 | 10 | 13 | 6 | 2 | 19 | 3 | 15 | 18 | 11 | 5 |
| 14 | 17 | 16 | 7 | 19 | 9 | 8 | 3 | 15 | 10 | 5 | 13 | 11 | 18 | 2 | 20 | 4 | 1 | 12 | 6 |
| 15 | 8 | 13 | 19 | 6 | 18 | 5 | 7 | 10 | 11 | 3 | 14 | 2 | 1 | 16 | 9 | 4 | 12 | 17 | 20 |
| 20 | 8 | 12 | 11 | 7 | 10 | 2 | 13 | 4 | 16 | 19 | 15 | 1 | 9 | 17 | 6 | 3 | 14 | 18 | 5 |
| 11 | 4 | 9 | 5 | 15 | 10 | 19 | 12 | 13 | 7 | 2 | 6 | 3 | 16 | 17 | 14 | 18 | 8 | 1 | 20 |
| 9 | 19 | 15 | 13 | 2 | 12 | 8 | 14 | 7 | 4 | 20 | 6 | 1 | 5 | 11 | 3 | 17 | 18 | 16 | 10 |
| 1 | 2 | 17 | 13 | 3 | 7 | 9 | 5 | 6 | 20 | 14 | 10 | 4 | 12 | 18 | 19 | 8 | 11 | 15 | 16 |
| 18 | 12 | 16 | 19 | 17 | 9 | 5 | 11 | 6 | 13 | 8 | 14 | 3 | 2 | 15 | 20 | 7 | 1 | 10 | 4 |
| 11 | 16 | 19 | 6 | 12 | 7 | 2 | 14 | 15 | 18 | 4 | 8 | 5 | 3 | 9 | 17 | 20 | 1 | 13 | 10 |
| 4 | 19 | 12 | 17 | 7 | 6 | 14 | 20 | 5 | 11 | 9 | 13 | 18 | 8 | 10 | 2 | 3 | 15 | 1 | 16 |
| 3 | 14 | 7 | 13 | 17 | 6 | 9 | 8 | 15 | 19 | 2 | 20 | 12 | 11 | 18 | 4 | 10 | 1 | 5 | 16 |
| 6 | 4 | 3 | 13 | 12 | 10 | 11 | 2 | 15 | 7 | 9 | 20 | 8 | 1 | 19 | 18 | 5 | 17 | 16 | 14 |
| 3 | 6 | 4 | 13 | 19 | 1 | 7 | 15 | 8 | 10 | 12 | 18 | 11 | 9 | 20 | 5 | 2 | 16 | 14 | 17 |
| 10 | 6 | 20 | 14 | 19 | 4 | 1 | 8 | 16 | 2 | 13 | 3 | 7 | 9 | 12 | 5 | 11 | 15 | 17 | 18 |
| 17 | 7 | 8 | 16 | 4 | 6 | 9 | 19 | 11 | 5 | 12 | 13 | 10 | 18 | 20 | 1 | 14 | 15 | 2 | 3 |
| 12 | 16 | 9 | 3 | 4 | 18 | 19 | 10 | 8 | 6 | 20 | 14 | 13 | 7 | 5 | 15 | 11 | 2 | 17 | 1 |
| 3 | 5 | 15 | 9 | 6 | 19 | 4 | 17 | 2 | 14 | 11 | 20 | 13 | 10 | 7 | 18 | 12 | 8 | 16 | 1 |
| 8 | 7 | 2 | 12 | 17 | 19 | 9 | 5 | 20 | 13 | 11 | 18 | 1 | 3 | 4 | 15 | 10 | 14 | 16 | 6 |
| 20 | 13 | 4 | 6 | 7 | 9 | 2 | 16 | 11 | 14 | 5 | 19 | 3 | 17 | 12 | 18 | 10 | 1 | 8 | 15 |
| 14 | 19 | 5 | 6 | 3 | 16 | 10 | 8 | 12 | 17 | 20 | 9 | 13 | 18 | 2 | 11 | 7 | 4 | 15 | 1 |
| 19 | 3 | 12 | 11 | 13 | 14 | 7 | 18 | 5 | 1 | 2 | 17 | 15 | 6 | 9 | 20 | 4 | 8 | 16 | 10 |
| 5 | 11 | 15 | 17 | 9 | 6 | 1 | 10 | 20 | 19 | 16 | 8 | 14 | 2 | 7 | 3 | 13 | 18 | 12 | 4 |

| | | | | | | | | | | | | | | | | | | | |
|---|---|---|---|---|---|---|---|---|---|---|---|---|---|---|---|---|---|---|---|
| 14 | 3 | 11 | 2 | 6 | 1 | 15 | 19 | 8 | 9 | 12 | 10 | 16 | 7 | 5 | 17 | 20 | 13 | 4 | 18 |
| 9 | 15 | 18 | 6 | 14 | 13 | 12 | 2 | 1 | 4 | 8 | 3 | 19 | 5 | 20 | 11 | 7 | 10 | 16 | 17 |
| 20 | 13 | 16 | 18 | 3 | 9 | 14 | 5 | 8 | 12 | 17 | 10 | 15 | 7 | 19 | 2 | 11 | 6 | 4 | 1 |
| 8 | 19 | 15 | 20 | 9 | 1 | 18 | 7 | 17 | 14 | 4 | 16 | 11 | 5 | 6 | 10 | 13 | 2 | 12 | 3 |
| 18 | 15 | 16 | 1 | 20 | 14 | 11 | 13 | 9 | 2 | 5 | 8 | 10 | 17 | 12 | 7 | 19 | 4 | 3 | 6 |
| | | | | | | | | | | | | | | | | | | | |
| 16 | 2 | 15 | 3 | 8 | 11 | 12 | 1 | 14 | 19 | 7 | 17 | 20 | 4 | 6 | 9 | 10 | 13 | 5 | 18 |
| 6 | 9 | 4 | 1 | 2 | 15 | 18 | 16 | 8 | 17 | 13 | 3 | 14 | 20 | 12 | 5 | 19 | 7 | 10 | 11 |
| 12 | 10 | 4 | 5 | 16 | 1 | 7 | 19 | 8 | 11 | 2 | 3 | 14 | 6 | 18 | 13 | 15 | 9 | 20 | 17 |
| 17 | 12 | 14 | 7 | 9 | 6 | 19 | 8 | 16 | 5 | 11 | 1 | 20 | 15 | 3 | 4 | 18 | 13 | 10 | 2 |
| 5 | 4 | 10 | 13 | 15 | 20 | 7 | 3 | 12 | 9 | 14 | 1 | 17 | 19 | 6 | 16 | 18 | 2 | 8 | 11 |
| | | | | | | | | | | | | | | | | | | | |
| 10 | 8 | 2 | 9 | 16 | 7 | 11 | 20 | 17 | 19 | 5 | 18 | 13 | 6 | 4 | 15 | 1 | 12 | 3 | 14 |
| 10 | 3 | 9 | 14 | 5 | 8 | 1 | 6 | 17 | 7 | 15 | 12 | 2 | 4 | 16 | 18 | 13 | 20 | 11 | 19 |
| 14 | 8 | 16 | 6 | 19 | 7 | 5 | 18 | 4 | 17 | 2 | 20 | 1 | 13 | 12 | 15 | 9 | 11 | 3 | 10 |
| 20 | 14 | 3 | 11 | 5 | 8 | 19 | 18 | 4 | 7 | 17 | 2 | 16 | 13 | 12 | 10 | 1 | 15 | 9 | 6 |
| 1 | 9 | 19 | 16 | 11 | 15 | 7 | 8 | 14 | 10 | 12 | 18 | 4 | 2 | 6 | 20 | 17 | 13 | 5 | 3 |
| | | | | | | | | | | | | | | | | | | | |
| 6 | 3 | 7 | 18 | 17 | 1 | 5 | 4 | 8 | 14 | 20 | 2 | 12 | 15 | 10 | 19 | 11 | 13 | 9 | 16 |
| 18 | 13 | 4 | 16 | 1 | 3 | 6 | 9 | 11 | 8 | 19 | 5 | 17 | 2 | 20 | 7 | 14 | 15 | 12 | 10 |
| 13 | 12 | 3 | 18 | 19 | 10 | 6 | 9 | 14 | 15 | 20 | 7 | 17 | 2 | 8 | 11 | 16 | 5 | 4 | 1 |
| 12 | 18 | 5 | 1 | 16 | 11 | 6 | 4 | 2 | 17 | 14 | 3 | 20 | 10 | 7 | 13 | 19 | 8 | 15 | 9 |
| 12 | 6 | 13 | 4 | 2 | 1 | 18 | 20 | 14 | 9 | 3 | 16 | 8 | 17 | 19 | 10 | 5 | 11 | 15 | 7 |
| | | | | | | | | | | | | | | | | | | | |
| 18 | 3 | 4 | 7 | 15 | 14 | 16 | 1 | 10 | 12 | 6 | 13 | 20 | 8 | 2 | 19 | 9 | 17 | 11 | 5 |
| 10 | 9 | 8 | 4 | 5 | 13 | 19 | 12 | 2 | 6 | 20 | 1 | 15 | 18 | 16 | 7 | 14 | 3 | 11 | 17 |
| 15 | 16 | 17 | 4 | 11 | 20 | 10 | 2 | 12 | 3 | 13 | 19 | 6 | 18 | 7 | 8 | 1 | 5 | 9 | 14 |
| 5 | 18 | 11 | 16 | 10 | 3 | 13 | 7 | 4 | 12 | 8 | 6 | 17 | 2 | 15 | 20 | 19 | 14 | 1 | 9 |
| 13 | 10 | 17 | 6 | 12 | 9 | 3 | 5 | 16 | 18 | 19 | 7 | 1 | 8 | 2 | 20 | 14 | 11 | 15 | 4 |
| | | | | | | | | | | | | | | | | | | | |
| 5 | 6 | 19 | 8 | 3 | 17 | 20 | 4 | 2 | 18 | 15 | 14 | 10 | 7 | 11 | 16 | 9 | 1 | 13 | 12 |
| 2 | 7 | 10 | 17 | 15 | 3 | 18 | 5 | 11 | 12 | 4 | 14 | 9 | 20 | 13 | 16 | 1 | 6 | 19 | 8 |
| 8 | 2 | 10 | 13 | 1 | 11 | 15 | 6 | 9 | 19 | 17 | 16 | 20 | 7 | 12 | 5 | 18 | 14 | 4 | 3 |
| 8 | 1 | 3 | 15 | 10 | 2 | 7 | 13 | 19 | 9 | 12 | 11 | 18 | 17 | 20 | 16 | 14 | 4 | 6 | 5 |
| 15 | 2 | 19 | 1 | 16 | 18 | 13 | 8 | 5 | 14 | 4 | 7 | 11 | 3 | 17 | 12 | 9 | 10 | 20 | 6 |
| | | | | | | | | | | | | | | | | | | | |
| 20 | 14 | 18 | 5 | 2 | 10 | 11 | 7 | 15 | 16 | 13 | 17 | 12 | 9 | 8 | 6 | 4 | 3 | 19 | 1 |
| 18 | 13 | 6 | 9 | 1 | 5 | 19 | 2 | 16 | 17 | 10 | 15 | 7 | 11 | 20 | 14 | 8 | 4 | 3 | 12 |
| 9 | 13 | 20 | 16 | 11 | 8 | 12 | 15 | 7 | 14 | 4 | 10 | 6 | 17 | 2 | 3 | 18 | 5 | 19 | 1 |
| 7 | 10 | 4 | 8 | 3 | 1 | 14 | 15 | 2 | 6 | 17 | 20 | 11 | 5 | 19 | 12 | 18 | 13 | 9 | 16 |
| 16 | 18 | 12 | 7 | 13 | 14 | 4 | 10 | 15 | 11 | 6 | 9 | 1 | 5 | 17 | 19 | 3 | 20 | 8 | 2 |
| | | | | | | | | | | | | | | | | | | | |
| 20 | 8 | 11 | 2 | 5 | 19 | 15 | 3 | 6 | 12 | 10 | 18 | 4 | 16 | 14 | 9 | 13 | 1 | 17 | 7 |
| 12 | 15 | 16 | 8 | 7 | 2 | 18 | 4 | 6 | 1 | 19 | 20 | 3 | 10 | 5 | 17 | 13 | 14 | 11 | 9 |
| 11 | 13 | 2 | 10 | 3 | 17 | 1 | 7 | 15 | 5 | 8 | 6 | 12 | 18 | 4 | 9 | 14 | 20 | 19 | 16 |
| 1 | 8 | 5 | 12 | 9 | 16 | 11 | 20 | 3 | 10 | 7 | 18 | 2 | 17 | 14 | 19 | 6 | 4 | 15 | 13 |
| 14 | 10 | 17 | 19 | 5 | 11 | 7 | 6 | 1 | 12 | 16 | 2 | 20 | 15 | 3 | 8 | 13 | 9 | 4 | 18 |
| | | | | | | | | | | | | | | | | | | | |
| 20 | 6 | 10 | 8 | 12 | 3 | 11 | 9 | 7 | 13 | 14 | 16 | 2 | 15 | 19 | 18 | 17 | 4 | 5 | 1 |
| 3 | 6 | 1 | 19 | 18 | 5 | 7 | 15 | 13 | 9 | 17 | 8 | 16 | 2 | 10 | 4 | 20 | 14 | 12 | 11 |
| 9 | 1 | 12 | 20 | 17 | 4 | 11 | 10 | 16 | 6 | 18 | 5 | 2 | 15 | 8 | 7 | 19 | 14 | 13 | 3 |
| 17 | 11 | 6 | 16 | 9 | 7 | 20 | 5 | 15 | 8 | 12 | 1 | 18 | 4 | 19 | 13 | 2 | 3 | 14 | 10 |
| 7 | 11 | 6 | 13 | 19 | 12 | 16 | 10 | 17 | 5 | 8 | 20 | 3 | 18 | 2 | 4 | 14 | 9 | 15 | 1 |
| | | | | | | | | | | | | | | | | | | | |
| 18 | 3 | 2 | 16 | 20 | 1 | 14 | 15 | 12 | 6 | 19 | 8 | 5 | 9 | 10 | 7 | 11 | 4 | 13 | 17 |
| 17 | 9 | 16 | 10 | 13 | 12 | 5 | 4 | 7 | 20 | 19 | 11 | 15 | 6 | 1 | 3 | 2 | 14 | 18 | 8 |
| 1 | 7 | 17 | 3 | 15 | 6 | 20 | 2 | 8 | 10 | 12 | 5 | 18 | 4 | 11 | 19 | 14 | 16 | 9 | 13 |
| 15 | 6 | 18 | 17 | 20 | 8 | 3 | 14 | 5 | 4 | 7 | 13 | 10 | 2 | 1 | 19 | 9 | 12 | 16 | 11 |
| 8 | 7 | 1 | 17 | 10 | 5 | 13 | 16 | 3 | 18 | 15 | 12 | 4 | 2 | 11 | 9 | 19 | 14 | 6 | 20 |
| | | | | | | | | | | | | | | | | | | | |
| 16 | 20 | 15 | 1 | 13 | 4 | 17 | 12 | 19 | 2 | 5 | 8 | 18 | 11 | 9 | 7 | 3 | 6 | 14 | 10 |
| 2 | 13 | 12 | 3 | 5 | 4 | 9 | 10 | 17 | 14 | 8 | 16 | 11 | 18 | 6 | 15 | 20 | 19 | 7 | 1 |
| 7 | 11 | 20 | 5 | 10 | 18 | 8 | 12 | 6 | 4 | 19 | 13 | 1 | 15 | 17 | 9 | 3 | 16 | 14 | 2 |
| 6 | 13 | 17 | 10 | 2 | 15 | 5 | 19 | 20 | 7 | 3 | 11 | 14 | 4 | 9 | 18 | 12 | 1 | 8 | 16 |
| 6 | 18 | 9 | 17 | 14 | 15 | 1 | 8 | 13 | 11 | 7 | 20 | 2 | 4 | 10 | 19 | 5 | 16 | 12 | 3 |
| | | | | | | | | | | | | | | | | | | | |
| 4 | 2 | 18 | 9 | 7 | 1 | 5 | 17 | 16 | 3 | 20 | 13 | 12 | 8 | 19 | 10 | 6 | 15 | 11 | 14 |
| 18 | 1 | 17 | 3 | 15 | 6 | 4 | 14 | 20 | 12 | 9 | 2 | 19 | 8 | 7 | 13 | 16 | 11 | 5 | 10 |
| 5 | 8 | 1 | 18 | 16 | 17 | 13 | 12 | 2 | 7 | 10 | 15 | 6 | 11 | 4 | 19 | 14 | 20 | 9 | 3 |
| 5 | 18 | 11 | 1 | 9 | 19 | 3 | 10 | 4 | 15 | 8 | 2 | 20 | 6 | 14 | 12 | 7 | 17 | 13 | 16 |
| 13 | 1 | 6 | 9 | 4 | 15 | 12 | 10 | 11 | 3 | 20 | 18 | 5 | 8 | 17 | 19 | 7 | 16 | 14 | 2 |

## Appendix Table 4—*continued*

| | | | | | | | | | | | | | | | | | | | |
|---|---|---|---|---|---|---|---|---|---|---|---|---|---|---|---|---|---|---|---|
| 15 | 14 | 11 | 19 | 6 | 10 | 12 | 8 | 4 | 18 | 13 | 20 | 9 | 3 | 17 | 16 | 2 | 7 | 5 | 1 |
| 13 | 12 | 16 | 5 | 10 | 4 | 19 | 15 | 18 | 1 | 2 | 8 | 20 | 17 | 7 | 3 | 9 | 11 | 6 | 14 |
| 8 | 2 | 16 | 10 | 18 | 4 | 9 | 6 | 12 | 5 | 15 | 17 | 20 | 3 | 1 | 14 | 11 | 13 | 7 | 19 |
| 8 | 13 | 6 | 12 | 9 | 14 | 20 | 7 | 4 | 19 | 10 | 5 | 11 | 17 | 1 | 18 | 3 | 15 | 2 | 16 |
| 3 | 8 | 11 | 2 | 18 | 15 | 9 | 1 | 10 | 13 | 20 | 5 | 14 | 4 | 17 | 19 | 6 | 7 | 12 | 16 |
| 16 | 17 | 12 | 2 | 15 | 4 | 19 | 10 | 7 | 1 | 3 | 9 | 11 | 5 | 13 | 6 | 20 | 8 | 14 | 18 |
| 19 | 3 | 18 | 10 | 15 | 8 | 12 | 13 | 11 | 17 | 6 | 14 | 9 | 20 | 1 | 5 | 2 | 16 | 7 | 4 |
| 19 | 9 | 3 | 5 | 8 | 6 | 11 | 16 | 4 | 15 | 2 | 18 | 10 | 20 | 14 | 7 | 12 | 17 | 13 | 1 |
| 6 | 7 | 8 | 14 | 16 | 12 | 11 | 2 | 17 | 3 | 5 | 1 | 4 | 10 | 18 | 13 | 15 | 19 | 9 | 20 |
| 9 | 20 | 17 | 5 | 19 | 13 | 6 | 12 | 15 | 14 | 3 | 11 | 16 | 8 | 18 | 7 | 10 | 4 | 2 | 1 |
| 12 | 14 | 19 | 16 | 10 | 1 | 13 | 5 | 8 | 4 | 18 | 17 | 9 | 6 | 11 | 15 | 7 | 3 | 2 | 20 |
| 18 | 1 | 2 | 8 | 4 | 17 | 7 | 15 | 19 | 5 | 12 | 6 | 20 | 16 | 13 | 11 | 14 | 10 | 3 | 9 |
| 8 | 6 | 5 | 11 | 13 | 20 | 7 | 2 | 4 | 17 | 3 | 10 | 1 | 15 | 14 | 9 | 12 | 16 | 19 | 18 |
| 8 | 11 | 16 | 20 | 10 | 19 | 6 | 1 | 15 | 2 | 14 | 7 | 13 | 4 | 5 | 18 | 3 | 9 | 17 | 12 |
| 2 | 7 | 9 | 6 | 15 | 10 | 3 | 18 | 17 | 1 | 5 | 4 | 19 | 11 | 8 | 14 | 16 | 12 | 13 | 20 |
| 5 | 8 | 1 | 15 | 18 | 7 | 3 | 4 | 12 | 16 | 10 | 19 | 14 | 20 | 6 | 17 | 9 | 2 | 13 | 11 |
| 15 | 5 | 20 | 18 | 9 | 6 | 17 | 8 | 10 | 11 | 3 | 2 | 12 | 4 | 7 | 13 | 14 | 19 | 16 | 1 |
| 14 | 3 | 4 | 11 | 1 | 20 | 17 | 15 | 10 | 13 | 2 | 6 | 7 | 9 | 19 | 8 | 5 | 12 | 18 | 16 |
| 8 | 10 | 14 | 5 | 6 | 11 | 7 | 15 | 20 | 3 | 12 | 19 | 13 | 1 | 16 | 4 | 17 | 18 | 9 | 2 |
| 12 | 2 | 19 | 10 | 20 | 17 | 15 | 16 | 3 | 11 | 5 | 4 | 8 | 18 | 9 | 6 | 1 | 14 | 13 | 7 |
| 18 | 10 | 14 | 3 | 13 | 19 | 20 | 15 | 1 | 12 | 16 | 7 | 5 | 17 | 8 | 6 | 11 | 9 | 4 | 2 |
| 2 | 6 | 11 | 8 | 3 | 5 | 12 | 10 | 20 | 13 | 19 | 15 | 17 | 9 | 7 | 16 | 14 | 4 | 1 | 18 |
| 18 | 11 | 10 | 13 | 8 | 20 | 7 | 6 | 9 | 19 | 14 | 5 | 12 | 1 | 17 | 3 | 16 | 15 | 2 | 4 |
| 20 | 5 | 19 | 7 | 10 | 17 | 9 | 3 | 14 | 1 | 16 | 8 | 15 | 18 | 11 | 4 | 12 | 2 | 6 | 13 |
| 7 | 17 | 10 | 15 | 4 | 2 | 13 | 1 | 5 | 14 | 9 | 16 | 18 | 3 | 12 | 11 | 8 | 20 | 19 | 6 |
| 19 | 8 | 11 | 14 | 9 | 17 | 5 | 2 | 13 | 10 | 16 | 6 | 1 | 4 | 12 | 20 | 18 | 7 | 15 | 3 |
| 2 | 4 | 15 | 3 | 13 | 7 | 16 | 20 | 6 | 10 | 8 | 19 | 17 | 5 | 14 | 11 | 12 | 1 | 9 | 18 |
| 18 | 5 | 9 | 13 | 7 | 1 | 12 | 6 | 14 | 15 | 2 | 16 | 19 | 17 | 4 | 3 | 10 | 8 | 20 | 11 |
| 11 | 12 | 14 | 10 | 20 | 9 | 8 | 4 | 15 | 17 | 19 | 1 | 3 | 18 | 7 | 5 | 16 | 6 | 13 | 2 |
| 9 | 18 | 17 | 8 | 4 | 5 | 6 | 2 | 14 | 13 | 7 | 15 | 10 | 3 | 12 | 19 | 16 | 20 | 11 | 1 |
| 1 | 9 | 2 | 18 | 6 | 8 | 12 | 19 | 20 | 15 | 4 | 3 | 13 | 16 | 5 | 14 | 11 | 17 | 7 | 10 |
| 13 | 11 | 14 | 19 | 18 | 15 | 20 | 5 | 10 | 17 | 7 | 8 | 9 | 2 | 16 | 1 | 6 | 3 | 12 | 4 |
| 3 | 14 | 11 | 6 | 18 | 10 | 2 | 15 | 7 | 9 | 19 | 4 | 17 | 20 | 12 | 1 | 5 | 16 | 8 | 13 |
| 18 | 1 | 20 | 7 | 3 | 11 | 13 | 15 | 17 | 10 | 16 | 4 | 6 | 5 | 2 | 12 | 8 | 9 | 19 | 14 |
| 10 | 20 | 7 | 18 | 9 | 5 | 6 | 15 | 2 | 17 | 16 | 19 | 13 | 14 | 12 | 1 | 8 | 11 | 3 | 4 |
| 4 | 14 | 20 | 19 | 6 | 13 | 17 | 8 | 10 | 7 | 5 | 12 | 11 | 2 | 18 | 3 | 9 | 15 | 16 | 1 |
| 6 | 5 | 2 | 8 | 20 | 9 | 15 | 1 | 7 | 10 | 17 | 14 | 4 | 19 | 16 | 13 | 12 | 11 | 3 | 18 |
| 13 | 9 | 2 | 12 | 14 | 18 | 6 | 11 | 20 | 4 | 8 | 19 | 15 | 5 | 7 | 3 | 17 | 1 | 16 | 10 |
| 12 | 17 | 6 | 3 | 18 | 1 | 15 | 9 | 11 | 14 | 20 | 5 | 7 | 19 | 2 | 13 | 8 | 10 | 4 | 16 |
| 7 | 12 | 3 | 10 | 16 | 20 | 13 | 6 | 18 | 2 | 17 | 14 | 4 | 5 | 1 | 11 | 9 | 8 | 19 | 15 |
| 1 | 4 | 18 | 17 | 16 | 10 | 5 | 14 | 20 | 15 | 9 | 3 | 13 | 2 | 7 | 6 | 8 | 11 | 12 | 19 |
| 18 | 9 | 4 | 2 | 16 | 11 | 5 | 19 | 14 | 1 | 12 | 15 | 8 | 17 | 13 | 7 | 20 | 10 | 3 | 6 |
| 3 | 1 | 16 | 18 | 14 | 11 | 4 | 15 | 5 | 13 | 19 | 17 | 6 | 12 | 10 | 7 | 8 | 2 | 20 | 9 |
| 10 | 19 | 7 | 5 | 20 | 3 | 2 | 13 | 14 | 9 | 8 | 12 | 6 | 15 | 4 | 17 | 16 | 11 | 18 | 1 |
| 20 | 15 | 19 | 6 | 7 | 8 | 9 | 2 | 3 | 12 | 18 | 11 | 14 | 16 | 13 | 10 | 5 | 1 | 4 | 17 |
| 6 | 7 | 3 | 17 | 5 | 9 | 11 | 4 | 1 | 13 | 18 | 2 | 8 | 20 | 10 | 16 | 12 | 14 | 15 | 19 |
| 10 | 3 | 16 | 4 | 6 | 2 | 11 | 9 | 19 | 17 | 8 | 1 | 14 | 7 | 5 | 20 | 13 | 12 | 15 | 18 |
| 13 | 5 | 6 | 16 | 10 | 7 | 8 | 12 | 2 | 20 | 3 | 4 | 17 | 11 | 9 | 1 | 15 | 19 | 18 | 14 |
| 10 | 5 | 15 | 3 | 2 | 19 | 13 | 18 | 9 | 14 | 16 | 4 | 20 | 17 | 12 | 11 | 8 | 1 | 6 | 7 |
| 10 | 18 | 12 | 19 | 11 | 14 | 4 | 3 | 8 | 2 | 7 | 20 | 5 | 17 | 16 | 6 | 15 | 13 | 1 | 9 |

# APPENDIX TABLE 5A

CONCORDANCE COEFFICIENT $W$. PROBABILITY THAT A GIVEN VALUE OF $S$ WILL BE ATTAINED OR EXCEEDED FOR $n = 3$ AND VALUES OF $m$ FROM 2 TO 10

Values of $m$

| $S$ | 2 | 3 | 4 | 5 | 6 | 7 | 8 | 9 | 10 |
|---|---|---|---|---|---|---|---|---|---|
| 0 | 1·000 | 1·000 | 1·000 | 1·000 | 1·000 | 1·000 | 1·000 | 1·000 | 1·000 |
| 2 | 0·833 | 0·944 | 0·931 | 0·954 | 0·956 | 0·964 | 0·967 | 0·971 | 0·974 |
| 6 | 0·500 | 0·528 | 0·653 | 0·691 | 0·740 | 0·768 | 0·794 | 0·814 | 0·830 |
| 8 | 0·167 | 0·361 | 0·431 | 0·522 | 0·570 | 0·620 | 0·654 | 0·685 | 0·710 |
| 14 | | 0·194 | 0·273 | 0·367 | 0·430 | 0·486 | 0·531 | 0·569 | 0·601 |
| 18 | | 0·028 | 0·125 | 0·182 | 0·252 | 0·305 | 0·355 | 0·398 | 0·436 |
| 24 | | | 0·069 | 0·124 | 0·184 | 0·237 | 0·285 | 0·328 | 0·368 |
| 26 | | | 0·042 | 0·093 | 0·142 | 0·192 | 0·236 | 0·278 | 0·316 |
| 32 | | | 0·0046 | 0·039 | 0·072 | 0·112 | 0·149 | 0·187 | 0·222 |
| 38 | | | | 0·024 | 0·052 | 0·085 | 0·120 | 0·154 | 0·187 |
| 42 | | | | 0·0085 | 0·029 | 0·051 | 0·079 | 0·107 | 0·135 |
| 50 | | | | 0·0$^3$77 | 0·012 | 0·027 | 0·047 | 0·069 | 0·092 |
| 54 | | | | | 0·0081 | 0·021 | 0·038 | 0·057 | 0·078 |
| 56 | | | | | 0·0055 | 0·016 | 0·030 | 0·048 | 0·066 |
| 62 | | | | | 0·0017 | 0·0084 | 0·018 | 0·031 | 0·046 |
| 72 | | | | | 0·0$^3$13 | 0·0036 | 0·0099 | 0·019 | 0·030 |
| 74 | | | | | | 0·0027 | 0·0080 | 0·016 | 0·026 |
| 78 | | | | | | 0·0012 | 0·0048 | 0·010 | 0·018 |
| 86 | | | | | | 0·0$^3$32 | 0·0024 | 0·0060 | 0·012 |
| 96 | | | | | | 0·0$^3$32 | 0·0011 | 0·0035 | 0·0075 |
| 98 | | | | | | 0·0$^4$21 | 0·0$^3$86 | 0·0029 | 0·0063 |
| 104 | | | | | | | 0·0$^3$26 | 0·0013 | 0·0034 |
| 114 | | | | | | | 0·0$^4$61 | 0·0$^3$66 | 0·0020 |
| 122 | | | | | | | 0·0$^4$61 | 0·0$^3$35 | 0·0013 |
| 126 | | | | | | | 0·0$^4$61 | 0·0$^3$20 | 0·0$^3$83 |
| 128 | | | | | | | 0·0$^5$36 | 0·0$^4$97 | 0·0$^3$51 |
| 134 | | | | | | | | 0·0$^4$54 | 0·0$^3$37 |
| 146 | | | | | | | | 0·0$^4$11 | 0·0$^3$18 |
| 150 | | | | | | | | 0·0$^4$11 | 0·0$^3$11 |
| 152 | | | | | | | | 0·0$^4$11 | 0·0$^4$85 |
| 158 | | | | | | | | 0·0$^4$11 | 0·0$^4$44 |
| 162 | | | | | | | | 0·0$^6$60 | 0·0$^4$20 |
| 168 | | | | | | | | | 0·0$^4$11 |
| 182 | | | | | | | | | 0·0$^5$21 |
| 200 | | | | | | | | | 0·0$^7$99 |

# APPENDIX TABLE 5B

CONCORDANCE COEFFICIENT $W$. PROBABILITY THAT A GIVEN VALUE OF $S$ WILL BE ATTAINED OR EXCEEDED FOR $n = 4$ AND $m = 3$ AND 5

| $S$ | $m = 3$ | $m = 5$ | $S$ | $m = 5$ |
|---|---|---|---|---|
| 1 | 1·000 | 1·000 | 61 | 0·055 |
| 3 | 0·958 | 0·975 | 65 | 0·044 |
| 5 | 0·910 | 0·944 | 67 | 0·034 |
| 9 | 0·727 | 0·857 | 69 | 0·031 |
| 11 | 0·608 | 0·771 | 73 | 0·023 |
| 13 | 0·524 | 0·709 | 75 | 0·020 |
| 17 | 0·446 | 0·652 | 77 | 0·017 |
| 19 | 0·342 | 0·561 | 81 | 0·012 |
| 21 | 0·300 | 0·521 | 83 | 0·0087 |
| 25 | 0·207 | 0·445 | 85 | 0·0067 |
| 27 | 0·175 | 0·408 | 89 | 0·0055 |
| 29 | 0·148 | 0·372 | 91 | 0·0031 |
| 33 | 0·075 | 0·298 | 93 | 0·0023 |
| 35 | 0·054 | 0·260 | 97 | 0·0018 |
| 37 | 0·033 | 0·226 | 99 | 0·0016 |
| 41 | 0·017 | 0·210 | 101 | 0·0014 |
| 43 | 0·0017 | 0·162 | 105 | $0{\cdot}0^{3}64$ |
| 45 | 0·0017 | 0·141 | 107 | $0{\cdot}0^{3}33$ |
| 49 | | 0·123 | 109 | $0{\cdot}0^{3}21$ |
| 51 | | 0·107 | 113 | $0{\cdot}0^{3}14$ |
| 53 | | 0·093 | 117 | $0{\cdot}0^{4}48$ |
| 57 | | 0·075 | 125 | $0{\cdot}0^{5}30$ |
| 59 | | 0·067 | | |

# APPENDIX TABLE 5c

CONCORDANCE COEFFICIENT $W$. PROBABILITY THAT A GIVEN VALUE OF $S$ WILL BE ATTAINED OR EXCEEDED FOR $n = 4$ AND $m = 2$, 4 AND 6

| $S$ | $m = 2$ | $m = 4$ | $m = 6$ | $S$ | $m = 6$ |
|---|---|---|---|---|---|
| 0 | 1·000 | 1·000 | 1·000 | 82 | 0·035 |
| 2 | 0·958 | 0·992 | 0·996 | 84 | 0·032 |
| 4 | 0·833 | 0·928 | 0·957 | 86 | 0·029 |
| 6 | 0·792 | 0·900 | 0·940 | 88 | 0·023 |
| 8 | 0·625 | 0·800 | 0·874 | 90 | 0·022 |
| 10 | 0·542 | 0·754 | 0·844 | 94 | 0·017 |
| 12 | 0·458 | 0·677 | 0·789 | 96 | 0·014 |
| 14 | 0·375 | 0·649 | 0·772 | 98 | 0·013 |
| 16 | 0·208 | 0·524 | 0·679 | 100 | 0·010 |
| 18 | 0·167 | 0·508 | 0·668 | 102 | 0·0096 |
| 20 | 0·042 | 0·432 | 0·609 | 104 | 0·0085 |
| 22 | | 0·389 | 0·574 | 106 | 0·0073 |
| 24 | | 0·355 | 0·541 | 108 | 0·0061 |
| 26 | | 0·324 | 0·512 | 110 | 0·0057 |
| 30 | | 0·242 | 0·431 | 114 | 0·0040 |
| 32 | | 0·200 | 0·386 | 116 | 0·0033 |
| 34 | | 0·190 | 0·375 | 118 | 0·0028 |
| 36 | | 0·158 | 0·338 | 120 | 0·0023 |
| 38 | | 0·141 | 0·317 | 122 | 0·0020 |
| 40 | | 0·105 | 0·270 | 126 | 0·0015 |
| 42 | | 0·094 | 0·256 | 128 | $0{\cdot}0^{3}90$ |
| 44 | | 0·077 | 0·230 | 130 | $0{\cdot}0^{3}87$ |
| 46 | | 0·068 | 0·218 | 132 | $0{\cdot}0^{3}73$ |
| 48 | | 0·054 | 0·197 | 134 | $0{\cdot}0^{3}65$ |
| 50 | | 0·052 | 0·194 | 136 | $0{\cdot}0^{3}40$ |
| 52 | | 0·036 | 0·163 | 138 | $0{\cdot}0^{3}36$ |
| 54 | | 0·033 | 0·155 | 140 | $0{\cdot}0^{3}28$ |
| 56 | | 0·019 | 0·127 | 144 | $0{\cdot}0^{3}24$ |
| 58 | | 0·014 | 0·114 | 146 | $0{\cdot}0^{3}22$ |
| 62 | | 0·012 | 0·108 | 148 | $0{\cdot}0^{3}12$ |
| 64 | | 0·0069 | 0·089 | 150 | $0{\cdot}0^{4}95$ |
| 66 | | 0·0062 | 0·088 | 152 | $0{\cdot}0^{4}62$ |
| 68 | | 0·0027 | 0·073 | 154 | $0{\cdot}0^{4}46$ |
| 70 | | 0·0027 | 0·066 | 158 | $0{\cdot}0^{4}24$ |
| 72 | | 0·0016 | 0·060 | 160 | $0{\cdot}0^{4}16$ |
| 74 | | $0{\cdot}0^{3}94$ | 0·056 | 162 | $0{\cdot}0^{4}12$ |
| 76 | | $0{\cdot}0^{3}94$ | 0·043 | 164 | $0{\cdot}0^{5}80$ |
| 78 | | $0{\cdot}0^{3}94$ | 0·041 | 170 | $0{\cdot}0^{5}24$ |
| 80 | | $0{\cdot}0^{4}72$ | 0·037 | 180 | $0{\cdot}0^{6}13$ |

# APPENDIX TABLE 5D

CONCORDANCE COEFFICIENT $W$. PROBABILITY THAT A GIVEN VALUE OF $S$ WILL BE ATTAINED OR EXCEEDED FOR $n = 5$ AND $m = 3$

| $S$ | $m = 3$ | $S$ | $m = 3$ |
|---|---|---|---|
| 0 | 1·000 | 44 | 0·236 |
| 2 | 1·000 | 46 | 0·213 |
| 4 | 0·988 | 48 | 0·172 |
| 6 | 0·972 | 50 | 0·163 |
| 8 | 0·941 | 52 | 0·127 |
| 10 | 0·914 | 54 | 0·117 |
| 12 | 0·845 | 56 | 0·096 |
| 14 | 0·831 | 58 | 0·080 |
| 16 | 0·768 | 60 | 0·063 |
| 18 | 0·720 | 62 | 0·056 |
| 20 | 0·682 | 64 | 0·045 |
| 22 | 0·649 | 66 | 0·038 |
| 24 | 0·595 | 68 | 0·028 |
| 26 | 0·559 | 70 | 0·026 |
| 28 | 0·493 | 72 | 0·017 |
| 30 | 0·475 | 74 | 0·015 |
| 32 | 0·432 | 76 | 0·0078 |
| 34 | 0·406 | 78 | 0·0053 |
| 36 | 0·347 | 80 | 0·0040 |
| 38 | 0·326 | 82 | 0·0028 |
| 40 | 0·291 | 86 | $0{\cdot}0^{3}90$ |
| 42 | 0·253 | 90 | $0{\cdot}0^{4}69$ |

# APPENDIX TABLE 6

SIGNIFICANCE POINTS OF $S$ (FOR THE COEFFICIENT OF CONCORDANCE $W$)

From Friedman (1940) by permission of the author and the Editor of the *Annals of Mathematical Statistics*

| $m$ | $n$ | | | | | Additional values for $n = 3$ | |
|---|---|---|---|---|---|---|---|
| | 3 | 4 | 5 | 6 | 7 | $m$ | $S$ |
| **Values at 0·05 Level of Significance** | | | | | | | |
| 3 | | | 64·4 | 103·9 | 157·3 | 9 | 54·0 |
| 4 | | 49·5 | 88·4 | 143·3 | 217·0 | 12 | 71·9 |
| 5 | | 62·6 | 112·3 | 182·4 | 276·2 | 14 | 83·8 |
| 6 | | 75·7 | 136·1 | 221·4 | 335·2 | 16 | 95·8 |
| 8 | 48·1 | 101·7 | 183·7 | 299·0 | 453·1 | 18 | 107·7 |
| 10 | 60·0 | 127·8 | 231·2 | 376·7 | 571·0 | | |
| 15 | 89·8 | 192·9 | 349·8 | 570·5 | 864·9 | | |
| 20 | 119·7 | 258·0 | 468·5 | 764·4 | 1158·7 | | |
| **Values at 0·01 Level of Significance** | | | | | | | |
| 3 | | | 75·6 | 122·8 | 185·6 | 9 | 75·9 |
| 4 | | 61·4 | 109·3 | 176·2 | 265·0 | 12 | 103·5 |
| 5 | | 80·5 | 142·8 | 229·4 | 343·8 | 14 | 121·9 |
| 6 | | 99·5 | 176·1 | 282·4 | 422·6 | 16 | 140·2 |
| 8 | 66·8 | 137·4 | 242·7 | 388·3 | 579·9 | 18 | 158·6 |
| 10 | 85·1 | 175·3 | 309·1 | 494·0 | 737·0 | | |
| 15 | 131·0 | 269·8 | 475·2 | 758·2 | 1129·5 | | |
| 20 | 177·0 | 364·2 | 641·2 | 1022·2 | 1521·9 | | |

# APPENDIX TABLE 7A

## 5 PER CENT POINTS OF THE DISTRIBUTION OF $z$

Reprinted from Table VI of Professor Sir R. A. Fisher's *Statistical Methods for Research Workers*, Oliver & Boyd, Ltd., Edinburgh, by permission of the author and publishers

| | Values of $\nu_1$. | | | | | | | | | |
|---|---|---|---|---|---|---|---|---|---|---|
| Values of $\nu_2$. | 1. | 2. | 3. | 4. | 5. | 6. | 8. | 12. | 24. | ∞. |
| 1 | 2·5421 | 2·6479 | 2·6870 | 2·7071 | 2·7194 | 2·7276 | 2·7380 | 2·7484 | 2·7588 | 2·7693 |
| 2 | 1·4592 | 1·4722 | 1·4765 | 1·4787 | 1·4800 | 1·4808 | 1·4819 | 1·4830 | 1·4840 | 1·4851 |
| 3 | 1·1577 | 1·1284 | 1·1137 | 1·1051 | 1·0994 | 1·0953 | 1·0899 | 1·0842 | 1·0781 | 1·0716 |
| 4 | 1·0212 | 0·9690 | 0·9429 | 0·9272 | 0·9168 | 0·9093 | 0·8993 | 0·8885 | 0·8767 | 0·8639 |
| 5 | 0·9441 | 0·8777 | 0·8441 | 0·8236 | 0·8097 | 0·7997 | 0·7862 | 0·7714 | 0·7550 | 0·7368 |
| 6 | 0·8948 | 0·8188 | 0·7798 | 0·7558 | 0·7394 | 0·7274 | 0·7112 | 0·6931 | 0·6729 | 0·6499 |
| 7 | 0·8606 | 0·7777 | 0·7347 | 0·7080 | 0·6896 | 0·6761 | 0·6576 | 0·6369 | 0·6134 | 0·5862 |
| 8 | 0·8355 | 0·7475 | 0·7014 | 0·6725 | 0·6525 | 0·6378 | 0·6175 | 0·5945 | 0·5682 | 0·5371 |
| 9 | 0·8163 | 0·7242 | 0·6757 | 0·6450 | 0·6238 | 0·6080 | 0·5862 | 0·5613 | 0·5324 | 0·4979 |
| 10 | 0·8012 | 0·7058 | 0·6553 | 0·6232 | 0·6009 | 0·5843 | 0·5611 | 0·5346 | 0·5035 | 0·4657 |
| 11 | 0·7889 | 0·6909 | 0·6387 | 0·6055 | 0·5822 | 0·5648 | 0·5406 | 0·5126 | 0·4795 | 0·4387 |
| 12 | 0·7788 | 0·6786 | 0·6250 | 0·5907 | 0·5666 | 0·5487 | 0·5234 | 0·4941 | 0·4592 | 0·4156 |
| 13 | 0·7703 | 0·6682 | 0·6134 | 0·5783 | 0·5535 | 0·5350 | 0·5089 | 0·4785 | 0·4419 | 0·3957 |
| 14 | 0·7630 | 0·6594 | 0·6036 | 0·5677 | 0·5423 | 0·5233 | 0·4964 | 0·4649 | 0·4269 | 0·3782 |
| 15 | 0·7568 | 0·6518 | 0·5950 | 0·5585 | 0·5326 | 0·5131 | 0·4855 | 0·4532 | 0·4138 | 0·3628 |
| 16 | 0·7514 | 0·6451 | 0·5876 | 0·5505 | 0·5241 | 0·5042 | 0·4760 | 0·4428 | 0·4022 | 0·3490 |
| 17 | 0·7466 | 0·6393 | 0·5811 | 0·5434 | 0·5166 | 0·4964 | 0·4676 | 0·4337 | 0·3919 | 0·3366 |
| 18 | 0·7424 | 0·6341 | 0·5753 | 0·5371 | 0·5099 | 0·4894 | 0·4602 | 0·4255 | 0·3827 | 0·3253 |
| 19 | 0·7386 | 0·6295 | 0·5701 | 0·5315 | 0·5040 | 0·4832 | 0·4535 | 0·4182 | 0·3743 | 0·3151 |
| 20 | 0·7352 | 0·6254 | 0·5654 | 0·5265 | 0·4986 | 0·4776 | 0·4474 | 0·4116 | 0·3668 | 0·3057 |
| 21 | 0·7322 | 0·6216 | 0·5612 | 0·5219 | 0·4938 | 0·4725 | 0·4420 | 0·4055 | 0·3599 | 0·2971 |
| 22 | 0·7294 | 0·6182 | 0·5574 | 0·5178 | 0·4894 | 0·4679 | 0·4370 | 0·4001 | 0·3536 | 0·2892 |
| 23 | 0·7269 | 0·6151 | 0·5540 | 0·5140 | 0·4854 | 0·4636 | 0·4325 | 0·3950 | 0·3478 | 0·2818 |
| 24 | 0·7246 | 0·6123 | 0·5508 | 0·5106 | 0·4817 | 0·4598 | 0·4283 | 0·3904 | 0·3425 | 0·2749 |
| 25 | 0·7225 | 0·6097 | 0·5478 | 0·5074 | 0·4783 | 0·4562 | 0·4244 | 0·3862 | 0·3376 | 0·2685 |
| 26 | 0·7205 | 0·6073 | 0·5451 | 0·5045 | 0·4752 | 0·4529 | 0·4209 | 0·3823 | 0·3330 | 0·2625 |
| 27 | 0·7187 | 0·6051 | 0·5427 | 0·5017 | 0·4723 | 0·4499 | 0·4176 | 0·3786 | 0·3287 | 0·2569 |
| 28 | 0·7171 | 0·6030 | 0·5403 | 0·4992 | 0·4696 | 0·4471 | 0·4146 | 0·3752 | 0·3248 | 0·2516 |
| 29 | 0·7155 | 0·6011 | 0·5382 | 0·4969 | 0·4671 | 0·4444 | 0·4117 | 0·3720 | 0·3211 | 0·2466 |
| 30 | 0·7141 | 0·5994 | 0·5362 | 0·4947 | 0·4648 | 0·4420 | 0·4090 | 0·3691 | 0·3176 | 0·2419 |
| 60 | 0·6933 | 0·5738 | 0·5073 | 0·4632 | 0·4311 | 0·4064 | 0·3702 | 0·3255 | 0·2654 | 0·1644 |
| ∞ | 0·6729 | 0·5486 | 0·4787 | 0·4319 | 0·3974 | 0·3706 | 0·3309 | 0·2804 | 0·2085 | 0 |

# APPENDIX TABLE 7B

## 1 Per Cent Points of the Distribution of $z$

**Reprinted from Table VI of Professor Sir R. A. Fisher's *Statistical Methods for Research Workers*, Oliver & Boyd, Ltd., Edinburgh, by permission of the author and publishers**

| Values of $\nu_2$ | Values of $\nu_1$: 1. | 2. | 3. | 4. | 5. | 6. | 8. | 12. | 24. | ∞. |
|---|---|---|---|---|---|---|---|---|---|---|
| 1 | 4·1535 | 4·2585 | 4·2974 | 4·3175 | 4·3297 | 4·3379 | 4·3482 | 4·3585 | 4·3689 | 4·3794 |
| 2 | 2·2950 | 2·2976 | 2·2984 | 2·2988 | 2·2991 | 2·2992 | 2·2994 | 2·2997 | 2·2999 | 2·3001 |
| 3 | 1·7649 | 1·7140 | 1·6915 | 1·6786 | 1·6703 | 1·6645 | 1·6569 | 1·6489 | 1·6404 | 1·6314 |
| 4 | 1·5270 | 1·4452 | 1·4075 | 1·3856 | 1·3711 | 1·3609 | 1·3473 | 1·3327 | 1·3170 | 1·3000 |
| 5 | 1·3943 | 1·2929 | 1·2449 | 1·2164 | 1·1974 | 1·1838 | 1·1656 | 1·1457 | 1·1239 | 1·0997 |
| 6 | 1·3103 | 1·1955 | 1·1401 | 1·1068 | 1·0843 | 1·0680 | 1·0460 | 1·0218 | 0·9948 | 0·9643 |
| 7 | 1·2526 | 1·1281 | 1·0672 | 1·0300 | 1·0048 | 0·9864 | 0·9614 | 0·9335 | 0·9020 | 0·8658 |
| 8 | 1·2106 | 1·0787 | 1·0135 | 0·9734 | 0·9459 | 0·9259 | 0·8983 | 0·8673 | 0·8319 | 0·7904 |
| 9 | 1·1786 | 1·0411 | 0·9724 | 0·9299 | 0·9006 | 0·8791 | 0·8494 | 0·8157 | 0·7769 | 0·7305 |
| 10 | 1·1535 | 1·0114 | 0·9399 | 0·8954 | 0·8646 | 0·8419 | 0·8104 | 0·7744 | 0·7324 | 0·6816 |
| 11 | 1·1333 | 0·9874 | 0·9136 | 0·8674 | 0·8354 | 0·8116 | 0·7785 | 0·7405 | 0·6958 | 0·6408 |
| 12 | 1·1166 | 0·9677 | 0·8919 | 0·8443 | 0·8111 | 0·7864 | 0·7520 | 0·7122 | 0·6649 | 0·6061 |
| 13 | 1·1027 | 0·9511 | 0·8737 | 0·8248 | 0·7907 | 0·7652 | 0·7295 | 0·6882 | 0·6386 | 0·5761 |
| 14 | 1·0909 | 0·9370 | 0·8581 | 0·8082 | 0·7732 | 0·7471 | 0·7103 | 0·6675 | 0·6159 | 0·5500 |
| 15 | 1·0807 | 0·9249 | 0·8448 | 0·7939 | 0·7582 | 0·7314 | 0·6937 | 0·6496 | 0·5961 | 0·5269 |
| 16 | 1·0719 | 0·9144 | 0·8331 | 0·7814 | 0·7450 | 0·7177 | 0·6791 | 0·6339 | 0·5786 | 0·5064 |
| 17 | 1·0641 | 0·9051 | 0·8229 | 0·7705 | 0·7335 | 0·7057 | 0·6663 | 0·6199 | 0·5630 | 0·4879 |
| 18 | 1·0572 | 0·8970 | 0·8138 | 0·7607 | 0·7232 | 0·6950 | 0·6549 | 0·6075 | 0·5491 | 0·4712 |
| 19 | 1·0511 | 0·8897 | 0·8057 | 0·7521 | 0·7140 | 0·6854 | 0·6447 | 0·5964 | 0·5366 | 0·4560 |
| 20 | 1·0457 | 0·8831 | 0·7985 | 0·7443 | 0·7058 | 0·6768 | 0·6355 | 0·5864 | 0·5253 | 0·4421 |
| 21 | 1·0408 | 0·8772 | 0·7920 | 0·7372 | 0·6984 | 0·6690 | 0·6272 | 0·5773 | 0·5150 | 0·4294 |
| 22 | 1·0363 | 0·8719 | 0·7860 | 0·7309 | 0·6916 | 0·6620 | 0·6196 | 0·5691 | 0·5056 | 0·4176 |
| 23 | 1·0322 | 0·8670 | 0·7806 | 0·7251 | 0·6855 | 0·6555 | 0·6127 | 0·5615 | 0·4969 | 0·4068 |
| 24 | 1·0285 | 0·8626 | 0·7757 | 0·7197 | 0·6799 | 0·6496 | 0·6064 | 0·5545 | 0·4890 | 0·3967 |
| 25 | 1·0251 | 0·8585 | 0·7712 | 0·7148 | 0·6747 | 0·6442 | 0·6006 | 0·5481 | 0·4816 | 0·3872 |
| 26 | 1·0220 | 0·8548 | 0·7670 | 0·7103 | 0·6699 | 0·6392 | 0·5952 | 0·5422 | 0·4748 | 0·3784 |
| 27 | 1·0191 | 0·8513 | 0·7631 | 0·7062 | 0·6655 | 0·6346 | 0·5902 | 0·5367 | 0·4685 | 0·3701 |
| 28 | 1·0164 | 0·8481 | 0·7595 | 0·7023 | 0·6614 | 0·6303 | 0·5856 | 0·5316 | 0·4626 | 0·3624 |
| 29 | 1·0139 | 0·8451 | 0·7562 | 0·6987 | 0·6576 | 0·6263 | 0·5813 | 0·5269 | 0·4570 | 0·3550 |
| 30 | 1·0116 | 0·8423 | 0·7531 | 0·6954 | 0·6540 | 0·6226 | 0·5773 | 0·5224 | 0·4519 | 0·3481 |
| 60 | 0·9784 | 0·8025 | 0·7086 | 0·6472 | 0·6028 | 0·5687 | 0·5189 | 0·4574 | 0·3746 | 0·2352 |
| ∞ | 0·9462 | 0·7636 | 0·6651 | 0·5999 | 0·5522 | 0·5152 | 0·4604 | 0·3908 | 0·2913 | 0 |

# APPENDIX TABLE 8

## SIGNIFICANCE POINTS OF $\chi^2$

Reproduced from Table III of Professor Sir R. A. Fisher's *Statistical Methods for Research Workers*, Oliver & Boyd, Ltd., Edinburgh, by permission of the author and publishers

| $\nu$ | $P$ = 0·99 | 0·98 | 0·95 | 0·90 | 0·80 | 0·70 | 0·50 | 0·30 | 0·20 | 0·10 | 0·05 | 0·02 | 0·01 |
|---|---|---|---|---|---|---|---|---|---|---|---|---|---|
| 1 | $0{\cdot}0^{3}157$ | $0{\cdot}0^{3}628$ | $0{\cdot}0^{2}393$ | 0·0158 | 0·0642 | 0·148 | 0·455 | 1·074 | 1·642 | 2·706 | 3·841 | 5·412 | 6·635 |
| 2 | 0·0201 | 0·0404 | 0·103 | 0·211 | 0·446 | 0·713 | 1·386 | 2·408 | 3·219 | 4·605 | 5·991 | 7·824 | 9·210 |
| 3 | 0·115 | 0·185 | 0·352 | 0·584 | 1·005 | 1·424 | 2·366 | 3·665 | 4·642 | 6·251 | 7·815 | 9·837 | 11·345 |
| 4 | 0·297 | 0·429 | 0·711 | 1·064 | 1·649 | 2·195 | 3·357 | 4·878 | 5·989 | 7·779 | 9·488 | 11·668 | 13·277 |
| 5 | 0·554 | 0·752 | 1·145 | 1·160 | 2·343 | 3·000 | 4·351 | 6·064 | 7·289 | 9·236 | 11·070 | 13·388 | 15·086 |
| 6 | 0·872 | 1·134 | 1·635 | 2·204 | 3·070 | 3·828 | 5·348 | 7·231 | 8·558 | 10·645 | 12·592 | 15·033 | 16·812 |
| 7 | 1·239 | 1·564 | 2·167 | 2·833 | 3·822 | 4·671 | 6·346 | 8·383 | 9·803 | 12·017 | 14·067 | 16·622 | 18·475 |
| 8 | 1·646 | 2·032 | 2·733 | 3·490 | 4·594 | 5·527 | 7·344 | 9·524 | 11·030 | 13·362 | 15·507 | 18·168 | 20·090 |
| 9 | 2·088 | 2·532 | 3·325 | 4·168 | 5·380 | 6·393 | 8·343 | 10·656 | 12·242 | 14·684 | 16·919 | 19·679 | 21·666 |
| 10 | 2·358 | 3·059 | 3·940 | 4·865 | 6·179 | 7·267 | 9·342 | 11·781 | 13·442 | 15·987 | 18·307 | 21·161 | 23·209 |
| 11 | 3·053 | 3·609 | 4·575 | 5·578 | 6·989 | 8·148 | 10·341 | 12·899 | 14·631 | 17·275 | 19·675 | 22·618 | 24·725 |
| 12 | 3·571 | 4·178 | 5·226 | 6·304 | 7·807 | 9·034 | 11·340 | 14·011 | 15·821 | 18·549 | 21·026 | 24·054 | 26·217 |
| 13 | 4·107 | 4·765 | 5·892 | 7·042 | 8·634 | 9·926 | 12·340 | 15·119 | 16·985 | 19·812 | 22·362 | 25·472 | 27·688 |
| 14 | 4·660 | 5·368 | 6·571 | 7·790 | 9·467 | 10·821 | 13·339 | 16·222 | 18·151 | 21·064 | 23·685 | 26·873 | 29·141 |
| 15 | 5·229 | 5·985 | 7·261 | 8·547 | 10·307 | 11·721 | 14·339 | 17·322 | 19·311 | 22·307 | 24·996 | 28·259 | 30·578 |
| 16 | 5·812 | 6·614 | 7·962 | 9·312 | 11·152 | 12·624 | 15·338 | 18·418 | 20·465 | 23·542 | 26·296 | 29·633 | 32·000 |
| 17 | 6·408 | 7·255 | 8·672 | 10·085 | 12·002 | 13·531 | 16·338 | 19·511 | 21·615 | 24·769 | 27·587 | 30·995 | 33·409 |
| 18 | 7·015 | 7·906 | 9·390 | 10·865 | 12·857 | 14·440 | 17·338 | 20·601 | 22·760 | 25·989 | 28·869 | 32·346 | 34·805 |
| 19 | 7·633 | 8·567 | 10·117 | 11·651 | 13·716 | 15·352 | 18·338 | 21·689 | 23·900 | 27·204 | 30·144 | 33·687 | 36·191 |
| 20 | 8·260 | 9·237 | 10·851 | 12·443 | 14·578 | 16·266 | 19·337 | 22·775 | 25·038 | 28·412 | 31·410 | 35·020 | 37·566 |
| 21 | 8·897 | 9·915 | 11·591 | 13·240 | 15·445 | 17·182 | 20·337 | 23·858 | 26·171 | 29·615 | 32·671 | 36·343 | 38·932 |
| 22 | 9·542 | 10·600 | 12·338 | 14·041 | 16·314 | 18·101 | 21·337 | 24·939 | 27·301 | 30·813 | 33·924 | 37·659 | 40·289 |
| 23 | 10·196 | 11·293 | 13·091 | 14·848 | 17·187 | 19·021 | 22·337 | 26·018 | 28·429 | 32·007 | 35·172 | 38·968 | 41·638 |
| 24 | 10·856 | 11·992 | 13·848 | 15·659 | 18·062 | 19·943 | 23·337 | 27·096 | 29·553 | 33·196 | 36·415 | 40·270 | 42·980 |
| 25 | 11·524 | 12·697 | 14·611 | 16·473 | 18·940 | 20·867 | 24·337 | 28·172 | 30·675 | 34·382 | 37·652 | 41·566 | 44·314 |
| 26 | 12·198 | 13·409 | 15·379 | 17·292 | 19·820 | 21·792 | 25·336 | 29·246 | 31·795 | 35·563 | 38·885 | 42·856 | 45·642 |
| 27 | 12·879 | 14·125 | 16·151 | 18·114 | 20·703 | 22·719 | 26·336 | 30·319 | 32·912 | 36·741 | 40·113 | 44·140 | 46·963 |
| 28 | 13·565 | 14·847 | 16·928 | 18·939 | 21·588 | 23·647 | 27·336 | 31·391 | 34·027 | 37·916 | 41·337 | 45·419 | 48·278 |
| 29 | 14·256 | 15·574 | 17·708 | 19·768 | 22·475 | 24·577 | 28·336 | 32·461 | 35·139 | 39·087 | 42·557 | 46·693 | 49·588 |
| 30 | 14·953 | 16·306 | 18·493 | 20·599 | 23·364 | 25·508 | 29·336 | 33·530 | 36·250 | 40·256 | 43·773 | 47·962 | 50·892 |

*Note.*—For values of $\nu$ greater than 30 the quantity $\sqrt{2\chi^2}$ may be taken to be distributed normally about mean $\sqrt{(2\nu - 1)}$ with unit variance.

# APPENDIX TABLE 9

PAIRED COMPARISONS. FREQUENCY ($f$) OF VALUES OF $d$ AND PROBABILITY ($P$) THAT VALUES WILL BE ATTAINED OR EXCEEDED

| Value of $d$ | $n = 2$ | | $n = 3$ | | $n = 4$ | | $n = 5$ | | $n = 6$ | | $n = 7$ | |
|---|---|---|---|---|---|---|---|---|---|---|---|---|
| | $f$ | $P$ | $f$ | $P$ | $f$ | $P$ | $f$ | $P$ | $f$ | $P$ | $f$ | $P$ |
| 0 | 2 | 1·000 | 6 | 1·000 | 24 | 1·000 | 120 | 1·000 | 720 | 1·000 | 5,040 | 1·000 |
| 1 | | | 2 | 0·250 | 16 | 0·625 | 120 | 0·883 | 960 | 0·978 | 8,400 | 0·998 |
| 2 | | | | | 24 | 0·375 | 240 | 0·766 | 2,240 | 0·949 | 21,840 | 0·994 |
| 3 | | | | | | | 240 | 0·531 | 2,880 | 0·880 | 33,600 | 0·983 |
| 4 | | | | | | | 280 | 0·297 | 6,240 | 0·792 | 75,600 | 0·967 |
| 5 | | | | | | | 24 | 0·023 | 3,648 | 0·602 | 90,384 | 0·931 |
| 6 | | | | | | | | | 8,640 | 0·491 | 179,760 | 0·888 |
| 7 | | | | | | | | | 4,800 | 0·227 | 188,160 | 0·802 |
| 8 | | | | | | | | | 2,640 | 0·081 | 277,200 | 0·713 |
| 9 | | | | | | | | | | | 280,560 | 0·580 |
| 10 | | | | | | | | | | | 384,048 | 0·447 |
| 11 | | | | | | | | | | | 244,160 | 0·263 |
| 12 | | | | | | | | | | | 233,520 | 0·147 |
| 13 | | | | | | | | | | | 72,240 | 0·036 |
| 14 | | | | | | | | | | | 2,640 | 0·001 |
| TOTAL | 2 | — | 8 | — | 64 | — | 1,024 | — | 32,768 | — | 2,097,152 | — |

# APPENDIX TABLE 10A

Agreement in Paired Comparisons. The Probability $P$ that a Value of $\Sigma$ (for $u$) will be attained or exceeded, for $m = 3$, $n = 2$ to 8

| $n = 2$ | | $n = 3$ | | $n = 4$ | | $n = 5$ | | $n = 6$ | | $n = 7$ | | $n = 8$ | |
|---|---|---|---|---|---|---|---|---|---|---|---|---|---|
| $\Sigma$ | $P$ | $\Sigma$ | $P$ | $\Sigma$ | $P$ | $\Sigma$ | $P$ | $\Sigma$ | $P$ | $\Sigma$ | $P$ | $\Sigma$ | $P$ |
| 1 | 1·000 | 3 | 1·000 | 6 | 1·000 | 10 | 1·000 | 15 | 1·000 | 21 | 1·000 | 28 | 1·000 |
| 3 | 0·250 | 5 | 0·578 | 8 | 0·822 | 12 | 0·944 | 17 | 0·987 | 23 | 0·998 | 30 | 1·000 |
| | | 7 | 0·156 | 10 | 0·466 | 14 | 0·756 | 19 | 0·920 | 25 | 0·981 | 32 | 0·997 |
| | | 9 | 0·016 | 12 | 0·169 | 16 | 0·474 | 21 | 0·764 | 27 | 0·925 | 34 | 0·983 |
| | | | | 14 | 0·038 | 18 | 0·224 | 23 | 0·539 | 29 | 0·808 | 36 | 0·945 |
| | | | | 16 | 0·0046 | 20 | 0·078 | 25 | 0·314 | 31 | 0·633 | 38 | 0·865 |
| | | | | 18 | $0{\cdot}0^{3}24$ | 22 | 0·020 | 27 | 0·148 | 33 | 0·433 | 40 | 0·736 |
| | | | | | | 24 | 0·0035 | 29 | 0·057 | 35 | 0·256 | 42 | 0·572 |
| | | | | | | 26 | $0{\cdot}0^{3}42$ | 31 | 0·017 | 37 | 0·130 | 44 | 0·400 |
| | | | | | | 28 | $0{\cdot}0^{4}30$ | 33 | 0·0042 | 39 | 0·056 | 46 | 0·250 |
| | | | | | | 30 | $0{\cdot}0^{6}95$ | 35 | $0{\cdot}0^{3}79$ | 41 | 0·021 | 48 | 0·138 |
| | | | | | | | | 37 | $0{\cdot}0^{3}12$ | 43 | 0·0064 | 50 | 0·068 |
| | | | | | | | | 39 | $0{\cdot}0^{4}12$ | 45 | 0·0017 | 52 | 0·029 |
| | | | | | | | | 41 | $0{\cdot}0^{6}92$ | 47 | $0{\cdot}0^{3}37$ | 54 | 0·011 |
| | | | | | | | | 43 | $0{\cdot}0^{7}43$ | 49 | $0{\cdot}0^{4}68$ | 56 | 0·0038 |
| | | | | | | | | 45 | $0{\cdot}0^{9}93$ | 51 | $0{\cdot}0^{4}10$ | 58 | 0·0011 |
| | | | | | | | | | | 53 | $0{\cdot}0^{5}12$ | 60 | $0{\cdot}0^{3}29$ |
| | | | | | | | | | | 55 | $0{\cdot}0^{6}12$ | 62 | $0{\cdot}0^{4}66$ |
| | | | | | | | | | | 57 | $0{\cdot}0^{8}86$ | 64 | $0{\cdot}0^{4}13$ |
| | | | | | | | | | | 59 | $0{\cdot}0^{9}44$ | 66 | $0{\cdot}0^{5}22$ |
| | | | | | | | | | | 61 | $0{\cdot}0^{10}15$ | 68 | $0{\cdot}0^{6}32$ |
| | | | | | | | | | | 63 | $0{\cdot}0^{12}23$ | 70 | $0{\cdot}0^{7}40$ |
| | | | | | | | | | | | | 72 | $0{\cdot}0^{8}42$ |
| | | | | | | | | | | | | 74 | $0{\cdot}0^{9}36$ |
| | | | | | | | | | | | | 76 | $0{\cdot}0^{10}24$ |
| | | | | | | | | | | | | 78 | $0{\cdot}0^{11}13$ |
| | | | | | | | | | | | | 80 | $0{\cdot}0^{13}48$ |
| | | | | | | | | | | | | 82 | $0{\cdot}0^{14}12$ |
| | | | | | | | | | | | | 84 | $0{\cdot}0^{16}14$ |

# APPENDIX TABLE 10B

AGREEMENT IN PAIRED COMPARISONS. THE PROBABILITY $P$ THAT A VALUE OF $\Sigma$ (FOR $u$) WILL BE ATTAINED OR EXCEEDED, FOR $m = 4$ AND $n = 2$ TO 6 (FOR $n = 6$ ONLY VALUES BEYOND THE 1 PER CENT POINT ARE GIVEN)

| $n = 2$ | | $n = 3$ | | $n = 4$ | | $n = 5$ | | $n = 5$ | | $n = 6$ | | $n = 6$ | |
|---|---|---|---|---|---|---|---|---|---|---|---|---|---|
| $\Sigma$ | $P$ | $\Sigma$ | $P$ | $\Sigma$ | $P$ | $\Sigma$ | $P$ | $\Sigma$ | $P$ | $\Sigma$ | $P$ | $\Sigma$ | $P$ |
| 2 | 1·000 | 6 | 1·000 | 12 | 1·000 | 20 | 1·000 | 42 | 0·0048 | 57 | 0·014 | 79 | $0{\cdot}0^{8}42$ |
| 3 | 0·625 | 7 | 0·947 | 13 | 0·997 | 21 | 1·000 | 43 | 0·0030 | 58 | 0·0092 | 80 | $0{\cdot}0^{8}28$ |
| 6 | 0·125 | 8 | 0·736 | 14 | 0·975 | 22 | 0·999 | 44 | 0·0017 | 59 | 0·0058 | 81 | $0{\cdot}0^{9}98$ |
| | | 9 | 0·455 | 15 | 0·901 | 23 | 0·995 | 45 | $0{\cdot}0^{3}73$ | 60 | 0·0037 | 82 | $0{\cdot}0^{9}15$ |
| | | 10 | 0·330 | 16 | 0·769 | 24 | 0·979 | 46 | $0{\cdot}0^{3}41$ | 61 | 0·0022 | 83 | $0{\cdot}0^{9}12$ |
| | | 11 | 0·277 | 17 | 0·632 | 25 | 0·942 | 47 | $0{\cdot}0^{3}24$ | 62 | 0·0013 | 84 | $0{\cdot}0^{10}51$ |
| | | 12 | 0·137 | 18 | 0·524 | 26 | 0·882 | 48 | $0{\cdot}0^{4}90$ | 63 | $0{\cdot}0^{3}76$ | 86 | $0{\cdot}0^{11}30$ |
| | | 14 | 0·043 | 19 | 0·410 | 27 | 0·805 | 49 | $0{\cdot}0^{4}37$ | 64 | $0{\cdot}0^{3}44$ | 87 | $0{\cdot}0^{11}17$ |
| | | 15 | 0·025 | 20 | 0·278 | 28 | 0·719 | 50 | $0{\cdot}0^{4}25$ | 65 | $0{\cdot}0^{3}23$ | 90 | $0{\cdot}0^{13}28$ |
| | | 18 | 0·0020 | 21 | 0·185 | 29 | 0·621 | 51 | $0{\cdot}0^{5}93$ | 66 | $0{\cdot}0^{3}13$ | | |
| | | | | 22 | 0·137 | 30 | 0·514 | 52 | $0{\cdot}0^{5}21$ | 67 | $0{\cdot}0^{4}72$ | | |
| | | | | 23 | 0·088 | 31 | 0·413 | 53 | $0{\cdot}0^{5}17$ | 68 | $0{\cdot}0^{4}36$ | | |
| | | | | 24 | 0·044 | 32 | 0·327 | 54 | $0{\cdot}0^{6}74$ | 69 | $0{\cdot}0^{4}18$ | | |
| | | | | 25 | 0·027 | 33 | 0·249 | 56 | $0{\cdot}0^{7}66$ | 70 | $0{\cdot}0^{5}97$ | | |
| | | | | 26 | 0·019 | 34 | 0·179 | 57 | $0{\cdot}0^{7}38$ | 71 | $0{\cdot}0^{5}47$ | | |
| | | | | 27 | 0·0079 | 35 | 0·127 | 60 | $0{\cdot}0^{9}93$ | 72 | $0{\cdot}0^{5}20$ | | |
| | | | | 28 | 0·0030 | 36 | 0·090 | | | 73 | $0{\cdot}0^{5}10$ | | |
| | | | | 29 | 0·0025 | 37 | 0·060 | | | 74 | $0{\cdot}0^{6}51$ | | |
| | | | | 30 | 0·0011 | 38 | 0·038 | | | 75 | $0{\cdot}0^{6}18$ | | |
| | | | | 32 | $0{\cdot}0^{3}16$ | 39 | 0·024 | | | 76 | $0{\cdot}0^{7}78$ | | |
| | | | | 33 | $0{\cdot}0^{4}95$ | 40 | 0·016 | | | 77 | $0{\cdot}0^{7}44$ | | |
| | | | | 36 | $0{\cdot}0^{5}38$ | 41 | 0·0088 | | | 78 | $0{\cdot}0^{7}15$ | | |

# APPENDIX TABLE 10c

**Agreement in Paired Comparisons. The Probability $P$ that a Value of $\Sigma$ (for $u$) will be attained or exceeded, for $m = 5$ and $n = 2$ to $5$**

| $n = 2$ | | $n = 3$ | | $n = 4$ | | $n = 5$ | | $n = 5$ | |
|---|---|---|---|---|---|---|---|---|---|
| $\Sigma$ | $P$ | $\Sigma$ | $P$ | $\Sigma$ | $P$ | $\Sigma$ | $P$ | $\Sigma$ | $P$ |
| 4 | 1·000 | 12 | 1·000 | 24 | 1·000 | 40 | 1·000 | 76 | $0{\cdot}0^{4}50$ |
| 6 | 0·375 | 14 | 0·756 | 26 | 0·940 | 42 | 0·991 | 78 | $0{\cdot}0^{4}16$ |
| 10 | 0·063 | 16 | 0·390 | 28 | 0·762 | 44 | 0·945 | 80 | $0{\cdot}0^{5}50$ |
| | | 18 | 0·207 | 30 | 0·538 | 46 | 0·843 | 82 | $0{\cdot}0^{5}15$ |
| | | 20 | 0·103 | 32 | 0·353 | 48 | 0·698 | 84 | $0{\cdot}0^{6}39$ |
| | | 22 | 0·030 | 34 | 0·208 | 50 | 0·537 | 86 | $0{\cdot}0^{6}10$ |
| | | 24 | 0·011 | 36 | 0·107 | 52 | 0·384 | 88 | $0{\cdot}0^{7}23$ |
| | | 26 | 0·0039 | 38 | 0·053 | 54 | 0·254 | 90 | $0{\cdot}0^{8}53$ |
| | | 30 | $0{\cdot}0^{3}24$ | 40 | 0·024 | 56 | 0·158 | 92 | $0{\cdot}0^{8}12$ |
| | | | | 42 | 0·0093 | 58 | 0·092 | 94 | $0{\cdot}0^{9}14$ |
| | | | | 44 | 0·0036 | 60 | 0·050 | 96 | $0{\cdot}0^{10}46$ |
| | | | | 46 | 0·0012 | 62 | 0·026 | 100 | $0{\cdot}0^{12}91$ |
| | | | | 48 | $0{\cdot}0^{3}36$ | 64 | 0·012 | | |
| | | | | 50 | $0{\cdot}0^{3}12$ | 66 | 0·0057 | | |
| | | | | 52 | $0{\cdot}0^{4}28$ | 68 | 0·0025 | | |
| | | | | 54 | $0{\cdot}0^{5}54$ | 70 | 0·0010 | | |
| | | | | 56 | $0{\cdot}0^{5}18$ | 72 | $0{\cdot}0^{3}39$ | | |
| | | | | 60 | $0{\cdot}0^{7}60$ | 74 | $0{\cdot}0^{3}14$ | | |

# APPENDIX TABLE 10D

AGREEMENT IN PAIRED COMPARISONS. THE PROBABILITY $P$ THAT A VALUE OF $\Sigma$ (FOR $u$) WILL BE ATTAINED OR EXCEEDED, FOR $m = 6$ AND $n = 2$ TO 4

| $n = 2$ | | $n = 3$ | | $n = 4$ | | $n = 4$ | | $n = 4$ | |
|---|---|---|---|---|---|---|---|---|---|
| $\Sigma$ | $P$ | $\Sigma$ | $P$ | $\Sigma$ | $P$ | $\Sigma$ | $P$ | $\Sigma$ | $P$ |
| 6 | 1·000 | 18 | 1·000 | 36 | 1·000 | 55 | 0·043 | 74 | $0{\cdot}0^{4}12$ |
| 7 | 0·688 | 19 | 0·969 | 37 | 0·999 | 56 | 0·029 | 75 | $0{\cdot}0^{5}89$ |
| 10 | 0·219 | 20 | 0·832 | 38 | 0·991 | 57 | 0·020 | 76 | $0{\cdot}0^{5}49$ |
| 15 | 0·031 | 21 | 0·626 | 39 | 0·959 | 58 | 0·016 | 77 | $0{\cdot}0^{5}32$ |
| | | 22 | 0·523 | 40 | 0·896 | 59 | 0·011 | 80 | $0{\cdot}0^{6}68$ |
| | | 23 | 0·468 | 41 | 0·822 | 60 | 0·0072 | 81 | $0{\cdot}0^{6}17$ |
| | | 24 | 0·303 | 42 | 0·755 | 61 | 0·0049 | 82 | $0{\cdot}0^{6}12$ |
| | | 26 | 0·180 | 43 | 0·669 | 62 | 0·0034 | 85 | $0{\cdot}0^{7}34$ |
| | | 27 | 0·147 | 44 | 0·556 | 63 | 0·0025 | 90 | $0{\cdot}0^{8}93$ |
| | | 28 | 0·088 | 45 | 0·466 | 64 | 0·0016 | | |
| | | 29 | 0·061 | 46 | 0·409 | 65 | $0{\cdot}0^{3}83$ | | |
| | | 30 | 0·040 | 47 | 0·337 | 66 | $0{\cdot}0^{3}66$ | | |
| | | 31 | 0·034 | 48 | 0·257 | 67 | $0{\cdot}0^{3}48$ | | |
| | | 32 | 0·023 | 49 | 0·209 | 68 | $0{\cdot}0^{3}26$ | | |
| | | 35 | 0·0062 | 50 | 0·175 | 69 | $0{\cdot}0^{3}16$ | | |
| | | 36 | 0·0029 | 51 | 0·133 | 70 | $0{\cdot}0^{4}86$ | | |
| | | 37 | 0·0020 | 52 | 0·097 | 71 | $0{\cdot}0^{4}68$ | | |
| | | 40 | $0{\cdot}0^{3}58$ | 53 | 0·073 | 72 | $0{\cdot}0^{4}48$ | | |
| | | 45 | $0{\cdot}0^{4}31$ | 54 | 0·057 | 73 | $0{\cdot}0^{4}16$ | | |

# INDEX

(Greek letters are indexed under their spelling in Roman letters, *e.g.* $\tau$ under tau. References are to pages.)